D1094535

How To Know

THE FRESH-
WATER ALGAE

An illustrated key for identifying the more common Fresh-water Algae to genus, with hundreds of species named and pictured and with numerous aids for their study.

G. W. PRESCOTT, Ph.D.

Professor of Botany
Michigan State University

WM. C. BROWN COMPANY PUBLISHERS
Dubuque, Iowa

THE PICTURED-KEY NATURE SERIES

"How to Know the Insects," Jaques, 1947

"Living Things—How to Know Them," Jaques, 1946

"How to Know the Trees," Jaques, 1946

"Plant Families—How to Know Them," Jaques, 1948

"How to Know the Economic Plants," Jaques, 1948, 1958

"How to Know the Spring Flowers," Cuthbert, 1943, 1949

"How to Know the Mosses and Liverworts," Conard, 1944, 1956

"How to Know the Land Birds," Jaques, 1947

"How to Know the Fall Flowers," Cuthbert, 1948

"How to Know the Immature Insects," Chu, 1949

"How to Know the Protozoa," Jahn, 1949

"How to Know the Mammals," Booth, 1949

"How to Know the Beetles," Jaques, 1951

"How to Know the Spiders," Kaston, 1952

"How to Know the Grasses," Pohl, 1953, 1968

"How to Know the Fresh-Water Algae," Prescott, 1954

"How to Know the Western Trees," Baerg, 1955

"How to Know the Seaweeds," Dawson, 1956

"How to Know the Freshwater Fishes," Eddy, 1957, 1969

"How to Know the Weeds," Jaques, 1959

"How to Know the Water Birds," Jaques-Ollivier, 1960

"How to Know the Butterflies," Ehrlich, 1961

"How to Know the Eastern Land Snails," Burch, 1962

"How to Know the Grasshoppers," Helfer, 1963

"How to Know the Cacti," Dawson, 1963

"How to Know the Aquatic Plants," Prescott, 1969

Other Subjects in Preparation

Printed in United States of America

INTRODUCTION

ARDLY any body of water or moist spot on the face of the earth is devoid of algae; they are as widely distributed almost as bacteria. The variety of form and of color exhibited by algae are seemingly endless and Nature has shown no bounds in designing these ornate plants, many of which have bizarre shapes and specialized habits.

Algae attract attention for many reasons, partly because of their bright colors or because of profuse and conspicuous growths in ponds, streams and along ocean shores. The more evident growths in fresh-water are usually referred to by those unacquainted with algae as "water-moss," "frog spittle," or pond-scums, pond-silks, etc. This illustrated, 'how-to-know' key is designed to give the student who is equipped with a microscope an opportunity to explore the world of fresh-water algae, and to give the correct scientific names (at least genus names) to the more common forms. The student may find to his surprise that a clot of "moss" will include half a dozen or more distinct and recognizable plants, each with its own characteristic form, method of reproduction, and life history. In some collections taken from acid bogs as many as 200 or more different species may be found.

It is hoped that this book will aid in identifying 440 fresh-water algal genera. To be sure, the naming of a plant or animal is not necessarily an end unto itself—but identification and naming must serve as a basis for any study of structure, physiology, life history, ecology and economic importance. Just as when one knows the name of a person and so then can learn more about him (or her), so the identification of algae can be the beginning of further investigations, for scientific pursuits or for the pure pleasure of getting better acquainted with the world of aquatic life.

Having found the generic names of fresh-water algae, the student may wish to identify plants according to their specific names. (See p. 3 for definitions). For this he will want to turn to some of the works listed in the bibliography. An attempt has been made in illustrating the genera to present their most common species. In many instances, among the one-celled and colonial genera especially, there is considerable variation in form among the species included in a genus. The student will need to keep this point in mind when matching a plant under consideration with the illustrations in the key. A plant in question may be a species somewhat or quite unlike the one shown.

The generic names used in the key are those of long-standing and the ones to be found in floras and handbooks the world over. In a few instances the names used here have been reduced elsewhere to synonymy by specialists who have critically examined old taxonomic literature and herbarium specimens for long-buried epithets. The advanced student is urged to look into the writings of specialists if he wishes to make comparisons of taxonomic terminologies.

East Lansing, Michigan
January, 1964

G. W. Prescott

Dr. Prescott's work with the Fresh-water Algae is well known. His book, first published in 1954 is widely used. Now he has given it a careful revision. A good number of genera have been added, making it a larger and more complete book. We are pleased to see this greater field of usefulness opening up for it.

H. E. JAQUES
Editor

TABLE OF CONTENTS

CHINESE IDIOGRAPH FOR THE
WORD ALGAE.

WHAT ARE ALGAE

ALTHOUGH most fresh-water algae are microscopic, many kinds are gregarious and occur in such numbers as to form the well-known "water-blooms" or pond scums. A few genera are individually large enough to be seen easily without the aid of a microscope, e.g., the stone-worts (Characeae), or some of the fresh-water red algae such as *Batrachospermum*, or colonial forms such as the blue-green alga *Nostoc*.

If it were possible for fresh-water algae to grow as large as some other plants (mosses and ferns for example) and to live upon land, they would be considered highly attractive indeed and would be much

cultivated as ornamentals. The symmetry of form and the patterns of external decorations possessed by many of them are not excelled in beauty by larger plants. The varied shapes of both marine and fresh-water algae, coupled with their many colors and hues have made them the subject of observation and wonderment for a long time, especially since the invention of the microscope. Indeed, the microscopic size of most of the fresh-water algae renders them all the more intriguing, and since the early days of the first microscopical club they have been used for pleasurable observation and speculation.

It is not the aesthetic quality of fresh-water algae alone, of course, which explains the amount of interest shown them. For small though they are, fresh-water algae (like some of their microscopic kin in the oceans) have many economic importances and considerable biological significance. Their relationship to aquatic biology problems of various kinds, their troublesome contamination of water supplies, and their use in general physiological research constitute just a few of the many aspects which lead to a study of them. Purely scientific problems, such as the role of algae in organic evolution, the biology of their reproduction and life histories, and their ecology are common subjects of investigation. Although much is still to be learned from them, the solution, or at least clarification, of many problems in general biology and physiology have been obtained from studies of algae. At this time, for example, much attention is being given algae in culture for the study of highly important and practical problems in photosynthesis and the products of algal metabolism. Some genera of unicellular algae are being used for the assay and detection of biologicals (vitamins and growth-promoting or growth-inhibiting substances). Some cancer research involves studies in the physiology and reproduction of algal cells. The use of algae in sewage oxidation and for oxygenation in space flights are other well-known fields of study.

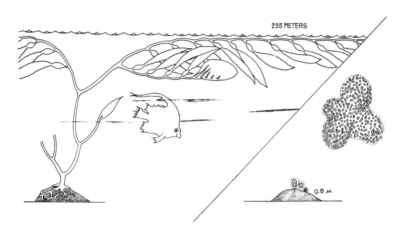

Whatever the interests in fresh-water algae may be, the student who has access to a microscope can find many hours of fascination in a few drops of pond water.

The term "algae" derived from the Latin name for sea-wrack, has come to be applied to all relatively simple (thalloid), marine and fresh-water vegetation. Actually, of course, many different kinds of organisms are included among the plants which lie outside (or below) the realm of mosses (Bryophyta), the ferns (Pteridophyta), and the seed-bearing plants (Spermatophyta). Included under "algae" are the smallest and most simple of chlorophyll-bearing organisms, the entire plant being but a single cell. Some of these may be less than 1 micron in diameter. At the other extreme, some of the brown algae, kelps (Phaeophyta) are the longest plants in the world. *Macrocystis* of the Pacific Ocean, for example, has been reported to reach as much as 700 feet, and even greater lengths have been claimed.

The student soon learns that "algae" include several divisions or phyla of the plant kingdom, and that there are incorporated even some groups of organisms which, strictly speaking, belong neither to the plant nor to the animal kingdom (Euglenophyta, Pyrrhophyta, and many of the yellow-green algae such as *Synura* and *Dinobryon).* These

are forms which usually are treated as chlorophyll-bearing protozoans in a reference work dealing with one-celled animals. Several
of the swimming, protozoan-like forms have definitely plant-like or
even non-motile relatives, however, which more than justify their
being given a place among the plant-like algae.

The reader who is not familiar with the classification of plants
and animals, nor with the terminology used for the different cate-
gories, may wish to refer to the following definitions.

SPECIES. A particular kind of plant or animal is called a species.
For example, a certain kind of rose, or a particular alga such as a
"pond silk," or a particular bird is known as a species and is given
an identifying or specific name. Because there are so many (although slight) variations between individuals which are, in general,
very much alike, the limitations or precise circumscriptions of a species
of plant or animal are often difficult, and subject to different interpretations by specialists.

GENUS. All plants which obviously are roses, but not all the same
kind, are grouped and constitute what is known as a genus (plural,
genera). Thus, all different species of roses are placed in the genus
Rosa, the Latin name for the genus. All species of "pond-silk" are
placed in the genus *Spirogyra*. The genus name, *Spirogyra*, and a
species name (a particular kind) together constitute the *scientific*
name. For example, *Spirogyra elongata* is the scientific name of a
species which has long cells; *Rosa cinnamonea* is the cinnamon rose.
This method of naming each kind of plant and animal with a double
name is known as the binomial system of nomenclature. The double
name identifies not only a particular kind of individual but also in-
dicates to what group (genus) it belongs.

FAMILY. The genus *Rosa* has much in common with the strawberry
genus *Fragaria*, and is much like the prune genus, *Prunus*. Similarly
Spirogyra has much in common with another group of species which
constitutes the genus *Mougeotia*. Therefore, *Rosa, Fragaria, Prunus*, and
other genera that have characteristics much in common are grouped
to form what is called a *family*. In this instance, the Rosaceae or
Rose family. *Spirogyra, Mougeotia, Zygnema* and some other algal
genera which have characteristics in common and which seem, therefore, to be related are grouped to form the family Zygnemataceae.

ORDER. In turn, families which are distinct from one another but
which, nevertheless, have some few characteristics in common are
grouped to form what is known as an order. Thus we have the Rosales,
the Zygnematales, etc.

DIVISION or PHYLUM. Several related orders form a major cate-
gory known as a Division or Phylum of the plant kingdom (or of the
animal kingdom). Thus several orders of the green algae constitute

3

the division (phylum) Chlorophyta. In many instances it may be convenient to subdivide the phylum into groups of orders called *classes*. Hence in the Chloroyhyta there are recognized 2 classes, Chlorophyceae and Charophyceae. In the key which follows only the genus names are given, with illustration of 1 or 2 common species. In so far as possible, the most distinctive features of the genus are shown in the illustrations.

In some instances a genus may be monotypic, *i.e.*, contains only 1 species, or a family may have only 1 known genus. For example, the family Microsporaceae includes only the genus *Microspora* (Fig. 194). Likewise, it is possible for a phylum of organisms to have but 1 order; all such compositions being subject to interpretations of specialists.

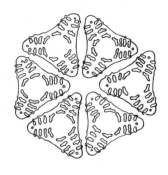

USE OF THE KEY

THE task of the writer in describing fresh-water algae is not made easier by their relatively small (mostly microscopic) size. Hence it is necessary to employ special descriptive terms to differentiate these minute organisms, and to assign them properly to the families and phyla to which they belong. Many of the terms are defined in the Pictured Glossary.

In such a treament as is presented here, only the more common and best-known genera in the United States (exclusive of Hawaii) can be given a place. The reader should have this in mind when using the key. He should avail himself of other less abridged or monographic works if satisfactory identification of a plant in which he is interested does not appear possible by the use of the following key. But the almost world-wide distribution of a majority of fresh-water genera gives such a key a usefulness beyond geographical limits. Such a key cannot be made as easy to use as are many keys to larger organisms. An attempt has been made to overcome some of the usual difficulties by keying out some genera at several different points, especially those genera which are so variable that selection of any one set of differentiating criteria for them is impossible.

A beginning student or one with limited familiarity with the algae must exercise patience until he has developed some degree of judgement and has become well-acquainted with the meaning of terms, and until he has discovered to what degree a plant may vary from the usual character which is employed in making an identification. Many times he will find it profitable, if not necessary, to 'back-track' in using the key and to follow down both dichotomies of choice before arriving at a satisfactory determination. As mentioned before, in making use of the illustrations it must be remembered that only 1 or 2 species of a genus are illustrated, and that the plant in question may not appear exactly like the forms which are figured. This is true for many of the genera in the Chlorococcales (*Scenedesmus, Oocystis, Tetraedron, etc.*) and of the Desmids (*Cosmarium, Euastrum, Micrasterias, e.g.*) also in the Chlorophyta.

One of the primary difficulties with which the inexperienced student is confronted when first using a general key to the algae is that of detecting and identifying colors, green, blue-green, yellow-green, *etc.* to which the key makes reference. Pigmentation in the different algal groups is a fundamental characteristic and one which is very helpful in making identification. But yellow-green algae at times may appear decidedly grass-green, and the brown-pigmented algae may have a distinct tinge of green, especially when artificial light is used

5

for the microscope. Hence, other characters, or a combination of characteristics excluding or in addition to color must be employed to make a choice in the key. Suggestions are given in appropriate places in the following key for making certain tests to help differentiate genera on the basis of color. Although it is a combination of characters which differentiates algae in the final analysis, the key can select these characters one by one only.

HOW AND WHERE TO COLLECT
FRESH-WATER ALGAE

ILAMENTOUS algae can be collected from mass growths by hand, of course, and representative tufts placed in vials or collecting jars. Less conspicuous forms may be found as fuzzy films on submerged grasses, old rush culms, and sticks. Using the fingers these growths can be lifted away or pulled from their attachment, or short sections of stems of aquatic plants and grass leaves can be placed in vials and the algae removed with scraping tools in the laboratory. A dropping pipette and a pair of tweezers are useful for collecting minute forms.

Using the back of the thumb nail, or a dull-edged knife will serve, greenish coatings on rocks and submerged wood can be scraped away. Such an instrument is useful for removing samples of green or brown felt-like or mucilaginous growths from wet stones about waterfalls, from dripping cliffs and rocky outcrops.

Submerged glass, shells, and bits of crockery in the water furnish substrates for many algae which occur as minute, green discs or tufts. Old, rotting wood may be perforated with algae which lie so far below the surface that they are scarcely visible, but wood that appears at all greenish from the exterior should be examined.

Feel under the rim of dams or along the edges of stones in flowing water. Many blue-green and also some of the more rare fresh-water red algae occur in such habitats.

On and in damp soil are to be found numerous species of Cyanophyta and Diatoms. Sometimes algae occur in pure 'stands' and sheets or films of a single species may be lifted or scraped from soil, wet boards, and the face of moist cliffs.

On beaches near the high water line, but back far enough where the sand lies unmolested most of the time, the upper dry layer of sand may be removed to disclose a densely green stratum of algae. The green sand can be scraped into a container and rinsed, and then when the water is poured off in the laboratory an interesting mixture of algae will be found, together with a variety of microscopic animals (protozoans, rotifers, copepods, etc.). This biotic cosmos is known as psammon and includes many organisms that normally occur in sandy beaches although not necessarily in the open water of a nearby lake or stream.

In *Nitella* (one of the larger green algae), in *Lemna trisulca* (one of the duckweeds), in *Ricciocarpus natans* and *Riccia fluitans* (floating

7

liverworts) occur various green and blue-green endophytic algae. Small portions of these aquatic plants, and others as well, may be allowed to age and to become discolored in laboratory dishes. The endophytes (and some epiphytes too) will then appear more clearly and can be dissected away for study.

In humid climates trunks of trees and surfaces of leaves may have epiphytic and endophytic (semi-parasitic) algae such as *Trentepohlia*, and *Cephaleuros*. *Arisaema* (Indian turnip) leaves invariably contain the parasitic alga *Phyllosiphon* which causes yellow or red spots in host tissue.

The habitats of fresh-water algae are diverse, some living in hot springs at 77° C.; others in snow fields at high altitudes, whereas others live in animals, or on them such as *Basicladia* on the snapping turtle.

One interesting habitat is the back of snapping turtles where the coarse, wiry filamentous alga *Basicladia* is invariably found. Other algae may be associated with *Basicladia* on the 'mossy' backs of turtles, whereas alligators are sometimes veritable algal gardens and offer a variety of species for the less timid collector. In the rain-forests of the tropics, Central America, e.g., the three-toed sloth harbors among its hair scales a minute red alga, *Cyanoderma bradypodis*, and a filamentous green alga, *Trichophilus welcheri*.

In alpine and subalpine regions where there are banks of permanent snow, red streaks will be found in the snow fields, or foot prints will turn red as the snow is compacted. The color is produced by unicellular green algae, especially *Chlamydomonas nivalis* which contain a red pigment, haematochrome, developed in many organisms exposed to intense illumination. Although such cells contain chlorophyll the green is masked by the more prevalent haematochrome. Occasionally green and yellow snow banks are found. A small quantity of red or 'bloody' snow when allowed to melt in a jar may yield a surprising quantity of such genera as *Scotiella, Ankistrodesmus, Mycanthococcus* and certain dinoflagellates.

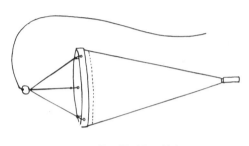

The Plankton Net

Specimens collected from the open water (planktonic organisms) are best taken with a cone-shaped, silk, bolting cloth net (No. 20 mesh). Plankton nets are obtainable from biological supply houses, or may be made up by securing a yard of the silk from an importer or from a flour mill. The American Limnological and Oceanography Society publishes periodically a list of commercial houses and firms where various kinds of collecting equipment may be obtained. A light-weight, brass (preferred) or thin galvanized iron ring (stout wire), or band may be used for the mouth of the net. A convenient size is a ring about 6 or 8 inches in diameter. Using a pattern, (See Welch, P. S. 1948. Limnological Methods, Blakiston Co., p. 234-235) cut the silk so that when attached to the ring a cone about 14 inches long is formed. The silk should not be attached directly to the ring but sewed first to a band of stout muslin which then may be sewed over the ring or metal band. If a flat band is used for the mouth of the net the edges should be filed smooth and rounded to eliminate as much cutting and fraying of the muslin as possible. The net may be used as a closed cone in which instance it must be turned inside out and rinsed into a dish or jar. More conveniently, the tip of the net may be cut off at a point about ½ in. or less from the end which will permit the insertion of a small homeopathic vial (4 to 6 dram capacity) which can be tied about its neck into the apex of the net. Thus the sample will become concentrated in the vial and when the net is reversed the collected material can be poured into a sample bottle, and the net then rinsed before another sample is taken. Of course the vial at the end of the neck can be untied with each use and another inserted. Better still, a small metal (aluminum) band, threaded to receive a 6-dram screw cap vial can be sewed into the tip of the net. Then the vial can be unscrewed and a fresh one inserted conveniently after each use. When comparative habitat studies are made much care should be used to see that the net is well-rinsed if it is to be used to collect from more than one habitat.

The net should have 3 leaders of equal length attached to the ring at regularly spaced points. The leaders should be tied to a small ring to which the tow cord is also attached. Use a heavy line such as a sash cord line for the pull cord and the leaders. Braided copper wire is sometimes used for the leaders but these become worn quickly at points of attachment and snap with resultant loss of equipment.

Utricularia, an under-water animal-trapping plant, is a veritable Christmas tree loaded with miscellaneous algae which are caught among the leaves, in the bladders, and held in the mucilage that envelopes the plant.

Microscopic forms of algae may be obtained in great numbers from the squeezing of *Sphagnum* (and other mosses), especially when the plants feel slippery or slimy. Small pools and seeps in *Sphagnum* bogs abound in many species of algae, especially Desmids. The moss or overhanging dead grass and stems of rushes can be squeezed directly into a vial, or if a gross, mass collection is desired, the moss can be squeezed into the plankton net so that a concentrated *purée* of algae is obtained. *Utricularia* (bladderwort), especially when it occurs in soft water or acid lakes, is a veritable net itself and handfuls of this plant can be squeezed into a plankton net with very fruitful results.

Specimens collected from the field should be put in receptacles with just enough water to cover them, leaving ample space for air, especially if the sample is to be stoppered for some time before arriving at the laboratory. Clots of larger, filamentous algae may have the excess water gently squeezed from them, rolled in wet and then dry paper (newspaper highly satisfactory) and so be kept in good condition for 24 hours or more.

Immediately upon returning from the field, vials or packets of material should be opened and poured into wide, shallow dishes so that they may be well aerated. If the collection is not too crowded in a dish of water the plants may be kept alive and in good condition almost indefinitely, especially if the dishes are stored in a cool place with reduced illumination such as in a north facing window. Some kinds of algae will remain in satisfactory condition for study (even though additional growth may not occur) when stored in a refrigerator kept at ordinary temperatures used in food storage.

Some collectors prefer to spread algae on cards or stiff paper to dry, and then make herbarium specimens of them. In working with such specimens later, a few drops of water placed on the dried plants will soak up the material well enough that it can be lifted away for mounting on a slide. Specimens so treated, however, are not satisfactory unless one has had a long experience in examining algae and is familiar with their appearance in the undried condition.

If it is desirable to keep a record of the location from which separate field collections are made, it is obviously necessary to give samples a code number or label at the time they are taken. One satisfactory way of doing this is to carry 3- x 5-inch cards, all but cut through into narrow strips which will fit into the collecting vials. A number then can be written on a slip which is torn off from the card and inserted. Information bearing the same code number can be written into a field notebook for future reference. In the laboratory a permanent number can be assigned to the vial and written on the cork if the material is to be saved for subsequent studies.

LABORATORY PROCEDURE

PRESERVING

I F samples are to be preserved an amount of 6-3-1 preservative equal to the volume of the specimen (and its water medium) may be added to the vial. This preservative is composed of 6 parts water, 3 parts 95% alcohol, and 1 part commercial formalin. If 5 cc. of glycerin are added to each 100 cc. of the preservative, a medium is produced which protects the specimen against total loss should the preservative evaporate. Cork-stoppered vials, as a rule, are much more serviceable than screw-cap vials which permit a greater amount of evaporation of the liquid because the tops loosen upon standing for a time.

Formalin-acetic acid-alcohol (FAA) makes an excellent preservative as well as a killing agent if material is later to be prepared for staining or cytological work. To 50 cc. of 95% alcohol add 5 cc. of glacial acetic acid, 10 cc. of commercial formalin, and 35 cc. of water. Proprionic acid may be substituted for the glacial acetic. This preservative is useless for Dinoflagellates with wall plates, however because the acid causes plates to dissociate.

For general and incidental preserving, ordinary 3% formalin may be used if the above ingredients are not available. (Add 3 cc. of commercial formalin to 37 cc. of water.)

PREPARING MOUNTS

For a study of most fresh-water algae a compound microscope is needed which has a 10X ocular and 10X and 43X objectives. Larger forms of algae such as the Characeae are best studied with a binocular dissecting microscope. Best illumination for the microscope is obtained from daylight because colors of the algal pigments appear more naturally. In lieu of good daylight (light from a northern window preferred), artificial light from a microscope lamp fitted with a daylight blue bulb is used, or a lamp which has a blue filter. Naturally, all optical parts of the microscope should be kept free of dust, moisture, and finger prints, using rice lens paper for cleaning. It is difficult enough to see micro-organisms clearly when optical conditions are perfect. An eye-piece micrometer and a stage micrometer for microscope calibration are essential of course if measurements are desired.

In preparing mounts for the study of algae *small* amounts of material should be used, and spread out evenly in a thin layer. Dense clumps and opaque masses of algae in a microscope mount produce only disappointment and headaches.

For the study of Diatoms it is necessary to have a clear and un-obstructed view of the wall and its markings, and of the details of internal wall structures, free from the chromatophores and other cell contents. There are several methods for cleaning and clearing Diatom cells (frustules), some of which are rather complex, involving boiling in acid, *etc.* A simple procedure which is satisfactory for generic de-termination is to spread a bit of material in a generous drop of water on a microscope slide. The slide is held over a flame and the water brought to a boil. The smear is steamed thus for a few seconds, after which a drop of water or of 5% glycerin can be used for a study slide.

For diatom techniques see Burke (1937) and Fleming (1949). If semi-permanent miscroscopic mounts are desired, specimens may be placed on a slide, evenly spread out in a large drop of 5% glycerin. The slide should be set away under a dust-proof cover. Once or twice a day for 2 or 3 days other drops of the glycerin solution are added until, through evaporation of the water, approximately 100% glycerin is obtained about the specimen. To this a small drop of melted gly-cerin jelly is added and the cover slip put in place. Care should be used to add just enough jelly to fill out the area under the cover slip so as not to allow leakage from beneath it. The cover may be ringed then with a sealing material such as balsam, colorless fingernail polish, Bismarck Black, or Gold Size. (See catalogues of biological supply houses which list these and other mounting and sealing materials.

A useful reagent to demonstrate the presence of starch ($C_6H_{10}O_5$ of the Chlorophyta) is I-KI. Commonly employed solutions are: 1) Iodine, 2 gs., Potassium Iodine, 1 g., Water, 200 cc; 2) Lugol's Iodine), Iodine 1 gr., Potassium Iodine 2 gs., Water 300 cc. A killing and fixing solu-tion may be prepared by adding to 200 cc. of water, 10 gs. of Iodine, 20 gs. of Potassium Iodide, and 20 cc. of Glacial Acetic Acid. Starch becomes dark, purplish-blue to black when stained with Iodine.

A depression slide may be used if specimens are to be examined over an extended period, for a study of motility, reproductive processes, *etc.* Rub a smear of vaseline around the margin of the depression. Place a drop of water or culture medium containing the specimen in the center of a coverglass. Then invert the coverglass with the drop suspended in the slide depression. Press down the margins of the coverglass in the vaseline film to seal the chamber. In such a cham-ber the supply of oxygen is limited of course. A similar and often more efficient type of mount is to seal a low plastic or glass collar to a slide (in a film of vaseline). Smear the top edge of the collar with vaseline and invert a hanging drop in the collar, pressing down the edges of the coverglass into the film of vaseline so as to seal the chamber. Such a mount can be used for low magnification study.

THE PHYLA OF ALGAE

HE organisms which constitute what are commonly known as "algae" are extremely diverse in form, color, habit, and in their habitats. Actually there are as many as 8 separate phyla or divisions of the plant kingdom included under "algae," (9 if Cryptophyceae, of uncertain position, are given a phylum status). Hence to write descriptively of algae one is confronted with almost as great a task as if he were treating all the phyla of land plants, fungi, mosses, ferns and seed plants, plus 3 or 4 additional groups. To be sure, all the phyla of algae do not include as many families and genera as do some of the higher plants, but the green algae alone include some 10 or 12 thousand species, distributed among about 375 genera.

The 3 major phyla of algae (those which are the most common) are the Chlorophyta (green), Cyanophyta (blue-green) and Chrysophyta (yellow- or brown-green). It is suggested that to facilitate the differentiation of these 3 groups and to become acquainted with the colors that characterize them, a known green alga *(Spirogyra)*, a blue-green *(Anabaena)* and a Diatom be mounted side by side on the same slide. This will permit the ready comparison of the colors and also a comparison of the wall features, cell contents, *etc.* Then a series of illustrations depicting these 3 groups should be examined so that gross morphology can become associated with the respective pigmentations.

The phyla of fresh-water algae herein recognized are as follows:

1 Chlorophyta (Green Algae).

Plants unicellular, colonial, or filamentous; floating, swimming, or attached and stationary; cells containing plastids (chloroplasts) in which chlorophyll (grass-green) is predominant, and in which there is usually a shiny, starch-storing body, the pyrenoid; pigments are 2 chlorophylls, 2 carotenes, 3 or 4 xanthophylls, and haematochrome sometimes present; starch test with iodine positive (in almost every instance); nucleus definite (although often small and inconspicuous); cell wall (rarely lacking) composed of cellulose and pectose; swimming cells or motile reproductive elements furnished with 2 (usually)—4 or rarely as many as 8 flagella of equal length and attached in the anterior end; sexual reproduction by iso- aniso- and by heterogametes.

2 Cyanophyta (Blue-Green Algae).

Plants unicellular, colonial, or in simple or branched (sometimes falsely branched) filaments; chloroplasts lacking, the pigments in solution and coloring the entire protoplast, often more densely in the peripheral region of the cell; pigments are cholorphyll-a, carotenes, 2 xanthophylls, phycoerythrin, phycocyanin; cell wall thin, a membrane which usually has a gelatinous outer sheath; contents often with false (pseudo-) vacuoles which refract light and obscure the true color of the cells which may be green, blue-green, gray-green, violet, tan, brown or purple; definite nucleus lacking but occurring as a cluster of granules in the midregion (central body) of the cell; motile cells and sexual reproduction wanting; asexual reproduction by cell division (fission) or by spores (endospores; akinetes); food storage questionably glycogen, possibly floridean starch; iodine test for starch negative.

3 Chrysophyta (Yellow-Green, or Yellow-Brown Algae).

Plants unicellular or colonial, rarely filamentous; pigments contained in chromatophores in which yellow or brown often predominates; pigments are chlorophyll-a, 1 carotene, fucoxanthin and usually lutein; food storage in the form of oil or leucosin, the latter often giving the cell a metallic lustre; starch test with iodine negative; wall relatively thick, pectin, often impregnated with silicon (especially in the Diatoms), and sometimes formed of 2 sections which overlap in the midregion; motile cells and swimming reproductive elements furnished with 2 flagella of unequal length, or with but 1 flagellum; rhizopodial (pseudopodial and amoeboid) extensions of the cell not uncommon in some families.

4 Euglenophyta (Euglenoids).

Cells solitary, swimming by 1 (usually) or by 2 (rarely 3) flagella; a gullet present in the anterior end of the cell in many members, as is also a red eye-spot; chloroplasts few to many, variously shaped bodies (a few members colorless); pigments are 2 chlorophylls, 1 carotene, 1, possibly 2 xanthophylls; pyrenoids usually present in some genera, either on the chloroplasts, or free in the cell; food reserve in the form of an insoluble starch, paramylum which is negative to the iodine test, and fatty substances; nucleus large and centrally located; cell membrane in the form of a pellicle, rigid or plastic, frequently striated; sexual reproduction lacking; vegetative reproduction by longitudinal cell division, and by encystment followed by multiplication of the cell.

5 Cryptophyta (Cryptophyceae of some authors) (Cryptomonads).

Cells solitary (rarely colonial), mostly swimming, protozoan-like organisms with 2, often laterally inserted or subapical flagella unequal in length; chromatophores few and large, brown or blue or red with pyrenoids commonly present; pigments are chlorophyll, xanthophylls, (others ?); food reserve in the form of solid starch or starch-like substances; iodine test sometimes positive; cell membrane a firm periplast; a gullet commonly present in the anterior end; reproduction by longitudinal cell division; sexual reproduction unknown.

6 Pyrrhophyta (Dinoflagellates).

Cells solitary (rarely filamentous in marine genera); mostly swimming by 2 flagella of approximately equal length, 1 wound about the cell in a transverse furrow, and 1 extended posteriorly from the point of attachment in a longitudinal furrow; cells mostly dorsiventrally flattened and differentiated, the longitudinal furrow extending along the ventral surface; cell wall (rarely absent) firm and simple or formed of regularly arranged, polygonal plates (as in the so-called armored or thecate Dinoflagellates); pigments are 2 chlorophylls, 1 carotene, 4 xanthophylls (especially peridinin and dinoxanthin), and phycopyrrin; the red peridinin sometimes predominating, giving the organisms in mass the characteristic color of the "red tide"; food reserve starch, starch-like substances and oil; a pigment-spot (possibly an eye-spot) commonly present; reproduction by longitudinal cell division; sexual reproduction unknown; asexual zoospores formed in some genera.

7 Rhodophyta (Red Algae).

Plants simple or branched filaments (unicellular in 1 questionable genus); pigments contained in chromatophores including 2 chlorophylls, 2 carotenes, lutein xanthophyll, phycoerthryin (usually predominant), and phycocyanin; (in fresh-water genera phycoerythrin is reduced and the plants are commonly gray-green, violet-green or tan-colored); food reserve in the form of floridean starch which is iodine-negative; walls relatively thick, often containing pores with intercellular connections, highly mucilaginous; sexual reproduction by heterogametes, the egg contained in a carpogonium, the antherozoids as non-motile elements cut off from the tips of special branches; asexual reproduction by monospores and by tetraspores (in some genera); motility of vegetative and reproductive cells lacking; thalli often macroscopic in size.

8 Chloromonadophyta (Chloromonads).

An obscure and little-understood group composed of but a few genera and species; cells solitary, swimming by 1 or 2 flagella, apically attached; chromatophores (when present) greenish with xanthophylls predominating over the chlorophyll; food reserve in the form of oils or a fat; contractile vacuoles and a reservoir in the anterior end of the cell; cell contents with trichocysts radiately arranged just within the cell membrane (in the genus Gonyostomum); reproduction by cell division; sexual reproduction unknown.

9 Phaeophyta (Brown Algae).

A phylum almost entirely marine, including the brown sea weeds (kelps); essentially filamentous (some microscopic) but mostly macroscopic robust and leathery; pigments are 2 chlorophylls, 1 carotene, 6 or more xanthophylls including fucoxanthins; food reserve in the form of laminarin or soluble carbohydrates including alcohol (mannitol); pyrenoids sometimes present; reproduction asexual by kidney-shaped zoospores with 2 lateral flagella, or sexual by iso- aniso- or heterogametes.

SYNOPSIS OF THE ALGAL PHYLA

OST phyla of the algae are present in both marine and fresh water, although some occur more abundantly in one or the other of the two habitats. The Phaeophyta, for example are almost entirely marine, the Euglenophyta almost all fresh-water in distribution. The following general key is presented to characterize the phyla and to facilitate a comparison.

1 Cells without chloroplasts or chromatophores; pigments blue-green, olive-green, or purplish, distributed throughout the entire protoplast (although cells may be somewhat less colored in the central region); wall usually thin (often showing as a membrane only) and generally with a mucilaginous sheath (wide or narrow, watery or firm and definite); food reserve in the form of glycogen or a starchlike substance; iodine test for starch negative; no motile cells; no sexual reproduction.......Blue-Green Algae.......CYANOPHYTA

1 Cells with chloroplasts or with chromatophores, the pigments not distributed throughout the protoplast; cell wall clearly evident (with rare exceptions, *Pyramimonas*, e.g., Fig. 38); stored food in the form of starch; iodine test for starch positive....................2

2 Cells with grass-green chloroplasts (but see some species of *Euglena* Fig. 9, or the filamentous alga *Trentepohlia*, Fig. 193 which although possessing chlorophyll, have the green color masked by an abundance of the red pigment, haematochrome).............3

2 Cells with chloroplasts or chromatophores some other color, gray-green, brown, violet-green, or yellow-green, sometimes purplish..5

3 Free-swimming, unicellular; with numerous ovoid, star-shaped, or plate-like chloroplasts which are grass-green; food stored as clearly evident grains of insoluble paramylum (sticks or plates); iodine test for starch negative; 1 or 2 (rarely 3) coarse flagella attached at the apex in a gullet; eye-spot usually evident.....................
Euglenoids ..................................EUGLENOPHYTA

3 Organisms not as above....................................4

4 Unicellular, without an eye-spot; chloroplasts numerous discs usually radially directed at the periphery of the cell; motile by means of 2 flagella inserted in an apical reservoir; trichocyst organelles usually present just within the cell membrane; food reserve oil...
............Chloromonads..............CHLOROMONADOPHYTA

4 Unicellular, colonial, or filamentous; swimming or not (often free-floating); when swimming using 2 to 4 fine flagella attached at the

apex of the cell in a colorless reservoir; chloroplasts 1 to several, usually with a conspicuous pyrenoid (starch-storing granule); iodine test for starch positive........Green Algae......CHLOROPHYTA

5 Chromatophores light olive-brown to dark brown; nearly all marine; essentially filamentous, but occurring mostly as thalli of macroscopic size (brown sea weeds); stored food in the form of laminarin and alcohol; starch test with iodine negative; motile cells with 2 laterally attached flagella...........Brown Algae...........PHAEOPHYTA

5 Plants marine or fresh-water, but not occurring as brown thalli of macroscopic size..6

6 Chromatophores yellow-green to yellow- or golden-brown; food in the form of leucosin or oil; starch test with iodine negative; plants unicellular, colonial or filamentous; sometimes swimming with apically attached flagella of unequal length, or with 1 flagellum; many forms (especially Diatoms, Figs. 387-443) with the cell wall impregnated with silicon; wall often in 2 adjoining or overlapping sections ....Yellow-Green Algae.............CHRYSOPHYTA

6 Chromatophores not yellow-green or pale green, but dark golden brown, gray-green, violet-green, rarely blue or red; food in the form of oil or starch-like carbohydrates; iodine test for starch usually negative 7

7 Unicellular, with dark, golden-brown chromatophores; swimming by 2 laterally attached flagella; a conspicuous eye-spot usually present; many forms with the cell wall composed of polygonal plates; cell with a transverse and a longitudinal furrow; reserve food in the form of starch or oil........Dinoflagellates........PYRRHOPHYTA

7 Organisms unicellular or filamentous, not motile or swimming by apical or subapical laterally attached flagella; chromatophores brown, green, bluish, violet-green or gray-green................8

8 Chromatophores violet or gray-green, sometimes bluish-green in fresh water, red in marine forms; occurring as filamentous thalli of macroscopic and microscopic size; food reserve starch-like carbohydrates; starch test with iodine negative......................
Red Algae ....RHODOPHYTA

8 Chromatophores 1 or 2 golden-brown (rarely blue or red) bodies; organisms unicellular (rarely colonial); swimming by sub-apically attached flagella; food reserve starch-like carbohydrates; iodine test for starch positive in some.....Cryptomonads.....CRYPTOPHYTA
(This class of the algae has several characteristics in common with Dinoflagellates and in some systems of classification they are included with the Pyrrhophyta.)

A Selected List of Books and Major Papers Dealing with the Classification of Fresh-water Algae

Atkinson, G. F. Monograph of the Lemaneaceae of the United States. Ann. Bot., 4: 177-229. Pls. 7-9.

Boyer, C. S. 1916. Diatomaceae of Philadelphia and Vicinity. Philadelphia.

Brunnthaler, J. 1915. Protococcales. In: A. Pascher. Die Süsswasserflora Deutschlands, Osterreichs und der Schweiz. Heft 5. Chlorophyceae 2: 52-205. Jena.

Burke, J. F. 1937. Collecting recent diatoms. Preparing recent diatoms. Mounting recent diatoms. New York. Microsc. Soc. Bull., 1(3): 9-12; 1(4): 13-16; 1(5): 17-20.

Chapman, V. J. 1962. The Algae. Macmillan Co., New York.

Collins, F. S. (1909) 1928. The Green Algae of North America. Tufts College Studies, Sci. Ser., 2(1909): 79-480. Pls. 1-18. Reprinted with supplements 1 and 2 by G. E. Stechert Co., New York. 1928.

Copeland, J. J. 1936. Yellowstone Thermal Myxophyceae. Ann. New York Acad. Sci., 36: 1-232. 73 Figs.

Drouet, F. and Daily, William A. 1952. A Revision of the Coccoid Myxophyceae. Butler Univ. Bot. Stud.,-12: 1-218.

Eddy, Samuel. 1930. The fresh-water armored or thecate Dinoflagellates. Trans. Amer. Microsc. Soc., 49: 277-321. Pls. 28-35.

Elmore, C. J. 1921. The Diatoms (Bacillarioideae) of Nebraska. Univ. Nebr. Stud., 21(1/4): 1-214. 23 Pls.

Fleming, W. D. 1949. Cleaning and preparation of diatoms for mounting. Bull. Amer. Soc. Amateur Microscopists, 5(3): 40-43.

Fritsch, F. E. 1935, 1945. The Structure and Reproduction of the Algae. Vols. I, II. Cambridge University Press.

Geitler, L. 1930-1931. Cyanophyceae. In: L. Rabenhorst, Kryptogamen-Flora von Deutschland, Osterreich under der Schweiz. 14 Lf., 1(1930): 1-288; Lf. 2(1931): 289-464. Figs. 1-131. Leipzig.

Gojdics, Mary. 1953. The Genus *Euglena*. Univer. Wisconsin Press, Madison.

Heering, W. 1914. Ulotrichales, Microsporales, Oedogoniales. In: A. Pascher. Die Süsswasserflora Deutschlands, Osterreich und der Schweiz. Heft. 6, Chlorophyceae 3: 1-250. Figs. 1-384. Jena.

Hustedt, F. Bacillariophyta. In: A Pascher. Die Süsswasser-flora Mitteleuropas. Heft. 10.

Irenée-Marie, Fr. 1939. Flore desmidiale de la region du Montréal. 547 pp. 69 Pls. La Prairie, Canada.

Jaques, H. E. 1948. Plant Families—How to Know Them. Wm. C. Brown Co., Dubuque, Iowa.

Krieger, W. 1933-1939. Die Desmidiaceen. In: L. Rabenhorst. Kryptogamen-Flora von Deutschland, Osterreich, und der Schweiz. 13 Abt. 1: 1-712. Pls. 1-96; Abt. 1, Teil 2: 1-117. Pls. 97-142. Leipzig.

Lemmermann, E. 1913. Euglenineae. Flagellatae 2. In: A Pascher, Die Süsswasserflora Deutschlands, Osterreich, und der Schweiz. Heft. 2: 115-174. Figs. 181-377. Jena.

Pascher, A. 1927. Volvocales-Phytomonadinae. In: Die Süsswasserflora Deutschlands, Osterreich, und der Schweiz. Heft 4: 1-506. Figs. 1-451. Jena.

Pascher, A. 1937-1939. Heterokonten. In: L. Rabenhorst. Kryptogamen-Flora von Deutschland, Osterreich und der Schweiz. XI: 1-1097. Figs. 1-912. Leipzig.

Prescott, G. W. 1927. The Motile Algae of Iowa. Univ. Iowa Stud. Nat. Hist., 12: 1-40. Pl. 1-10.

Prescott, G. W. 1962. Algae of the Western Great Lakes Area. IInd Ed., 977 pp., 143 pls. Wm. C. Brown Co., Dubuque, Iowa.

Schiller, J. 1933-1937. Dinoflagellatae. In: L. Rabenhorst. Kryptogamen-Flora von Deutschland, Osterreich und der Schweiz. X(1933), Teil 1: 1-617; Teil 2, Lf. 1(1935): 1-160; Lf. 2(1935): 161-320; Lf. 3(1937): 321-480; Lf. 4(1937): 481-590. Leipzig.

Smith, G. M. 1920, 1924. Phytoplankton of the Inland Lakes of Wisconsin. I, II. Wis. Geol. & Nat. Hist. Surv. Bull. 57. Madison.

Smith, G. M. 1950. Freshwater Algae of the United States. IInd Ed. 719 pp., 559 Figs. McGraw-Hill Book Co.

Tiffany, L. H. 1937. Oedogoniales, Oedogoniaceae. North American Flora, 11, Part I. 102 pp. New York Botanical Garden.

Tiffany, L. H. and Britton, M. E. 1952. The Algae of Illinois. 407 pp., 108 Pls. Univer. Chicago Press.

Tilden, Josephine E. 1910. Minnesota Algae. I. Univ. Minnesota Press, Minneapolis.

Tilden, Josephine E. 1935. The Algae and Their Life Relations. 550 pp., Figs. 1-257. Univ. Minnesota Press, Minneapolis.

West, W. and West, G. S. 1904-1912. A Monograph of the British Desmidiaceae. Vols. I-IV. Ray Society London. -and Carter, Nellie, 1924. Vol. V. Ray Society, London.

Wolle, F. 1887. Freshwater Algae of the United States. Vols. I, II. Bethlehem, Pa.

Wolle, F. 1892. Desmids of the United States and List of American Pediastrums. Bethlehem, Pa.

PICTURED-KEY TO THE COMMON GENERA OF FRESH-WATER ALGAE

1a Plants macroscopic, up to 40 or more cm. high, growing erect, with stem-like axes bearing whorls of branches and forked 'leaves' clearly visible to the unaided eye. Figs. 1-3. Family Characeae......2

1b Plants microscopic, or if macroscopic with cellular structures and branches not visible to the unaided eye, or scarcely so.........4

2a Branching unsymmetrical, with dense heads of short branches and scraggly longer ones; microscopically showing globular male organs (globules or 'antheridia') lateral, beside the oval, female organs (nucules or 'oogonia'). Fig. 1......................*TOLYPELLA*

Fig. 1. *Tolypella intricata* (Trentep.) v. Leonh. (a) portion of plant showing habit of branching and the heads of short branches in which the reproductive organs are located; (b) a node showing 4 "oogonia" and 1 "antheridium"; (c) an oogonium showing the 'crown' cells; (d) tip of branch.

Three species of this genus occur throughout the United States, but rather rarely. In general they appear as scraggly *Chara* (Fig. 2) plants, but growing singly rather than in dense beds, and usually in shallow, hard water lakes or in slowly flowing streams. Under the hand lens or microscope, however, *Tolypella* shows its true relationship to *Nitella* (Fig. 3) and the tribe Nitelleae by not having column-like or fluting cells along the stems and branches. The sex organs are produced in the 'heads' of short branches.

2b Branching symmetrical with rather evenly spaced whorls of equal-length branches at nodes of the stem; globules ('antheridia') above or below the nucules ('oogonia')..............................3

3a Plants coarse and usually rough with lime; ill-smelling (garlic or skunk odor); microscopically showing globules ('antheridia') lateral and below the oval nucules ('oogonia'), although some species are dioecious; with nodes and internodes; with elongate, corticating, columnar cells inclosing the main axial filament. Fig. 2....*CHARA*

22

(*Chara coronata* and *C. Braunii* have no corticating cells however; differentiated and identified by the habit of branching and location of the sex organs.)

Fig. 2. (a) *Chara canescens* Lois.-Des., portion of a plant in which thorn-like cells arising from the corticating elements give a spiny appearance; (b) *C. excelsa* Allen, showing the oval oogonium (nucule) above and the globular antheridium (globule) below.

Most of the species, of which there are many occurring in North America, are world-wide in their distribution, although many are endemic in Japan, in Australia, South Africa, etc. They are to be found usually in slow-flowing streams or in alkaline or hard water lakes in which calcium is abundant in the form of carbonates or bicarbonates. In their physiology the plants cause lime to become deposited on stems and 'leaves,' sometimes to the detriment of the plant. This encrustation is responsible for the common name of "stonewort." Marl and other kinds of calcareous deposits may be formed largely by *Chara* over long periods of time.

3b **Plant delicate, or if relatively stout not roughened with lime; dark green, not ill-smelling; microscopically with globules terminal on a short pedicel within a cluster of branches and above the nucules; main axis not corticated. Fig. 3** . . . . **NITELLA**

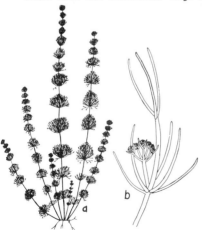

Species of *Nitella* are not seen as often as are Charas because they usually grow more deeply, thriving in soft water or acid lakes rather than in hard water situations. Some species occur in bog lakes that are darkly stained with humic and tannic acids and are collected only by dredging with a plant hook. The plants are greener than *Chara* because they are not encrusted with lime; are not ill-smelling; often have a glistening or translucent appearance.

Fig. 3. (a) *Nitella tenuissima* (Desv.) Kuetz., habit; (b), *N. flexilis* (L.) C. A. Agardh, portion of plant showing habit of branching.

4a (1) Cells containing chloroplasts (bodies with green pigment predominating), or chromatophores (bodies with colors other than green predominating) 5

4b Cells without chloroplasts or chromatophores, with pigments in solution and more or less evenly diffused throughout the entire protoplast 419

5a Plant grass- or leaf-green to gray-green; photosynthetic product starch (iodine test positive), or paramylum (iodine test negative),[2] or floridean starch in the fresh-water red algae which are greenish or violet-green (iodine test negative)[1].........................6

5b Plant not grass- or leaf-green (but see *Botrydium*, Fig. 242 and *Vaucheria*, Fig. 226 which are green but belong to the Chrysophyta, the yellow-green algae); color light green, violet-green, yellowish or brown; iodine test for starch negative (except in some Dinoflagellates) 304

6a Plants swimming in the vegetative state, solitary or colonial. (Preserved specimens should be examined for 2 or more minute protuberances at the anterior end of the cell which locate the position of flagella (organs of locomotion) that may have been retracted or lost. Use 5% glycerin for mounts. (See Fig. 9)................7

6b Plants not motile in the vegetative state (check to be certain the organism is not a motile one at rest. See *Trachelomonas*, Fig. 5 (which, although motile, is commonly found as a non-motile, brown shell (lorica) from which the swimming protoplast has escaped). Solitary, colonial, or filamentous...........................42

---

[1]Several genera of the Chlorophyta often have their green color partly or completely masked by a brick-red pigment, haematochrome. See the unicellular genera *Haematococcus* (24a); *Chlamydomonas* (35b); *Dunaliella* (40a), and *Urococcus* (185a). Also see the parasitic filamentous genus *Rhodochytrium* (133a) and the subaerial genus *Trentepohlia* (254a).

[2]See *Euglena* (Fig. 9) which although containing chlorophyll may have the green color masked by the red pigment, haematochrome.

7a Cells broadly ovoid or oval in outline, flattened as seen from the
side; chloroplasts radiately d'';posed at the periphery of the cell;
i' ;gella 2, 1 trailing. Fig. 4. Division Chloromonadophyta........
....GONYOSTOMUM

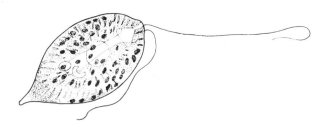

Fig. 4. *Gonyostomum serren* (Ehr.) Stein, showing the numerous, ovoid chloroplasts (shaded) and the radiately arranged
trichocysts (stinging organs). It is normal for 1 flagellum to
be directed forward, the other trailing.

This rare swimmer occurs mostly in acid bogs and in shallow lakes,
accompanying certain species of *Euglena* (Fig. 9). Under the microscope it reminds one of a flat, green bottle; usually is quiet in the
microscope field but moves with sudden jerky motions for short dis-
tances. Among the peripheral chloroplasts are slender trichocysts
which throw out threads upon stimulation. The forward directed flagellum is at least twice the length of the cell.

7b Cells round or oval when seen in both front and side view, sometimes slightly flattened, but with flagella directed forward; chloroplasts not arranged as above; no trichocysts; flagella 2, 4, or 1....8

8a Cells with numerous, disc-like (rarely ribbon-like) chloroplasts; food
reserve in the form of variously shaped, colorless or white paramylum bodies (see Fig. 9) which do not stain blue-black with iodine;
slow-moving by 1 (usually) or more stout flagella (see Fig. 9b); a
red eye-spot usually evident. Division Euglenophyta...........9

8b Cells with 1 cup-shaped or star-shaped cloroplast, usually containing 1 or more conspicuous pyrenoids (doughnut-like, shiny bodies
buried in the chloroplast or on its surface); food reserve starch,
iodine test positive; lens-shaped eye-spot usually evident, actively
swimming with fine, often obscure flagella. (See Fig. 31.) Add
5% glycerin to microscope mount to slow down organisms for observation). Division Chlorophyta (in part).....................13

9a Cells inclosed in a brown shell (test or lorica), variously shaped (round, oval, flask-shaped), often with a collar about the aperture through which a single flagellum extends. (The shells frequently are found empty, yellow to dark brown, smooth or decorated, with or without a tail piece). Fig. 5.................TRACHELOMONAS

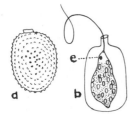

Fig. 5. (a) *Trachelomonas granulosa* Playf., a short-collared species which has a warty shell; (b) *T. euchlora* (Ehr.) Lemm., protoplast within shell, showing eye-spot(e), chloroplasts and flagellum.

There are several hundred species of *Trachelomonas*, each showing a differently shaped shell or lorica, and each having its own special pattern or type of decoration. The amount of iron present in the shell determines the intensity of the color. The colorless forms have been grouped to form the genus *Strombomonas* by some students. *Trachelomonas* species are found intermingled among other algae in shallow water of ditches and bogs, or among aquatic weed beds near the shores of lakes.

9b Cells not inclosed in a lorica..............................10

10a Cells flattened as seen from the side, and often twisted; broadly fusiform or nearly round in outline when seen from the front; paramylum in the form of 1 to several 'doughnut' rings or discs. Fig. 6...PHACUS

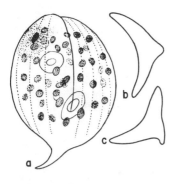

Fig. 6. (a) *Phacus curvicauda* Swir., front or ventral view showing eye-spot, chloroplasts and 2 ring-shaped paramylum bodies (food reserve); (b), (c) *P. triqueter* (Ehr.) Duj. as seen in end view, the triangular shape being produced by a flange on the dorsal surface of the cell.

Although some species are spirally twisted and 'top'-shaped most are flat or at most are only slightly saucer-shaped or pancake-like, with a long or short tail-piece. The rings of paramylum are usually very conspicuous, sometimes so large as to fill nearly the entire diameter of the cell.

10b Cells not flattened, round in cross section; either elongate-fusiform or oval to round or somewhat pear-shaped in outline; paramylum bodies different from above 11

11a Cells round, oval or pear-shaped; highly plastic and changeable in shape; flagella 2; gullet conspicuous in the anterior end; numerous, disc-like chloroplasts. Fig. 7. .... *EUTREPTIA*

These cells are fusiform when normally extended and bluntly truncate at the anterior end. Posteriorly they are abruptly narrowed into a caudal extension. There is an eye-spot and a gullet with small adjacent vacuoles in the anterior end. Under favorable optical conditions a granular swelling can be discerned at the base of each flagellum. The periplast, like many Euglenoids, is spirally striated.

Fig. 7. *Eutreptia viridis* Perty. (Redrawn from Lemmermann.)

11b Cells other shapes; 1 flagellum 12

12a Cells round, oval or pear-shaped; rigid, fixed in shape when swimming; paramylum in the form of 2 (or 4) large, lateral rings; tailpiece, if present, usually in the form of a short, sharp projection from the rounded posterior end. Fig. 8. .... *LEPOCINCLIS*

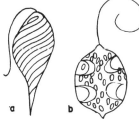

There are many species of this genus, world-wide in distribution, never forming pure growths but often intermingled with species of *Euglena* (Fig. 9). In optical section the cells are round and in many the periplast is spirally striated. On either side is a folded ring of paramylum; sometimes 2 such rings on each side. They swim more actively than *Euglena*.

Fig. 8. (a) *Lepocinclis acuta* Presc., showing spiral markings of the periplast (membrane); (b) *L. glabra* fa. *minor* Presc., showing 4, lateral, band-like paramylum bodies.

12b Cells elongate, fusiform or nearly cylindrical; rigid and fixed in shape or changeable (metabolic); paramylum in the form of a few and large, or numerous and small, colorless rods or sticks; tail-piece sometimes present, formed by gradual narrowing of the cell. Fig. 9...EUGLENA

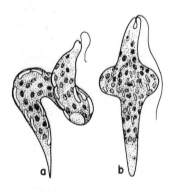

Fig. 9. (a) *Euglena convoluta* Korsch., showing lateral paramylum plates as seen on edge, one in flat view; (b) *E. elastica* Presc. Both of these are metabolic species, changing shape while moving, whereas some forms are rigid.

There is a gullet at the anterior end of *Euglena* cells and 1 or more contractile vacuoles. The eye-spot is usually conspicuous. In some species there are pyrenoids. Although usually green, these elongate, slowly moving organisms sometimes are colored red because of a pigment haematochrome. A pond or slough may have a bright red film produced by a *Euglena* 'bloom' because of the pigment, produced as a response to intense light. *Euglena* species are often found in the psammon.

13a (8) Plant a colony of 4 or more cells, either closely adjoined, or free from one another within a gelatinous envelope. Division Chlorophyta (in part)......................................14

13b Plant a solitary cell. Division Chlorophyta (in part)...........24

14a Cells arranged in a plane, forming a plate, flat or twisted....15

14b Cells arranged to form a spherical, ovoid or spheroidal colony..16

15a Colony horseshoe-shaped, flat or twisted. Fig. 10. .*PLATYDORINA*

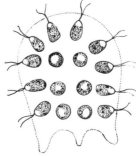

Although rare and seldom seen this plant can be easily identified by the flattened, slightly twisted, horseshoe-shaped colony. It is to be found in the same habitats with other members of the Volvocaceae such as *Eudorina* (Fig. 19) and *Pandorina* (Fig. 15).

Fig. 10. *Platydorina caudatum* Kofoid. The flagella of the organisms in the center of the colony are directed vertically to the surface.

15b Colony a circular or subquadrangular plate. Fig. 11. . . . *GONIUM*

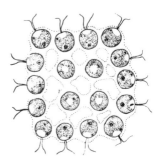

The number of cells in a colony may vary, according to species, from 4 to 32 or 64. The rectangular plates tumble over and over in locomotion. The flagella of the inner cells are directed at right angles to the colony plane; those of the lateral cells are directed outward in the colony plane.

Fig. 11. *Gonium pectorale* Muell. An 18-celled colony.

16a (14) Colony oblong or pear-shaped, with the cells densely clustered and all directed anteriorly, without an enveloping colonial mucilage 17

16b Colony globular or ovoid; cells inclosed in a mucilage sheath, but not all directed one way 19

17a Colonies small (2 to 4 cells). Fig. 12............*PASCHERIELLA*

Rare. Occurs in small rain water pools and catch basins of temporary duration. Unlike most members of this group of the algae the chloroplast is a laminate, parietal plate rather than cup-shaped.

Fig. 12. *Pascheri-ella tetras* Korsch. Cells showing eye-spot, and subflagellar vacuoles at the apex.

17b Colonies of 8 or 16 cells....................................18

18a Cells with 4 flagella arising from a protuberance at the broad anterior end. Fog. 13.....................*SPONDYLOMORUM*

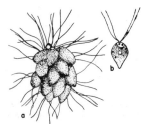

Pear-shaped cells huddled together with their broad ends all directed the same way; eye-spot is posterior rather than anterior. The 4 flagella are difficult of determination except under favorable optical conditions.

Fig. 13. *Spondylomorum quaternarium* Ehr. (a) colony; (b) single organism showing posterior eye-spot and subflagellar vacuoles.

18b Cells with 2 flagella. Fig. 14....*PYROBOTRYS (Chlamydobotrys)*

Like *Spondylomorum* (Fig. 13) cells of this colonial organism are closely grouped; have 2 long flagella and a conspicuous eye-spot, anterior or posterior. The chloroplast is massive and without pyrenoids.

Fig. 14. *Pyrobotrys gracilis* Korsch. A colony of individuals with posterior eyespots.

19a (16) Colony spheroidal or oval; cells pear-shaped, crowded together with broad ends all directed outwardly. Fig. 15 . . . .
. . . . *PANDORINA*

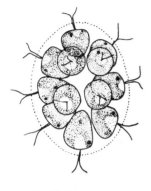

This is a tumbling colony which is usually more oval than spherical, with the cells rather compactly arranged. The flagella extend through the gelatinous sheath parallel and then flare widely. Often colonies are found in which each cell has undergone cleavage to form daughter colonies. *Pandorina morum* is world-wide in distribution whereas *P. charkowiensis* Korshikov, also found in the United States, is relatively rare.

Fig. 15. *Pandorina morum* Bory. Cells are pear-shaped and often are more compactly arranged than shown in the illustration.

19b Colony globular or broadly ovoid; cells not crowded but evenly spaced (even though close together) 20

20a Colonies large, containing hundreds or thousands of cells. Fig. 16 . . . . *VOLVOX*

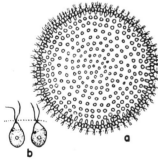

This globular colony containing thousands of cells usually can be seen easily with the unaided eye. It occurs in water that is rich in nitrogenous substances (frequently) and sometime produces "blooms" of short duration during summer months. It is often accompanied by *Pleordorina* (Fig. 20) and *Eudorina* (Fig. 19).

Fig. 16. *Volvox tertius* Meyen. (a) colony showing only vegetative cells; (b) two organisms showing eye-spot . Other species have colonies containing a larger number of cells, and some have intercellular connections.

20b Colonies composed of 8-16-64-128 cells 21

21a Cells fusiform with sharply pointed, lateral processes or extensions of the protoplast. Fig. 17 . . . .*STEPHANOSPHAERA*

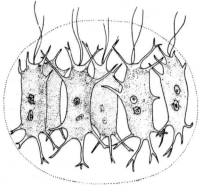

Like *Pascheriella* (Fig. 12) this plant occurs in small temporary pools in rocks, sometimes at high altitudes. The cells are all directed one way, lying in an equatorial belt with the flagella all directed forward.

Fig. 17. *Stephanosphaera pluvialis* Cohn. Oval colony with organisms forming a median band. The cells commonly show 2 pyrenoids (starch-storing bodies).

21b Cells round or ovoid, without lateral processes 22

22a Cells arranged at the equator of a spherical or oval gelatinous envelope; cells in 2 tiers, 8 or 16 in number. Fig. 18 . . . .
. . . . .*STEPHANOON*

This genus is a clear, oblate, gelatinous sphere with 1 or 2 series of cells encircling it at the equator. The cells are similar to other volvocoids but possess 2 flagella of unusual length. Each cell forms a daughter colony as in *Pandorina* (Fig. 15).

Fig. 18. *Stephanoon Askenasii* Schew.

22b Cells not arranged at the equator of a gelatinous sphere, but distributed throughout...23

23a Cells all the same size within the colony. Fig. 19....*EUDORINA*

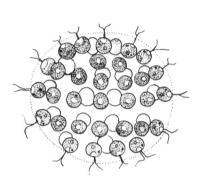

Fig. 19. *Eudorina elegans* Ehr. In this species the cells have a tendency to be arranged in transverse bands or tiers; occurs along with *Volvox* (Fig. 16) and *Pleodorina* (Fig. 20).

Unlike *Pandorina* (Fig. 15) the cells are round or oval and rather evenly spaced within the colonial mucilage and near the periphery, although they sometimes show a tiered arrangement. *Eudorina elegans*, the common species with world-wide distribution occurs with other colonial Volvocales in both tycho- and euplankton. *Eudorina unicocca* G. M. Smith is known also from the United States and from Panama. It is differentiated by the colony showing a more definite polarity, with the sheath forming lobes at the posterior end.

23b Cells of 2 sizes within the same colony, the smaller arranged at one pole of the envelope. Fig. 20.................*PLEODORINA*

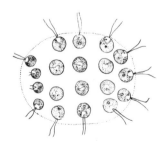

Fig. 20. *Pleodorina illinoisensis* Kofoid. Another common species, *P. californica* Shaw has about one-half of the cells larger (reproductive cells), the smaller cells being strictly vegetative.

24a (13) Protoplast at a considerable distance within the cell wall and connected to it by fine, radiating processes; cells with a mass of red pigment (haematochrome) often present in the center of the protoplast (sometimes masking the green color); usually encysted and quiescent, forming rust-colored, encrusting growths in bird baths and cemented pools. Fig. 21..........*HAEMATOCOCCUS*

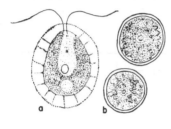

Fig. 21. *Haematococcus lacustris* (Girod.) Rostaf. (a) swimming cell showing protoplast with radiating processes; (b) cysts (which usually are brick-red in color).

Although motile, this organism is more frequently found as a conspicuous coating of red cysts in the bottom of shallow pools. In the swimming state it is readily identified by the fine fibrils which extend from the protoplast to the wall. The space between the wall and the protoplast is filled with colorless, watery mucilage.

29a Lorica colorless, rectangular in front view, with the corners produced into horns. Fig. 22 . . . . *PTEROMONAS*

Fig. 22. *Pteromonas aculeata* Lemm. Other species are truncately oval or quadrangular in shape as seen in front view.

This genus takes its name from the winged appearance of the envelope. Although there are about 7 species known, the most common is perhaps *Pteromonas aculeata* Lemm. recognizable by the rectangular appearance in 'front' view. Like *Phacotus* (Fig. 25) *Pteromonas* commonly occurs in the plankton of rivers. See *Scotiella* (Fig. 145) a genus which has been regarded by Pascher as belonging to *Pteromonas*.

29b Lorica globular or obversely pyriform 30

30a Lorica globular, not granular but punctate and often appearing rough or granular. Fig. 23 . . . . *DYSMORPHOCOCCUS*

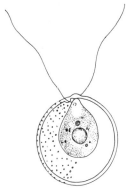

This genus has a broadly oval lorica which is different in shape from the inclosed protoplast that lies some distance within the shell. The lorica has numerous small pores, giving a dotted appearance and there are 2 separate pores through which the flagella extend. An eye-spot is present, and 1 or more pyrenoids in the parietal, cup-shaped chloroplast.

Fig. 23. *Dysmorphococcus variabilis* Takeda, showing a sample of the markings of the lorica.

30b Lorica obversely pyriform in 'front' view, compressed when seen from the side or top. Fig. 24.................CEPHALOMONAS

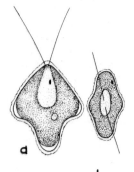

These cells have a colorless lorica which is close-fitting. The anterior end is broadly rounded, the posterior narrowed. The flagella are diagonally widely divergent.

Fig. 24. *Cephalomonas granulata* Higin. (a) front view; (b) apical view. (Redrawn from Higinbotham.)

31a (28) Lorica oval or elliptic in 'front' view, usually warty, dark colored and bivalved, the edges of the adjoining valves evident when the cell is seen from the side. Fig. 25.............PHACOTUS

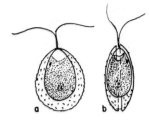

This genus is relatively rare, but is often abundant in collections from habitats where it occurs. It is both euplanktonic and tychoplanktonic and may occur in rivers as well as in lakes. The lorica and the protoplast are both egg-shaped in 'front' view, with a distinct space between them.

Fig. 25. *Phacotus lenticularis* (Ehr.) Stein. (a) front view; (b) side view showing bivalve structure of the cell wall.

31b Lorica roughened or warty, not dark colored, cordate in 'front' view, compressed when seen from the side, but extended into 2 posterior and 2 anterior lobes. Fig. 26............*WISLOUCHIELLA*

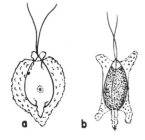

Named for the biologist Wislouch, this biflagellated organism is identified quickly by the oddly-shaped lobes or processes of the wall which extend in several planes. Rare.

Fig. 26. *Wislouchiella planctonica* Skvor. (a) front view; (b) side view.

32a (27) Cells elongate or fusiform. Fig. 27........*CHLOROGONIUM*

Of the 8 species in this genus only 3 are reported from the United States. They are all more elongate than any other members of the Volvocales. Usually found in swamps and shallow ponds, they sometimes appear abundantly in laboratory aquaria.

Fig. 27. *Chlorogonium* sp., with parietal chloroplast covering nearly the entire wall.

32b Cells oval, elliptic, or lobed...............................33

33a Cells lobed...34

33b Cells smooth-walled, without lobes or extensions.............35

34a Cells with 4 posterior lobes; quadrate in end view. Fig. 28......
....*BRACHIOMONAS*

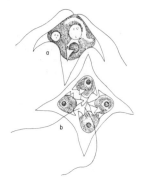

Brachiomonas is a marine genus that often occurs in brackish water and tide pools. The 2 flagella arise from the narrow anterior end of a cell which is 4-lobed (quadrate as seen in end view) and which has an extended, cone-like posterior end.

Fig. 28. *Brachiomonas Westiana* Pascher. (a) vegetative cell; (b) zoospore-formation. (Redrawn from West.)

34b Cell wall irregularly lobed throughout (lumpy), the protoplast often withdrawn from the wall. Fig. 29...........*LOBOMONAS*

The irregular, lumpy appearance of this genus is its chief characteristic. The organisms appear in the same habitat with *Haematococcus* (Fig. 21), i.e., temporary rain water pools and cement basins.

Fig. 29. *Lobomonas rostrata* Hazen.

35a (33) Protoplast with an envelope, decidedly narrowed anteriorly, not the same shape as the envelope. Fig. 30.................
....*SPHAERELLOPSIS*

The genus probably should be classified under *Chlamydomonas* (Fig. 31) although specialists separate its 2 species on the basis of the very wide gelatinous sheath being different in shape from that of the protoplast. It occurs in the tychoplankton of lakes and ponds.

Fig. 30. *Sphaerellopsis fluviatilis* Pascher.

35b Protoplast not narrowed decidedly anteriorly, the protoplast the same shape as the gelatinous envelope, or without an envelope. Fig. 31.................................*CHLAMYDOMONAS*

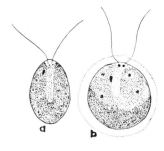

Fig. 31. (a) *Chlamydomonas polypyrenoideum* Presc.; (b) *C. sphagnicolo* Fritsch & Takeda, a species with bipapillate protrusions at the anterior end of the sheath.

Whereas this common genus is represented by approximately 507 described species it is doubtful that they are all distinct. Unless specimens are given careful study they may be confused with other biflagellated genera, or with the motile reproductive cells of other algae. The species of this genus are encountered more frequently than any other members of the Volvocales and are to be found in a great variety of habitats; eu- and tychoplankton, in small rock pools, rain barrels, laboratory aquaria. A favorable place for them is the barnyard pool or watering trough. *C. nivalis* (Bauer) Wille produces red snow at high altitudes.

36a (26) Cells compressed, broadly oval in end view, the 4 flagella inserted in 2 separated pairs. Fig. 32..............PLATYMONAS

Although usually found in brackish water, this genus contains at least 1 species that appears in fresh-water. To make identification the cells should be seen from the top or side to determine whether they are flattened.

Fig. 32. *Platymonas elliptica* G. M. Smith. (a) front view; (b) end view.

36b Cells round in end view, the 4 flagella arising from one point. Fig. 33 ....CARTERIA

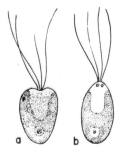

Like *Platymonas* (Fig. 32) this genus is characterized by having 4 flagella, but the cells are round when seen in end view. The chloroplast is variable in shape and may not appear as shown in the illustration. It may be a thin plate along the wall, cup-shaped and covering most of the wall except at the anterior end, or H-shaped.

Fig. 33. *Carteria cordiformis* (Carter) Dies.; (b) *C. Klebsii* Dill.

37a (25) Cells with a single flagellum. Fig. 34......PEDINOMONAS

Cells in this genus have no wall. They are circular or oval and possess a single flagellum which is directed posteriorly so that the organism swims backward. The chloroplast lies basally and along one side. There is a pyrenoid but no eye-spot.

Fig. 34. *Pedinomonas rotunda* Korsch. (Redrawn from Korschikoff.)

39a Cells pear-shaped or oval but with longitudinal folds, 4- to 6-lobed when seen in vertical view. Fig. 35...........STEPHANOPTERA

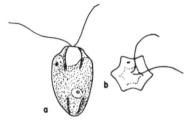

These pyriform motile cells without walls have longitudinal folds (wings) and when seen from the end are 6-radiate and star-like. The chloroplast also has longitudinal flanges which extend into the folds of the cell wall. The eye-spot is rod-like.

Fig. 35. *Stephanoptera gracilis* (Artari) G. M. Smith. (a) front view; (b) end view showing point of attachment of flagella.

39b Cells not pear-shaped, without longitudinal folds..............40

40a Cells oval or pear-shaped, the contents often colored with haematochrome; inhabiting brackish or saline water. Fig. 36.........
....DUNALIELLA

This species and 2 others are apparently the only ones described thus far for the genus, but they are widely distributed judging from reports of them in different parts of the world, occurring in brackish or saline waters. The chloroplast lies in the posterior part of the cell.

Fig. 36. *Dunaliella salina* Teodor. Two differently shaped individuals.

40b Cells inhabiting fresh water; broadly reniform or hexagonal in 'front' view but strongly compressed and narrowed when seen from the side. Fig. 37 . . . . .HETEROMASTIX

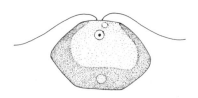

In this genus the cells are transversely, angularly oval with the chloroplast lying along the posterior wall. The 2 flagella are unequal in length, a feature difficult of determination. There is a large, conspicuous pyrenoid and a less conspicuous eye-spot (sometimes lacking).

Fig. 37. *Heteromastix angulata* Korsch.

41a (38) Cells with 4 flagella; pyriform, 4-lobed when seen in vertical view. Fig. 38 . . . . .PYRAMIMONAS

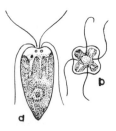

This is *Pyramidomonas* of some authors; contains at least 20 species all of which are 4-lobed when seen in end view. There is a flagellum attached in each of the 4 depressions, between the lobes.

Fig. 38. *Pyramimonas tetrarhynchus* S c h m a r. (a) front view; (b) end view showing points of attachment of the flagella.

41b Cells with 6 or 8 flagella; oval or pyriform, round in end view. Fig. 39 . . . . .POLYBLEPHARIDES

This genus is identified by having a veritable tuft of flagella (usually 8) which are relatively short. There are several contractile vacuoles at the anterior end. If there is an eye-spot it lies lateral about midway in the cell. There may or may not be a pyrenoid. Thus far the only 2 species in the United States have been reported from the Atlantic seaboard.

Fig. 39. *Polyblepharides fragariiformis* Hazen, showing 3 of the contractile vacuoles at the anterior end. (Redrawn from Hazen.)

42a (6) Plant a filament (cells in continuous or in interrupted series) with or without branches; or a flat expanse or an attached cushion with the branches closely appressed so that the basic filamentous plan is not clearly evident; or a tubular, thread-like thallus without cross walls (coenocytic)..204

42b Plants not filamentous, not as above, but solitary cells, or a colony of 2 or more cells inclosed by mucilage or by old mother-cell walls (see Oocystis, Fig. 96), or cells variously adjoined to one another (see Scenedesmus, Fig. 85; Pediastrum, Fig. 81)...............43

43a Cells solitary or gregarious but not adjoined to form colonies. .120

43b Cells adjoined or arranged in colonies......................44

44a Colony composed of 2 trapezoidal cells adjoined along their bases. Fig. 40..EUASTROPSIS

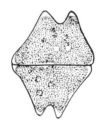

This is the only species of the genus on record. The two cells which compose the 'colony' appear much like those of Pediastrum (Fig. 81). The cell walls are smooth and in general appearance are unlike those of Pediastrum. Euastropsis occurs in tychoplankton and is widely distributed; not uncommon in arctic Alaska.

Fig. 40. *Euastropsis Richteri* (Schmid.) Lag.

44b Colony composed otherwise.................................45

45a Colony composed of cells invested by a common mucilage. (See Oocystis, Fig. 96), with the cells inclosed by old, expanded mother-cell wall, not by mucilage.).................................46

45b Colony composed of an aggregate of cells not inclosed by mucilage, but may be inclosed by old mother-cell wall or fragments of it..82

46a (45) Colony attached or adherent...........................47

46b Colony free-floating or entangled among other algae, but not growing attached. (Frequently algae which are normally attached become separated from their substrate. Look for attaching stalk, disc, or other evidence of the plant having been once attached)......56

47a (46) Colonies in the form of compact packets, free-living or more commonly among the epidermal cells of aquatic plants. Fig. 41..
..CHLOROSARCINA

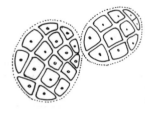

The cells are usually angular from mutual compression and ordinarily are inclosed by a gelatinous sheath. There are 5 species but only 1, *C. consociata* seems to be common in the United States, found in the duckweed *Lemna*. Old, colorless thalli of *Lemna trisulca* often show the green flecks of this and other endophytic algae (*Chlorochytrium Lemnae*, Fig. 107). Two other species are known.

Fig. 41. *Chlorosarcina consociata* (Klebs) G. M. Smith.

47b Colonies not endophytic in the tissues of aquatic plants.......48

48a (47) Colonial mucilage sac-like, balloon-shaped or intestiniform, often macroscopic...49

48b Colonial mucilage of other shapes, or if sac-like, microscopic..50

49a Aquatic; cells without individual sheaths, definitely arranged in 4's (except in age), mostly at the periphery of their common mucilage; under favorable optical conditions showing long, fine, hairlike pseudocilia (false flagella). Fig. 42...........TETRASPORA

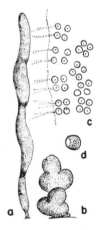

Early in the spring, or throughout the summer in cold running water, gelatinous, balloon-like or intestiniform strands of *Tetraspora* may be found attached to submerged substrates. At times thalli 2 or 3 feet long develop. Most of the dozen or so recognized species are macroscopic, but a few appear as microscopic, floating thalli. Especially when the thalli are young favorable optical conditions will disclose long, fine, shadowy pseudocilia which extend through the colonial mucilage. Compare with *Gloeocystis*. (Fig. 48) which has larger and fewer cells in a colony; no pseudocilia.

Fig. 42. (a) *Tetraspora cylindrica* (Wahl.) C. A. Agardh, habit of colony; (b) *T. gelatinosa* (Vauch) Desvaux, habit of colony; (c) enlargement of *Tetraspora* cells; (d) single cell showing cup-shaped chloroplast.

44

49b Terrestrial (usually); cells sometimes with indistinct sheaths within the colonial mucilage; not definitely arranged in 4's. Fig. 43....
....*PALMELLA*

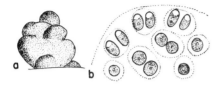

Fig. 43. *Palmella miniata* Liebl. (a) habit of colony; (b) portion of colony showing arrangement of cells and individual cell sheaths.

This plant forms lumpy, gelatinous masses, 2 to 8 mm. in diameter on damp soil or on dripping rocks. The cells of *P. miniata* are often red with the pigment haematochrome, whereas *P. mucosa* Kuetz. (without individual cellular sheaths) is always green. The oval cells, scattered throughout the mucilage may have indistinct, individual sheaths. Like *Gloeocystis* (Fig. 48) which has cup-shaped chloroplasts, *Palmella* may be confused with other gelatinous genera.

50a (48) Colony balloon-like or pear-shaped, narrowed at base to form a stalk-like attachment; pseudocilia usually clearly visible under high magnification. Fig. 44.....................*APIOCYSTIS*

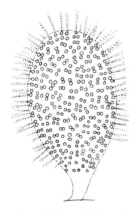

This plant is always in the form of a microscopic, balloon-like sac growing attached to filamentous algae or to aquatic plant stems. The cells are arranged somewhat irregularly in 2's and 4's. The pseudocilia are very long in this genus. *Apiocystis Brauniana* is relatively common, but in the Alaskan Arctic there is a rare species in which the gelatinous sac has a very thick and lamellated sheath and attains a much larger size.

Fig. 44. *Apiocystis Brauniana* Naeg. Diagram of a colony showing cell arrangement and pseudocilia.

50b Colony some other shape; pseudocilia absent..................51

51a Colonial mucilage forming a fusiform-shaped envelope; cells similarly shaped as the envelope, with long axes more or less parallel. Fig. 45 . . . . ***ELAKATOTHRIX***

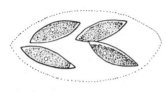

In this genus the cells are somewhat 'cigar'-shaped and occur end to end in pairs or side by side in a fusiform gelatinous sheath. *E. gelatinosa* Wille has both ends of the cell pointed whereas other species have the adjoined poles truncate. In one of the 3 species found in this country, *E. americana* Wille the gelatinous, colonial sheath is irregularly lacy or fringed.

Fig. 45. *Elakatothrix viridis* (Snow) Printz.

51b Colonial mucilage not fusiform **52**

52a Cells cylindrical or elongate-ovoid, scattered throughout amorphous mucilage. Fig. 46 . . . . ***COCCOMYXA***

There are four recorded species of this genus but only *C. dispar* seems to have been found in this country, forming gelatinous masses of varying extent on damp soil, on wet wood, on old fungal sporophores; rarely is free-floating. It has been found also attached to wooden flumes of swiftly flowing water. In subaerial habitats they are often intermingled and closely associated with other unicellular and colonial algae; often show a great variation in size.

Fig. 46. *Coccomyxa dispar* Schmidle. The end of a gelatinous strand, showing oval or bacilliform cells, each with a parietal chloroplast.

52b Cells shaped otherwise **53**

53a Cells elliptical or nearly spherical, arranged in 2's and 4's within ungelatinized walls of mother-cell; eye-spot usually evident. Fig. 47..................PALMELLA-STAGE OF CHLAMYDOMONAS

Fig. 47. *Palmella*-stage of *Chlamydomonas*.

Chlamydomonas (Fig. 31) often becomes quiescent under unfavorable conditions, or as a normal stage in its life history. The cells adhere to a substrate, lose their flagella, but continue to divide, inclosing themselves in mucilage, and form extensive gelatinous masses. The cells are arranged in 2's and 4's, surrounded by muciliaginous sheaths, thus somewhat resembling *Palmella*. (Fig. 43.) In this form *Chlamydomonas* is often mistaken for *Gloeocystis* (Fig. 48). Laboratory aquaria often contain *Chlamydomonas* in this stage. The cells may become actively motile again by developing new flagella.

53b Cells spherical (sometimes oval), irregularly scattered throughout mucilage, or in groups of 4; orange-colored oil globules sometimes present; eye-spot lacking....................................54

54a Cells inclosed by concentric layers of mucilage, individual cell sheaths distinct. Fig. 48.......................GLOEOCYSTIS

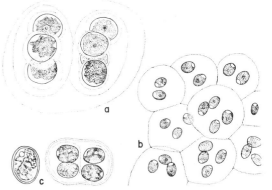

Fig. 48. (a) *Gloeocystis gigas* (Kuetz.) Lag:; (b) G. *ampla* (Kuetz.) Lag; (c) G. *major* Gerneck, showing dense, cup-shaped chloroplast.

There are several species of *Gloeocystis* and all are very common. They are not very distinctive plants and therefore many small, round or oval green cells, especially when inclosed in mucilage, belonging to other genera may be mistaken for them. The concentric layers of mucilage about the cells provide a helpful character for identification. *Gloeocystis ampla* (Kuetz.) Lag. does not always have mucilage in layers, however, but this free-floating species is identified by its oblong or oval cells.

54b Cells without evident individual sheaths; mucilage not in concentric layers..**55**

55a Chloroplast cup-shaped, not covering the entire wall; cells all the same size within the colonial mucilage; not in groups of 4. (See Fig. 43.)...*PALMELLA*

55b Chloroplast covering almost the entire wall; cells variable in size within the colonial mucilage. Fig. 49.........*CHLOROCOCCUM*

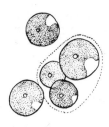

Although this plant occurs on soil it reproduces by swimming reproductive cells (zoospores). Another species, *Chlorococcum infusionum* (Schrank) Menegh. is aquatic and is differentiated from *C. humicola* by the fact that its cells are all uniform in size and shape. Old, wet bones and rocks under dripping water are favorable places for both species. Unless it is *Pleurococcus (Protococcus)*, (Fig. 77), *Chlorococcum humicola* is probably the most widely distributed algal species in the world.

Fig. 49. *Chlorococcum humicola* (Naeg.) Rab. Cells occasionally are seen to be inclosed in a mucilaginous sheath.

56a (46) Colony fusiform, definite in shape. (See Fig. 45.).........
....*ELAKATOTHRIX*

56b Colony not fusiform, but cubical, globular-quadrate, or irregular in shape..**57**

57a Colony regularly spherical, or oval, or a rectangular plate....**69**

57b Colony irregular or some other shape than above (but young stages of *Tetraspora*, Fig. 42, may be somewhat spherical)......**58**

58a Colony of 4 cells in one plane, interconnected by strands, the cells bearing a scale-like fragment of mother-cell wall. Fig. 50...
....*CORONASTRUM*

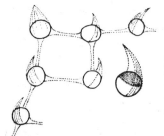

This is a very rare alga and the only one of 3 species in the genus which has been reported in the United States. The arrangement of the cells and their distinctive wing-like scale make identification certain.

Fig. 50. *Coronastrum aestivale* Thompson. (Redrawn from Thompson.)

58b Colony formed otherwise.................................59

59a Colony cubical, consisting of 4 cells at the corners of a hollow cube, the sides of which are formed of gelatinous strands. Fig. 51 ....*PECTODICTYON*

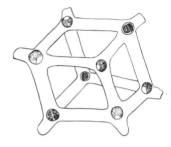

There are two species known for this genus. *P. cubicum* Taft has been found but once since it was originally described from Ohio. It is to be expected in open water plankton.

Fig. 51. *Pectodictyon cubicum* Taft. (Redrawn from Taft.)

59b Colony formed otherwise.................................60

60a Cells arranged in a linear series within gelatinous tubes or strands which are often branched. Fig. 52.............*PALMODICTYON*

Fig. 52. *Palmodictyon viride* Kuetz.

This species and *P. varium* (Naeg.) Lemm. are fairly common in mixtures of algae from the shallow water of ponds and swamps. The former has cells inclosed in individual sheaths, whereas the latter is without cellular sheaths. Some strands of colonial mucilage may be simple, others irregularly branched and sometimes anastomosing.

60b Cells arranged otherwise.................................61

61a Cells cylindrical or elongate-ellipsoid.......................62

61b Cells other shapes....................................63

62a Chloroplast axial, with 1 to several pyrenoids. Fig. 53........
....*MESOTAENIUM*

These oval or oblong cells have an axial, plate-like chloroplast and a wall that is all in one piece (Saccoderm Desmid). Although some of the 14 species occurring in this country are free-floating, others such as *M. macrococcum* (Kuetz.) Roy & Biss. usually occur among mosses and in gelatinous masses on rocky seeps, often at high altitudes.

Fig. 53. *Mesotaenium Greyii* Turner, Fa., showing variation in cell shape.

62b Chloroplast a parietal plate, without a pyrenoid. (See Fig. 46.)..
....*COCCOMYXA*

63a (61) Colony forming stringy, intestiniform masses, sometimes perforated skeins. (See Fig. 42.)....................*TETRASPORA*

63b Colony shaped otherwise...................................64

64a Colony composed of a few (2 to 4) oval cells inclosed in an irregularly shaped, layered, gelatinous sheath. Fig. 54.........
....*DACTYLOTHECE*

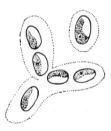

Cells in this genus are shaped as in *Mesotaenium* (Fig. 53) but they are much smaller (not more than 3 μ in diameter) and have a laminate, parietal chloroplast. The cells are inclosed in mucilage and form thin expanded masses on moist rocks. *D. confluens* (Kuetz.) Hansg. is the only species reported from North America.

Fig. 54. *Dactylothece confluens* (Kuetz.) Lag.

64b Colony composed of round, pyriform or oval cells; gelatinous sheath not stratified..65

65a Semicircular fragments of old mother-cell walls partly inclosing daughter cells, or lying about in the mucilage. Fig. 55........
....*SCHIZOCHLAMYS*

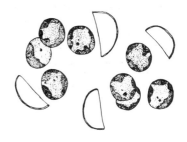

At times the free-floating, gelatinous masses of this plant may be of macroscopic size and so abundant that they may be scooped from the surface of the water by hand. More frequently the growths are less extensive and small aggregates of cells occur intermingled with other algae in shallow water situations. The fragments of old mother-cell walls help in identification of this plant. Un-

Fig. 55. *Schizochlamys gelatinosa* A. Braun.

der favorable optical conditions a tuft of long, fine pseudocilia are discernible, 4 to 8 from each cell. The chloroplasts are usually plate-like and parietal, but may appear massive. This is an anomalous plant, placed in the Tetrasporales because of the gelatinous colony and the pseudocilia. The presence of oil rather than starch as a reserve food raises a question as to its true affinity.

65b Fragments of old mother-cell walls not apparent..............66

66a Colonies sac-like or irregularly globose; cells arranged in 4's. (See Fig. 42.)....................................*TETRASPORA*

66b Colonies shaped otherwise; cells not arranged in 4's........67

67a Cells ovoid, compactly arranged in semi-opaque mucilage which is often brown or yellow and so obscures the cells; colonies frequently compounded by interconnecting strands of tough mucilage between clusters of cells. Fig. 56........*BOTRYOCOCCUS*

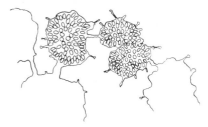

Fig. 56. *Botryococcus Braunii* Kuetz., showing an expression in which a colonial complex is formed by interconnecting strands of tough mucilage. Colonies frequently appear solitary and as a yellowish-brown lump in which individual cells can scarcely be seen, if at all. The color of the colony lies mostly in the mucilage. The species often forms blooms, especially in hard water lakes.

67b Cells round, oval or pyriform, not arranged in semi-opaque mucilage (mucilage of juvenile *Botryococcus* is colorless)..........68

68a Cells round or oval, in 2's or 4's within gelatinous sheaths; colonies solitary or aggregated. (See Fig. 48.)...........*GLOEOCYSTIS*

68b Cells pyriform, radiately disposed within an irregularly shaped gelatinous matrix; colony sometimes adherent. Fig. 57........
....*ASKENASYELLA*

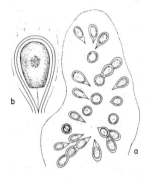

The gelatinous matrix which incloses the pear-shaped cells may be nearly globular, or irregular in outline. The cells are radiately arranged with the narrow end directed inward. The parietal chloroplast is in the broad anterior end. A fine, protoplasmic thread extends to the posterior end of the cell from the chloroplast. Tychoplanktonic, or attached.

Fig. 57. *Askenasyella chlamydopus* Schm. (Redrawn from Schmidle.). (a) colony; (b) single cell.

69a (57) Cells incised or constricted in the midregion to form semicells (cell halves), the cells often interconnected by fine, gelatinous strands. Fig. 58.............................*COSMOCLADIUM*

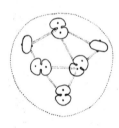

Fig. 58. *Cosmocladium tuberculatum* Presc.

This species has every appearance of a tiny *Cosmarium*-like Desmid in which the cells are enveloped in a colorless, gelatinous sheath. *Cosmocladium* belongs to the Placoderm Desmids, those which have the wall in 2 sections that adjoin in the midregion, usually with an incision (sinus) forming an isthmus between 2 semicells. There are but few species in the genus. Like the majority of Desmids it occurs in soft or acid water bogs. Under properly reduced light the fine, often double gelatinous strands interconnecting the cells can be determined.

69b Cells not constricted to form semicells.......................70

70a Chloroplast star-shaped, the radiating processes with their outer ends flattened against the wall. Fig. 59........*ASTEROCOCCUS*

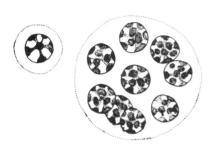

This species and *A. limneticus* G. M. Smith are the only ones known to occur in North America. *A. superbus* may occur singly or in small colonies of 2 or 4 cells and shows the star-shaped chloroplast more clearly than does the former which has smaller cells, 8 to 12, rarely 16 in number within a common envelop. *A. limneticus*, as the name suggests, is found ın open water plankton.

Fig. 59. *Asterococcus superbus* (Cienk.) Scherf.

70b Chloroplast not star-shaped.................................**71**

71a Cells arranged in groups of 4 at the ends of branching, mucilaginous strands (focus carefully into the colony). See Fig. 60......**72**

71b Cells not arranged at the ends of branching strands..........**73**

72a Cells appearing both reniform (bean-shaped) and ovoid in the same colony. Fig. 60......................*DIMORPHOCOCCUS*

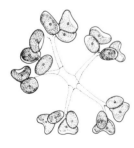

In this plant the cells are in clusters of 4, 2 of which when seen in 'top' view appear oval, whereas others, seen from the side, appear reniform or somewhat crescent-shaped, hence the genus name. *Dimorphococcus lunatus* A. Br. is often abundant in soft-water lakes, whereas the other species known from this country, *D. cordatus* Wolle, is less frequently found. Both species may occur in open-water plankton or in the tychoplankton near shore. A character that is helpful in identification is a negative one, the absence of a conspicuous gelatinous sheath inclosing the colony.

Fig. 60. *Dimorphococcus lunatus* A. Braun.

72b Cells spherical or broadly oval, all the same shape within the colony. Fig. 61 . . . . *DICTYOSPHAERIUM*

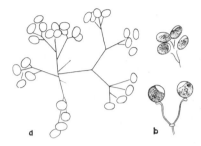

Cells are in clusters of 4, as in *Dimorphococcus* (Fig. 60), but all the same shape, round or oval. The interconnecting fibers, the remains of the old mother-cell wall are finer than in that genus. Sometimes an indefinite gelatinous envelope is seen. The chloroplast is a cup-shaped, parietal layer covering most of the wall.

Fig. 61. *Dictyosphaerium pulchellum* Wood. (a) habit of colony; (b) individual cells at ends of strands.

73a (71) Cells globular **74**

73b Cells other shapes, ovoid, fusiform, crescent-shaped, or bean-shaped **76**

74a Cells with distinct sheaths; cells inclosed in layered, colonial mucilage. (See Fig. 48.) . . . . *GLOEOCYSTIS*

74b Cells without distinct sheaths; colonial mucilage not layered . . . **75**

75a Chloroplast cup-shaped with a conspicuous pyrenoid (a doughnut-shaped, starch-storing body, usually shiny); colony often including clusters of smaller daughter cells. Fig. 62 . . . .
. . . . *SPHAEROCYSTIS*

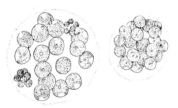

This plant, of which there is only 1 species in North American records, should be compared with *Planktosphaeria* (Fig. 63). There is 1, cup-shaped chloroplast, and the colony almost invariably shows clusters of small cells formed by the division of the parent cell into 4 or 8 daughter cells. There is a wide gelatinous sheath but the individual cells do not

Fig. 62. *Sphaerocystis Schroeteri* Chod.

show the lamellated envelope of *Gloeocystis* (Fig. 48) a genus which may be confused with *Sphaerocystis*. Young cells of *Planktosphaeria* may have a cup-shaped chloroplast.

75b Chloroplasts several polygonal plates, each with a pyrenoid (chloroplast single when cells are young); colony not containing clusters of daughter cells. Fig. 63..................*PLANKTOSPHAERIA*

This plant, only 1 species known, occurs mostly in the tychoplankton among other algae, but may also appear in the euplankton incidentally. Unless care is used this plant may be confused with *Gloeocystis* (Fig. 48), *Sphaerocystis* (Fig. 62) or other spherical algal cells within a mucilaginous sheath. When mature the cells are recognizable by their angular, 5-sided chloroplasts, each of which contains a pyrenoid. The colonial sheath is often very thin and difficult of determination.

Fig. 63. *Plankto-sphaeria gelatinosa* G. M. Smith.

76a (73) Cells lunate or sickle-shaped, tapered and pointed at the apices. 77

76b Cells bean-shaped, oval or spindle-shaped, the apices sometimes tapered, but rounded or blunt at the poles...................78

77a Cells decidedly curved, with the 2 poles nearly touching one another, arranged irregularly in groups of 4 with the convex walls apposed. Fig. 64..............................*KIRCHNERIELLA*

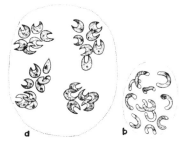

The crescent-shaped or arcuate cells of this genus are inclosed in a mucilage which sometimes is indistinct. *Kirchneriella*, of which there are 5 species in the United States, usually occurs in open-water plankton. The species are differentiated by degrees of curvature and variations in stoutness. The cells are mostly so sharply curved that their apices nearly touch whereas in *Selenastrum* (Fig. 78), with which *Kirchneriella* should be compared, the cells are symmetrically crescent-shaped and they are not inclosed by a gelatinous sheath.

Fig. 64. (a) *Kirchneriella lunaris* (Kirch.) Moebius; (b) *K. obesa* var. *major* (Ber.) G. M. Smith.

77b Cells symmetrically crescent-shaped, in groups of 4, 2 of which face one another (concave margins apposed). Fig. 65.........
....*TETRALLANTOS*

This rare species (the only one in the genus) is widely distributed. The characteristic arrangement of the cells is determined at the time that they are formed in groups of 4 within the mother cell. After the mother-cell wall breaks down to release the daughter-cells fragments of the wall may persist as interconnecting or radiating threads within the colonial mucilage which is often very thin and difficult of determination.

Fig. 65. *Tetrallantos Lagerheimii* Teiling.

78a (76) Cells curved sausage-shaped with rounded ends, adjoined to one another by fine threads; gelatinous sheath wide. Fig. 66....
....*TOMACULUM*

These sausage-like cells, sometimes with lateral, lobe-like extensions, are interconnected by thread-like strands. Upward of 20 such joined cells are inclosed in a hyaline, gelatinous sheath to form free-floating colonies. There are 1 or 2 parietal chloroplasts, each with a pyrenoid. The single species has been found only in North Carolina.

Fig. 66. *Tomaculum catenatum* Whitford. (Redrawn from Whitford.) (a) Colony; (b) single cell.

78b Cells shaped or arranged otherwise...........................79

79a Cells fusiform or spindle-shaped..............................81

79b Cells ovate, bean-shaped, or oblong..........................80

80a Cells oval, somewhat irregularly arranged in 4's, forming a flat plate. Fig. 67 . . . .*DISPORA*

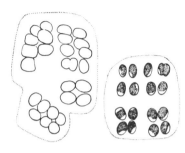

There is only one species of *Dispora* in the United States and apparently is rare. The cells are in irregular rectilinear series and usually show something of a quartet arrangement within a flat, gelatinous sheath. The plant should be compared with *Crucigenia* (Fig. 83). especially *C. irregularis* in which cells are indefinitely arranged in 4's.

Fig. 67. *Dispora crucigenioides* Printz.

80b Cells bean-shaped or oblong, reproducing by autospores which are retained within the enlarged mother-cell wall (the wall may gelatinize and appear as a mucilaginous sheath). Fig. 68 . . . .
. . . .*NEPHROCYTIUM*

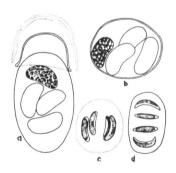

Most of the 7 species of this genus which occur in the United States have reniform or bean-shaped cells, often with 1 convex lateral wall and 1 flattened or slightly concave. They occur in mixtures of algae in the tychoplankton, although 2 species, *N. Agardhianum* Naeg. and *N. limneticum* G. M. Smith are usually found in the euplankton. The former has elongate, almost vermiform cells which are sometimes curved or spirally twisted.

Fig. 68. (a) *Nephrocytium ecdysiscepanum* W. West; (b) *N. obesum* W. & G. S. West; (a) *N. limneticum* (G. M. Smith) G. M. Smith; (d) *N. lunatum* W. West.

81a (79) Cells in linear pairs, 1 or several pairs within a common mucilaginous investment (cells with long axes approximately parallel, sometimes solitary). (See Fig. 45.) . . . .*ELAKATOTHRIX*

81b Cells arranged in parallel bundles, reproducing by autospores (daughter colonies forming within the mother-cell). Fig. 69.....
....*QUADRIGULA*

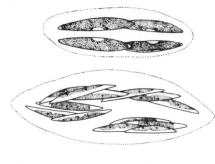

There are 4 species found in the euplankton of lakes, all of which have elongate-fusiform or 'cigar'-shaped cells. The species illustrated has cells with bluntly rounded poles whereas the other two have pointed apices. The cells occur in rather compact bundles of 4, all lying parallel in the the colonial envelope.

Fig. 69. *Quadrigula Chodatii* (Tanner-Fullman) G. M. Smith.

82a (45) Cells (or some of them in the colony) bearing long, gelatinous bristles or scales, or hairs.............................83

82b Cells without gelatinous bristles; with or without spines, shorter or longer than the cell.....................................87

83a Cells arranged in a quadrate colony of 4, interconnected by strands, each cell bearing a scale-like fragment of mother-cell wall. (See Fig. 50.)...........................*CORONASTRUM*

83b Colony formed otherwise.....................................84

84a Cells in clusters of from 2 to 6 (rarely solitary), bearing more than 1 hair...85

84b Cells bearing but 1 hair-like bristle...........................86

85a Hair with a gelatinous sheath at the base . Fig. 70..*CONOCHAETE*

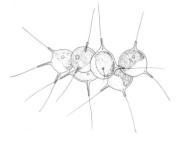

The globular cells of this genus are epiphytic and are inclosed by a gelatinous envelope from which 2 or 3 setae arise, the bases sheathed.

Fig. 70. *Conochaete comosa* Klebahn.

85b Hairs without a gelatinous sheath at the base. Fig. 71. . . . .
. . . .*OLIGOCHAETOPHORA*

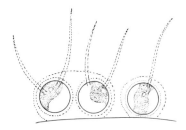

The epiphytic cells bear 2 or 3 simple, unsheathed spine-like bristles. The cells occur solitary or in clumps of from 2 to 4 inclosed by a common gelatinous sheath. Compare with Co*n-ochaete* (Fig. 70) and *Chaetosphaeridium* (Fig. 73).

Fig. 71. *Oligochaetophora simplex* G. S. West.

86a (84) Cells forming an attached, compact cluster within the mother-cell wall which bears a branched hair that has no sheath. Fig. 72 . . . .*DICRANOCHAETE*

Although this curious plant usually occurs as single cells, the individuals may be clustered as a result of recent cell division. It grows on filamentous algae and other submerged aquatic plants and apparently is very rare. The unique branched seta which is produced from the lower side of the cell makes identification certain.

Fig. 72. *Dicranochaete reniformis* Heiron.

86b Cells loosely arranged side by side in a cluster, each bearing an unbranched hair with a basal sheath. Fig. 73. . . . .
. . . .*CHAETOSPHAERIDIUM*

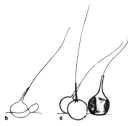

Fig. 73. *Chaetosphaeridium globosum* (Nordst.) Klebahn. (a) group of cells; (b) one cell showing tube-like utricle which may extend from one cell to another and so form a sort of colony.

The globular, hair-bearing cells of this genus occur either single or in aggregations of from 2 to 8, living epiphytically on larger algae or aquatic plants. Frequently the cells are loosened from their substrate and are found floating free. This genus and *Dicranochaete* (Fig. 72) are anomalous members of the Coleochaetaceae. They are included there because of the type of sheathed bristle, in spite of the fact that they are not filamentous.

87a (82) Cells attached at the ends of branching, gelatinous stalks, epizoic on microcrustaceans **88**

87b Cells not at the ends of branching, gelatinous strands; not epizoic **89**

88a Cells ellipsoid or somewhat fusiform; chloroplast 1 or 2 longitudinal, lateral bands. Fig. 74 .... *CHLORANGIUM*

This organism becomes attached, anterior end down, to small crustaceans and other microscopic animals by means of a gelatinous stalk. Although a swimming cell, the flagella are thrown off when the cells become attached but the cells continue to divide, forming a stalk which branches as new cells are formed so that a colony is produced. Some small animals such as *Cyclops* may go swimming about with veritable plumes of the green cells growing on their antennae. The cells have 2 elongate, parietal chloroplasts. *Chlorangium* is a sedentary member of the Volvocales according to some systems of classification. Compare *Chlorangium* with *Colacium* (Fig. 75) a member of the Euglenophyta.

Fig. 74. *Chlorangium stentorinum* (Ehr.) Stein.

88b Cells ovate to oblong or ovoid; chloroplasts numerous, ovoid discs. Fig. 75 .... *COLACIUM*

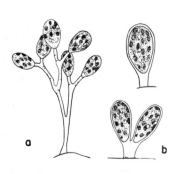

Microscopic animals, especially crustaceans, may appear green because of the large numbers of *Colacium* individuals attached to them, either singly or in plume-like clusters. Like *Chlorangium* (Fig. 74) this organism is a motile green cell which, however, has numerous *Euglena*-like chloroplasts (Fig. 9) and a conspicuous red eye-spot. The rather specific association of the algal cells with the animal host incites speculation as to how this relationship is maintained.

a

b

Fig. 75. (a) *Colacium arbuscula* Stein; (b) *C. vesiculosum* Ehr.

89a (87) Cells ellipsoid or spindle-shaped, attached end to end, forming loose, branching chains . Fig. 76. . . . . .DACTYLOCOCCUS

This anomalous genus is known from soil collections of algae. The characteristic chain-like arrangement of the cells develops as the cells are cultivated whereas they probably are solitary in nature.

Fig. 76. *Dactylococcus infusionum* Naeg. (Redrawn from Smith.)

89b Cells not arranged in branching chains. 90

90a Cells globose or flattened on some sides from mutual compression; forming green films on moist substrates. Fig. 77. . . . .
. . . . . .PROTOCOCCUS

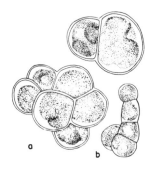

This plant, also known the world over as *Pleurococcus vulgaris* Menegh., forms the familiar green film on the moist side of trees, rocks, boards, *etc.* Essentially unicellular, it forms clumps from repeated cell division and the occasional tendency to form filaments has led students of the algae to classify it in the fliamentous order Ulotrichales, and to consider it as having been reduced to its present simple morphological condition. It reproduces only by cell division and is easily distributed by wind, water and insects so that it appears throughout the world almost everywhere that subaerial life can exist. There is an interesting selectivity exhibited, however, in respect to moisture and chemistry of the substrate. It is more commonly found on the damp bark of deciduous or hardwood trees rather than on conifers.

Fig. 77. *Protococcus viridis* Ag. (a) clump of cell; (b) filamentous tendency in the cell arrangement.

90b Cells differently shaped, not producing films on aerial substrates
. 91

91a Cells crescent-shaped or sharply acicular (or needle-shaped). . .92

91b Cells some other shape. 93

92a Cells strongly crescent-shaped, closely clustered but not entangled. Fig. 78..*SELENASTRUM*

Fig. 78. *Selenastrum gracile* Reinsch.

These gracefully curved cells occur in clusters of from 4 to 32, with a tendency to have the convex or 'outer' walls approximated. The curvature of the 'outer' and 'inner' walls of the crescent are more nearly equal than in the somewhat similarly shaped cells of *Kirchneriella* (Fig. 64), a genus which has cells irregularly arranged within a gelatinous envelope. Four species are commonly found in this country, mostly differentiated by size of cell and degree of curvature. Mixtures of algae from shallow water situations often include *Selenastrum* but they may be found also in euplankton.

92b Cells straight, or acicular, or only slightly crescent-shaped, loosely entangled about one another (frequently solitary rather than colonial). Fig. 79............................*ANKISTRODESMUS*

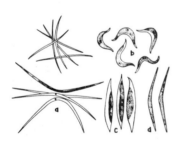

Fig. 79. (a) *Ankistrodesmus falcatus* (Corda) Ralfs; (b) *A. convolutus* Corda; (c) *A. Braunii* (Naeg.) Brunn.; (d) *A. fractus* (W. &. G. S. West) Brunn.

Although there are about 12 species of this genus common in the United States, *A. falcatus* is probably the one most frequently collected. It occurs as solitary or loosely clustered needles or slightly fusiform-shaped cells intermingled with other algae, or sometimes forming almost pure growths in artificial pools or in laboratory aquaria. One species, *A. spiralis* (Turn.) Lemm., has needle-shaped cells spirally twisted about one another to form bundles.

93a (91) Cells attached either along their side or end walls to form definite patterns, nets, plates, triangular clusters or short rows..**94**

93b Cells attached otherwise; if adjoined by lateral walls then not forming definite patterns....................................**109**

94a Cells cylindrical, 1 cell attached by 2 others at end walls repeatedly to form a network. Fig. 80............HYDRODICTYON

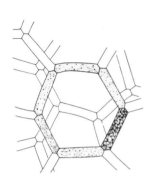

This is the familiar "water net" which often grows in such dense mats in lakes, small ponds and irrigation ditches as to become a troublesome weed. This unique alga is able to reproduce very rapidly because each cell of the net in turn produces a new cylindrical net of small cells within it, which upon escape enlarges enormously, each cell again producing a net. The nets are of macroscopic size and there is a report of one found more than 2 feet in length. It is thought that the 'irst written record referring to a specific ilga is of Hydrodictyon in ancient Chinese literature.

Fig. 80. *Hydrodictyon reticulatum* (L.) Lagerheim.

94b Cells some other shape, not attached to form a network.......95

95a Cells arranged to form flat, circular or rectangular plates. (Fig. 81) 96

95b Cells not arranged to form flat plates.......................99

96a Cells forming circular plates (sometimes irregularly subcircular), the marginal cells sometimes different in shape from those within. Fig. 81....................................PEDIASTRUM

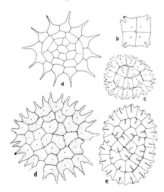

Although there are many species of this genus the cells all have a great similarity, varying only slightly in shape and wall markings. They can be identified as *Pediastrum* by the plate-like arrangement of the cells. In some species the plate is continuous whereas in others there are interstices and fenestrations. Commonly the cells at the margin differ in shape from those within. One species, *P. tetras* (Ehr.) Ralfs, contains only 4 cells in the colony but there may be as many as 32 or 64 (always some multiple of 2). Rarely a 2-celled colony may be seen in which instance it might be mistaken for *Euastropsis* (Fig. 40). *Pediastrum* cell walls are highly resistant to decay and many species are found in fossil or semi-fossil condition. The author knows of no instance

Fig. 81. (a) *Pediastrum simplex* (Meyen) Lemm.; (b) *P. tetras* (Ehr.) Ralfs; (c) *P. biradiatum* var. *emarginatum* fa. *convexum* Presc.; (d) *P. Boryanum* (Turp.) Menegh; (e) *P. obtusum* Lucks.

in which *Pediastrum* cells have been found parasitized by aquatic fungi or bacteria. Colonies are often found in the psammon.

96b Cells not arranged to form circular plates...................97

97a Cells triangular or ovoid, forming quadrangular plates, bearing 1 or more spines. Fig. 82........................*TETRASTRUM*

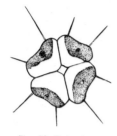

There are probably 7 species of this genus reported from the United States. They occur in the euplankton and are readily identified by their arrangement in flat plates of 4, the cells bearing 1 to 4 spines on the outer free walls. The cells are oval or heart-shaped or angular from mutual compression.

Fig. 82. *Tetrastrum heterocanthum (Nordst.) Chod.*

97b Cells rectangular or trapezoidal, or if oval, without spines......98

98a Cells rectangular, oval or trapezoidal, the outer walls entire (not incised); arranged in 4's to form quadrate plates, or in multiples of 4. Fig. 83.....................................*CRUCIGENIA*

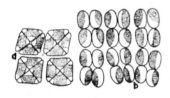

These cells (like *Tetrastrum*, Fig. 82) occur in 4's but usually form multiple colonies or groups of rectangular plates. There are about 15 species in the United States, differentiated by the shape of the cell which may be oval, triangular, or elliptic in outline.

Fig. 83. (a) *Crucigenia tetrapedia* (Kirch.) W. & G. S. West; (b) *C. rectangularis* (A. Braun) Gay.

98b Cells trapezoidal, the outer free walls deeply incised, forming oval or somewhat angular plates (only 4 cells present in some colonies). (See Fig. 81.)..........................*PEDIASTRUM*

99a (95)Cell wall with spines....................................100

99b Cell wall without spines....................................103

100a Cells ellipsoid, spines numerous, needle-like; cells (usually solitary) arranged side by side because of interlocking of spines which are indefinite in number. Fig. 84............*FRANCEIA*

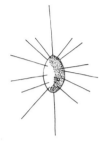

This and 2 other species occur in the euplankton of lakes but rather rarely. The cells are solitary but they may be clustered from the interlocking of the needle-like spines which cover the wall. *Lagerheimia* (Fig. 134) has a similar shape and needle-like spines that are confined to the poles or to the midregion of the cell.

Fig. 84. *Franceia Droescheri* (Lemm.) G. M. Smith.

100b Cells ovoid or spherical; spines few (1 to 4); cells definitely arranged and definite in number.........................101

101a Cells ovoid, arranged side by side in 1, or 2 alternating rows; spines short, mostly arising from the poles of the cells only. Fig. 85.....................................*SCENEDESMUS*

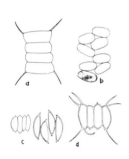

There are numerous species and varieties of this genus, occurring in both tycho- and euplankton. The cells are oval, fusiform, or crescent-shaped according to species. In some species there are two shapes of cells within the same colony. Although usually in a row of 4, some species have cells in a double, alternating series, and sometimes there may be a single row of 12 cells. *Scenedesmus* species invariably appear in laboratory cultures and aquaria, often coloring the water green; are frequently found in the psammon. Under unnatural conditions the plants may appear as single cells. Perhaps the most common species is *S. quadricauda* and its varieties (Fig. 85a).

Fig. 85. (a) *Scenedesmus quadricauda* (Turp.) de Bréb.; (b) *S. bijuga* var. *alternans* (Reinsch) Hansg.; (c) *S. incrassatulus* var. *mononae* G. M. Smith (Redrawn from Tiffany); (d) *S. opoliensis* P. Richter.

101b Cells spherical, in groups of 4 or in multiples of 4 to form compound colonies; outer walls bearing long, slender spines....102

102a Colony triangular; spines 1 to 7. Fig. 86.......*MICRACTINIUM*

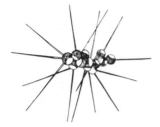

This rare alga occurs in the euplankton, having clusters of 4 round cells arranged in the form of a pyramid. Each cell bears 1 to several long, tapering spines. Another species which is also seldom seen is *M. quadrisetum* (Lemm.) G. M. Smith, having oval or elliptic cells.

Fig. 86. *Micractinium pusillum* Fres.

102b Colony pyramidal, with outer free wall of cells bearing a single stout spine. Fig. 87..............................*ERRERELLA*

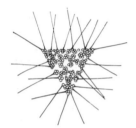

Cells of this plant, of which there is but a single species, are arranged to form a 3-dimension pyramid. It is known only from the euplankton and apparently is very rare, although it has been reported from several parts of the United States.

Fig. 87. *Errerella bornhemiensis* Conrad.

103a (99) Cells spherical or polygonal, arranged to form hollow, spherical or many-sided colonies; cells adjoining by interconnecting protuberances of the mucilaginous sheath. Fig. 88..*COELASTRUM*

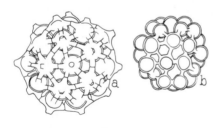

As the genus name suggests, cells of this plant are arranged to form a hollow colony. In some species the cells are closely associated and the hollow feature is discerned with difficulty, whereas in others the cells are clearly separated in a peripheral layer and interconnected by prominent 'arms' of the mucilaginous sheath. There are about

Fig. 88. (a) *Coelastrum cambricum* Archer (Redrawn from Smith); (b) *C. microporum* Naegeli.

14 species known from the United States. These differ in respect to the shape of the cell and the length of the processes of the sheath which in some produce marginal protuberances. *Coelastrum microporum* is especially common in both eu- and tychoplankton.

103b Cells not forming hollow colonies, not so adjoined..........104

104a Cells fusiform, radiating from a common center. Fig. 89.......
....ACTINASTRUM

Tnese 'cigar'-shaped cells are arranged in radiating colonies. The species illustrated here is more common in the plankton than *A. gracillimum* G. M. Smith which has cells about as wide at the apices as in the midregion.

Fig. 89. *Actinastrum Hantz-schii* Lag.

104b Cells shaped otherwise, not forming a colony of radiating cells
....105

105a Cells ellipsoid to fusiform, adjoined end to end, forming chain-like series. (See Fig. 76.)...................*DACTYLOCOCCUS*

105b Cells not forming chains................................106

106a Cells ovoid, ellipsoid or fusiform, adjoined by their lateral walls to form a row of 4 in a single series, or a double series in which the cells are alternating. (See Fig. 85).........*SCENEDESMUS*

106b Cells globular or variously shaped, not attached side by side in one plane...107

107a Cells fusiform or trapezoidal, attached with their long axes parallel about a common center. Fig. 90.............*TETRADESMUS*

This plant resembles some *Scenedesmus* species (Fig. 85) but differs in having the cells quadrately arranged rather than in a series in 1 plane. There are but 2 species known in the United States, both of them from the euplankton of Wisconsin lakes. *T. wisconsinense* G. M. Smith has trapezoidal cells.

Fig. 90. *Tetrades-mus Smithii* Presc.

107b Cells some other shape and not attached about a common center 108

108a Cells crescent-shaped, in groups of 4, 2 with concave sides toward one another, the other 2 cells in another plane with the poles at one end only in juxtaposition. (See Fig. 65.)..........
....*TETRALLANTOS*

108b Cells sickle-shaped, fusiform or crescent-shaped, twisted about one another. (See Fig. 79.)................*ANKISTRODESMUS*

109a (93) Cells adjoined by gelatinous strands or threads formed from the remains of old mother-cell walls......................110

109b Cells not adjoined by remains of old mother-cell walls......112

110a Cells spindle-shaped, in clusters of 4-8-16 at the ends of radiating gelatinous stalks. Fig. 91..................*ACTIDESMIUM*

This rare plant occurs in the tychoplankton of shallow pools; also including the Arctic. The star-shaped clusters of cells at the end of radiating (sometimes dichotomously branched) gelatinous stalks render it certain of identification. The clusters of cells result from the fact that zoospores formed in the cells remain clustered at the tip of the mother-cell. The chloroplast is parietal or diffuse and does not contain a pyrenoid as far as known.

Fig. 91. *Actidesmium Hookeri* Reinsch.

110b Cells shaped or arranged otherwise......................111

111a Cells globose, in clumps of 4-8, the groups held together by looplike fragments of old mother-cell wall. Fig. 92.......*WESTELLA*

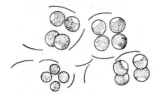

This plant should be compared with *Dictyosphaerium* (Fig. 61) which it may resemble superficially at times. *Westella* has no gelatinous envelope and although there are strands left by the old mother-cell wall they do not produce the regular, radiate structures as in *Dictyosphaerium*.

Fig. 92. *Westella botryoides* (W. West) de Wild.

111b Cells appearing oval and bean-shaped in the same colony, in clusters at the ends of radiating, branched strands. (See Fig. 60.)
....*DIMORPHOCOCCUS*

112a (109) Cells pear-shaped, bean-shaped or somewhat crescent-shaped; cells arranged at the ends of radiating, stout, gelatinous strands to form a globular colony. Fig. 93 . . . . *SORASTRUM*

There are only 4 species of this genus reported from the United States, of which *S. spinulosum* Naeg. is probably the most common in plankton. This species has relatively stout, short spines and the basal pedicel is scarcely developed so that the colony appears as a compact cluster.

Fig. 93. *Sorastrum americanum* (Bohlin) Schmidle.

112b Cells not so arranged, without spines or with spines different than above 113
113a Cells spherical or oval, in 2's and 4's, separated from one another by semi-opaque masses of dark mucilage which form X-shaped bands. Fig. 94 . . . . *GLOEOTAENIUM*

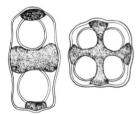

This unique plant is rare but widely distributed. When it occurs at all it is relatively abundant in a habitat. Collections of miscellaneous algae in shallow pools and from the margins of lakes often yield this species.

Fig. 94. *Gloeotaenium Loitelsbergerianum* Hansg.

113b Cells not separated from one another by masses of dark mucilage 114
114a Cells bearing long, needle-like spines (colonial only because of entangled spines). Fig. 95 . . . . *GOLENKINIA*

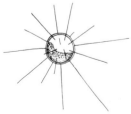

There are but 3 species of this genus reported, all of them common in tow samples from the open water of lakes. *G. radiata* Chod. has spines 2 to 3 times the diameter of the cell in length, whereas *G. paucispina* West & West has more numerous spines that are about equal to the cell diameter in length.

Fig. 95. *Golenkinia radiata* (Chodat) Wille.

114b Cells without spines...................................115

115a Cells inclosed by old mother-cell wall.....................116

115b Cells not inclosed by old mother-cell wall..................117

116a Cells somewhat bean-shaped or kidney-shaped, or broadly elliptic (old mother-cell wall often appearing as a mucilaginous sheath). (See Fig. 68.)...............................*NEPHROCYTIUM*

116b Cells elliptic, lemon-shaped, or nearly cylindrical, 1 or more generations of mother-cell walls inclosing daughter cells. Fig. 96 ....*OOCYSTIS*

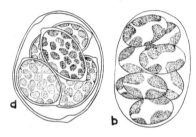

Fig. 96. (a) *Oocystis Eremosphaeria* G. M. Smith; (b) *O. Borgei* Snow.

There are several species of this genus common in both euplankton and tychoplankton. The various forms are differentiated by the presence or absence of nodules at the poles, and by the number of chloroplasts. Two or 3 generations of cell walls may be inclosed within an original mother-cell wall which enlarges so that it often appears as a gelatinous sheath and therefore is misleading as a differentiating genus character.

117a (115) Cells spherical, occurring as evenly distributed clumps within the gelatinous sheaths which sometimes are lacking (or invisible); chloroplasts several angular plates. (See Fig. 63.)............
....*PLANKTOSPHAERIA*

117b Cells variously shaped but not distributed in clumps as above; often densely aggregated; chloroplast 1, parietal...........118

118a Cells spherical or angular from mutual compression when occurring in clumps; subaerial............................119

118b Cells fusiform or needle-shaped; aquatic. (See Fig. 79.)........
....*ANKISTRODESMUS*

119a Cells spherical, clustered but not adjoined, sometimes solitary. See Fig. 49................................*CHLOROCOCCUM*

119b Cells in dense clumps, forming a film or layer on moist subaerial substrates; cells spherical or angular from mutual compression. (See Fig. 77.)......................*PROTOCOCCUS*
(*Pleurococcus*)

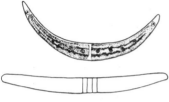

Fig. 97. *Closterium* spp. Two of the many variations in curvature and cell proportions in this genus. Some species have almost straight cells, or only slightly bowed.

This Desmid usually has distinctly lunate or crescent-shaped cells, but some species are nearly straight, or have one margin bowed and the other almost straight. A few species have the poles extended to form long, nearly straight processes which may be swollen slightly at the tip. Although this genus does not show the constriction of the cell to form 2 semicells characteristic of the Placoderm Desmids, the cell contents are symmetrically divided into 2 portions with the nucleus centrally located. A never-failing characteristic of *Closterium* is the polar vacuoles containing vibrating granules of gypsum. In most species the wall is striated, sometimes obscurely.

123a Cells attached by a slender stipe to other algae or to micro-fauna. Fig. 98..................................*CHARACIUM*

There are numerous species in this genus, differentiated by shape of cell and by presence or absence of a stalk. Some are very minute and are easily overlooked, whereas others are larger and grow in associations so as to form patches on filamentous algae or on small animals. The genus *Characiopsis* (Fig. 245) contains species shaped like some of those of *Characium* and care should

Fig. 98. (a) *Characium Debaryanum* (Reinsch) De Toni; (b) *C. ornithocephalum* A. Braun; (c) *C. rostratum* Reinhard.

be used in determining the color of the chloroplast and the presence or absence of a pyrenoid. *Characiopsis* has a yellow pigment predominating and the starch test is negative; is a member of the Chrysophyta.

123b Cells not attached by a stipe..............................**124**

124a Wall at the poles of the cell extended to form a slender seta, one of which may be forked; chloroplasts extending the full length of the cell. Fig. 99.....................*SCHROEDERIA*

Of the 3 species found in the United States, *S. setigera* (Schröd.) Lemm., is the most common. The cells have a spine at both poles which is undivided, whereas *S. ancora* G. M. Smith, also fairly common in plankton, has one polar process forked at the tip. In a Michigan pond the former species occurred as practically the only member of the plankton throughout winter months.

Fig. 99. *Schroederia Judayi* G. M. Smith.

124b Tips of the cells narrowed to fine points at least at one end with the poles narrowly rounded, tip not seta-like but narrowly pointed; chloroplast not extending the full length of the cell. Fig. 100......................................*OUROCOCCUS*

This rare plant might be confused easily with *Ankistrodesmus* spp. (Fig. 79) but the cells are usually stouter. It is closely related to *Elakatothrix* (Fig. 45) in the Order Tetrasporales because the cells retain the ability to divide vegetatively to form new individuals, whereas in the Order Chlorococcales, which includes cells similar in shape to *Ourococcus*, the cells cannot undergo division but must form new individuals within the wall of the parent cell.

Fig. 100. *Ourococcus bicaudatus* Grob. (Redrawn from G. M. Smith.)

125a (122) Cells very slender, needle-like or sometimes fusiform (usually in clusters but may be solitary), often only slightly crescent-shaped; chloroplast parietal, the outline often discerned with difficulty. (See Fig. 79).....................*ANKISTRODESMUS*

125b Cells stouter, not needle-like; definitely crescent-shaped, the chloroplast parietal and definite in outline......................126

126a Cells bearing a stout spine at either end. Fig. 101............
....*CLOSTERIDIUM*

This species has 2 relatives which are nearly straight. It can be differentiated from *Closterium* (Fig. 97) by the fact that there is but a single chloroplast, and by the absence of terminal vacuoles with vibrating granules.

Fig. 101. *Closteridium lunula* Reinsch.

126b Cells without a stout spine at the poles.....................127

127a Cells inclosed in a mucilage (usually in clusters but sometimes solitary); in some species the curvature is so great that the tips nearly touch. (See Fig. 64.)............*KIRCHNERIELLA*

127b Cells not inclosed in mucilage (rarely in mucilage; see Fig. 78); usually in clusters but sometimes solitary; curvature of the inner margin nearly that of the outer; tips of cell not almost touching. (See Fig. 78.).................................*SELENASTRUM*

128a (126) Living in the tissues of higher plants, or in animals, or their eggs 129

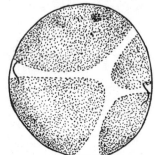

129a Globular cells inhabiting the envelope of salamander or frog eggs. Fig. 102................OOPHILA

Fig. 102. *Oophila Amblystomatis* Lambert.

130a Cells globose, numerous and minute, within the bodies of Protozoa, sponges, *Hydra, et al.* Fig. 103............CHLORELLA

Fig. 103. (a) *Chlorella (Zoochlorella) parasitica* Brandt (in *Ophrydium* sp., a colonial ciliate); (b) *C. (Zoochlorella) conductrix* Brandt (in *Hydra*); (c) *C. ellipsoidea* Gerneck, two cells enlarged to show parietal chloroplast.

These small cells occur singly or in gregarious masses, either free-living or contained within the bodies of animals such as Protozoa, especially Ciliata, and sponges. As endozoic plants they are often known as Zoochlorella. Species are not well-defined and mostly are differentiated by size and by the number of pyrenoids. The chloroplast is thin and cup-shaped. Like other members of the Chlorococcales, reproduction takes place by internal cell division (in this instance forming non-motile autospores). *Chlorella* is a genus that has been and is now being used in culture for investigations of the process of photosynthesis and in the synthesis of proteins, antibiotics, *etc.*

131a Plant a branched tube with globose swellings at the tips growing on and among the cells of Sphagnum. Fig. 104. . . . .
. . . .*PHYLLOBIUM*

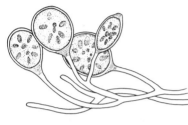

This thallus consists of almost colorless, branched threads growing within and among leaves of *Sphagnum*. The contents of the tubes accumulate at the tips of branches to form thick-walled akinetes. There are numerous ellipsoid chloroplasts radiately arranged in the apical swellings.

Fig. 104. *Phyllobium sphagnicola* G. S. West, a few colorless strands with terminal akinetes, from among cells of *Sphagnum* leaves.

131b Plant formed otherwise; not living on Sphagnum. 132

132a Plant a much-branched, coenocytic tube (multinucleate and without cross walls), growing in leaves of Araceae such as the Indian Turnip. Fig. 105. . . . . .PHYLLOSIPHON

This branched, tubular plant is non-cellular; forms green patches in the leaves of higher plants which become discolored. It may be more widely distributed than appears to be the situation at present, but so far it is known in the United States only from northern and eastern sections.

Fig. 105. *Phyllosiphon Arisari* Kuhn. (a) portion of thallus showing tangled threads; (b) habit of thallus in tissue of host. (Redrawn from Just.)

132b Plant not a branched coenocytic tube. 133

133a An irregularly shaped, flask-like cell in the tissues of Ambrosia (ragweed), and other plants. Fig. 106. . . . . . . .RHODOCHYTRIUM

This curiously shaped, unicellular parasite occurs on a greater variety of hosts than does *Phyllosiphon* (Fig. 105), but seems to be most frequent in ragweed. It is quickly identified by the red color and the large number of starch grains. The chloroplast is massive and indefinite.

Fig. 106. *Rhodochytrium spilanthidis* Lag.

133b An irregularly oval, thick-walled cell in the tissues of Lemna (duckweed). Fig. 107......................CHLOROCHYTRIUM

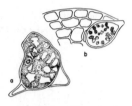

Fig. 107. *Chlorochytri-um Lemnae* Cohn. (a) showing net-like chloroplast (Redrawn from Bristol Roach.); (b) cell in host tissue.

There are probably three other species in the United States, differentiated by cell-size and thickness of the wall which is usually much lamellated. Plants of *Lemna trisulca*, when allowed to become colorless in the laboratory, show green spots locating the position of the endophytic alga.

134a (128) Cells in the form of vesicles on moist soil, with a colorless subterranean, rhizoid-like extension. Fig. 108....PROTOSIPHON

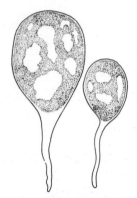

Protosiphon is a single-celled, coenocytic and bulbous plant inhabiting moist soil. The balloon-like portion has a colorless, subterranean, rhizoidal extension. There is a reticulate, sheet-like chloroplast covering most of the wall. The plants are usually found growing among *Botrydium* (Fig. 242) a member of the Chrysophyta in which leucosin rather than starch accumulates as a food reserve.

Fig. 108. *Protosiphon botryoides* (Kuetz.) Klebs, showing clathrate, parietal chloroplast.

137b Setae branched. (See Fig. 72.)..............*DICRANOCHAETE*

138a (136) Cells on a slender stalk or with the basal portion of the cell narrowed to form a stalk..........................139

138b Cells globular, attached by a broad, short stalk. Fig. 109......
....*MALLEOCHLORIS*

Fig. 109. *Malle-ochloris sessilis* Pascher. (Redrawn from Pascher.)

This rare plant is to be sought on filamentous algae such as members of the Cladophoraceae. The sheath that incloses the cell is often reddish. Reproduction (similar to other Tetrasporales) is by swimming spores and by isogametes.

139a Cells globular, with chloroplast lying along the outer free wall; growing on *Anabaena* and *Coelosphaerium*. Fig. 110.........
....*STYLOSPHAERIDIUM*

This curious epiphyte is found in abundance when it occurs at all as minute "hat pins" in the mucilage of colonial blue-green algae. Planktonic species of *Anabaena* and *Coelosphaerium* at certain times of the year and usually when they are in 'bloom' condition are often densely beset with the epiphytes.

Fig. 110. *Stylo-sphaeridium stipi-tatum* (Bach.) Geit. & Gimesi (a) habit of cells in colonial envelope; (b) single cell showing apical position of chlor-oplast.

139b Cells elongate-ovoid, or fusiform, or if globular with a chloroplast parietal along the lateral walls. (See Fig. 98.).....*CHARACIUM*

140a (135) Cells elongate-fusiform, or rod-shaped, crescent-shaped, slightly curved, or straight; several to many times longer than their diameter..141

140b Cells oval, circular (or nearly so), pyramidal, trapezoidal, or star-shaped; isodiametrically angular, not more than 3 times the diameter in length...160

141a Cells with narrowed apices, sometimes sharply pointed....142

141b Cells with broadly rounded or truncate apices.............147

142a Chloroplasts 2, axial, one in either horn of a crescent-shaped cell which may be only slightly curved. (See Fig. 97.).......... ....*CLOSTERIUM*

142b Chloroplasts otherwise; cell not so shaped.................143

143a Cells decidedly fusiform, one or both poles extended into setae or sharp points...144

143b Cells not broadly fusiform...............................146

144a Cells actually globular but inclosed in a fusiform sheath with longitudinal ridges. Fig. 111................*DESMATRACTUM*

These unique species, 2 of which occur in this country, are rather rare but seem to be widely distributed in the plankton of both streams and lakes. The wall is very wide and transparent, forming a sheath-like envelope.

Fig. 111. *Desmatractum bipyramidatum* (Chod.) Pascher.

144b Cells themselves fusiform; without such a sheath...........145

145a Setae formed by a narrowing of the cell to a fine point; chloroplast laminate (plate-like), not extending the full length of the cell. (See Fig. 100.)............................*OUROCOCCUS*

145b Setae formed by a fine spine on the wall, extending from the narrowed tips of the cells. (See Fig. 99.).......*SCHROEDERIA*

146a (143) Cells many times (20 or more) longer than wide; the chloroplast with a row of pyrenoids. Fig. 112......*CLOSTERIOPSIS*

Fig. 112. *Closteriopsis longissima* Lemm.

There is but 1 species reported from this country. Although it superficially resembles a *Closterium* (Fig. 97) it is easily separated on the basis of the single, plate-like chloroplast which may be notched or crenulate along the margin. At times the cells are slightly curved but usually are more nearly straight than any of the species of *Closterium*.

146b Cells less than 20 times the diameter long; slender needles or narrowly fusiform cells with 1 pyrenoid sometimes evident. (See Fig. 79.)................................*ANKISTRODESMUS*

147a (141) With a notch in the ends of the cell. Fig. 113...........
....*TETMEMORUS*

Fig. 113. *Tetmemorus laevis*
(Kuetz.) Ralfs.

This genus belongs to the Placoderm Desmids, having a wall in 2 pieces that adjoin in the midregion. Species that are found in this country seem to be confined to highly acid situations. There are several species reported from the United States, some with cylindrical shapes, others with ends tapering, but always with a prominent polar notch.

147b Without a notch in the ends of the cell....................148

148a Cells crescent-shaped, with an axial chloroplast bearing ridges in each horn. (See Fig. 97.)....................*CLOSTERIUM*

148b Cells not crescent-shaped, or with other types of chloroplasts..149

149a Cells constricted in the midregion to form 2 semicells which are mirror images of one another............................150

149b Cells not constricted in the midregion to form semicells......155
150a Cells furnished with whorls of protuberances which bear 1 or 2 spines; poles of the cell forked. Fig. 114.........*TRIPLOCERAS*

Fig. 114. *Triploceras gracile* Bailey.

There are only 2 species of this Placoderm Desmid in the United States, easily identified by the whorls of spine-bearing protuberances on the walls. Like many other Desmid genera this one seems to be confined to acid waters, especially in *Sphagnum* bogs.

150b Cells not furnished with whorls of spiny protuberances.....151

151a Cells 10 or more times longer than broad, usually cylindrical or nearly so, with margins smooth or undulate................152

151b Cells less than 10 times their diameter in length; cylindric, fusiform, or tumid, usually straight but sometimes slightly curved..153

152a With a circle of folds or creases at the base of the semicell, with a tooth on each fold. Fig. 115......................DOCIDIUM

Fig. 115. *Docidium undulatum* Bailey.

This genus is scarcely to be separated from *Pleurotaenium* (Fig. 116). In cells that are living, the density of the chloroplast makes obscure the characteristic creases in the wall where the 2 semicells are adjoined. One needs to focus carefully to see these folds which produce teeth-like projections at the very outer margin of the bases of the semicell, especially in examining those individuals which have a granule on the fold. Another species, *D. Baculum* Bréb., less common than the species illustrated, has smooth lateral walls.

152b Without a circle of creases at the base of the semicell. Fig. 116..
..PLEUROTAENIUM

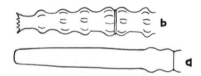

Fig. 116. (a) *Pleurotaenium trabecula* (Ehr.) Naegeli; (b) *P. nodosum* Bailey.

There are more species and a greater variety of shapes in this genus than in *Docidium* (Fig. 115) and they are more widely distributed. Although all of them are elongate and usually have subparallel margins, there is considerable variation in details of the wall decoration. In some species the walls are nodose or undulate; some spiny. Usually there is a circle of granules around the poles of the cell. Some species are not so restricted in their distribution as most Desmids and may occur in basic or slightly alkaline waters as well as in acid or soft waters.

153a (151) Cells with 2 star-shaped chloroplasts, 1 in each semicell.
Fig. 117.....................................CYLINDROCYSTIS

Fig. 117. *Cylindrocystis Brebissonii* Menegh.

Although some of the half-dozen species of this Saccoderm Desmid have slightly constricted cells, they have a wall composed of 1 piece and have no wall pores nor other decorations. There is a star-shaped chloroplast with a large pyrenoid in each half of the cell. This genus is not confined to acid habitats; may occur in alkaline bogs or among mosses, or may form gelatinous masses on wet stones in alpine situations.

153b Cell with other types of chloroplasts......................154

154a Cells short-cylindric, or subcylindrical; chloroplasts 1 in each semicell (rarely 3 or 4 chloroplasts forming transverse zones in the cell); no vacuoles with moving granules in the poles of the cell. Fig. 118...*PENIUM*

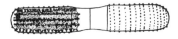

Fig. 118. *Penium margaritaceum* (Ehr.) Bréb.

Some species of this genus are shaped somewhat like those in *Cylindrocystis* (Fig. 117), but *Penium* is a Placoderm Desmid and has a wall in two sections which adjoin in the mid-region. The wall usually shows coarse punctations or granules, sometimes arranged in spiral rows. In general *Penium* cells are more cylindrical than *Cylindrocystis* and because new wall sections are formed when the cell divides they may become as long as some small species of *Pleurotaenium*.

154b Cells slightly attenuated at the apices; cholorplasts with several pyrenoids; vacuoles with moving granules in the poles of the cell. (See Fig. 97.)..............................*CLOSTERIUM*

155a (149) Chloroplasts spiral ribbons...........................156

155b Chloroplasts some other shape...........................157

**156a Cells 'cigar'-shaped, the poles rounded. Fig. 119............
....*SPIROTAENIA***

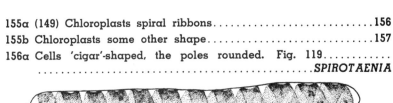

Fig. 119. *Spirotaenia condensata* Bréb.

This cylindrical cell is usually straight but may be slightly bent. Although 1 species in the United States has an axial chloroplast, the others have a characteristically spiral or at least twisted one.

156b Cells cylindrical with truncate poles. Fig. 120....*GENICULARIA*

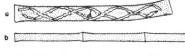

Fig. 120. *Genicularia elegans* West. (a) single cell; (b) Filamentous arrangement.

In this genus the cells may be solitary or adjoined end to end to form short or relatively long filaments. Although the chloroplasts are spirally twisted and show a resemblance of *Spirogyra* (Fig. 167) this genus is usually identifiable by the cells being slightly enlarged at the poles. Also the walls are usually densely beset with short, sharp granules. *Genicularia* is a member of the Gonatozygaceae, closely related to the true Desmids and found associated with them in nature.

157a (155) Cells cylindrical, 10 or more times the diameter in length, the poles truncate; wall spiny. Fig. 121..........*GONATOZYGON*

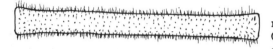

Fig. 121. *Gonatozygon aculeatum* Hastings.

This Desmid-like genus, a member of the Gonatozygaceae, has solitary cells which are nearly always a little crooked; have walls bearing long or short spines; are not constricted in the midregion. Although usually free-floating and intermingled with Desmids, the cells may be adherent to submerged plants. There is a ribbon-like chloroplast that is axial rather than parietal as in *Genicularia* (Fig. 120). One classification system places *Gonatozygon* in the Mesotaeniaceae.

157b Cells fusiform, short-cylindric, less than 10 times the diameter in length; wall smooth..158

158a Cells broadly fusiform or subcylindrical; 2 chloroplasts, 1 in each half of the cell, bearing longitudinal ridges and with notched margins. Fig. 122....................................*NETRIUM*

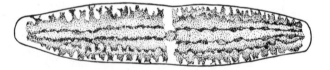

Fig. 122. *Netrium digitus* (Ehr.) Its. & Rothe.

These are "watermelon" or "cucumber"-shaped cells which are Saccoderm Desmids with scarcely any or no constriction in the midregion. Like other members of the Mesotaeniaceae the cell contents are conspicuously symmetrically divided into 2 portions. The chloroplasts are axial bodies with longitudinal ridges that have fimbriate margins.

158b Cells cylindrical or narrowly fusiform, with 1 chloroplast in the cell 159

159a Cells 'cigar'-shaped; chloroplast axial with 4 to 6 pyrenoids. Fig. 123 ....*ROYA*

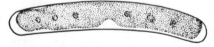

Fig. 123. *Roya obtusa* (Bréb.) W. & G. S. West.

This rather rare Saccoderm Desmid has slightly curved, cylindrical cells in which there is but a single chloroplast that is notched in the midregion where the nucleus is located. There is a row of pyrenoids.

159b Cells elongate-ellipsoid or ovoid to subcylindrical; 1 parietal chloroplast; cell contents violet-colored. (See Fig. 53.)............
....*MESOTAENIUM*

160a (140) Cells constricted in the midregion....................161

160b Cells not constricted in the midregion.....................168

161a Cells flat and nearly circular in proportions, star-like in front view, the median incision very deep; semicell deeply lobed or incised, in some species with secondary lobes and lobules. Fig. 124..*MICRASTERIAS*

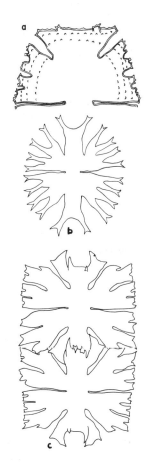

These are true Desmids and include some of the most beautiful microscopic objects. Although the outline of the cell varies greatly among the 20 or more species in this country, they can be identified by the flat, disc-like shape. One species, *M. foliacea* Bailey, has hooks on the polar lobes which enmesh with those of newly-formed cells so that false filaments are produced.

Fig. 124. (a) *Micrasterias americana* var. *Boldtii* Gutw.; (b) *M. radiata* Hass. var.; (c) *M. foliacea* Bailey.

161b Cells not flat and disc-like................................162

162a Cells with a shallow and broad, or a deep and narrow notch in the apex of the semicell. Fig. 125.............EUASTRUM

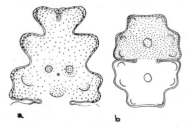

Fig. 125. (a) *Euastrum pinnatum* Ralfs; (b) *E. pectinatum* var. *inevolutum* W. & G. S. West.

There are numerous species in this Placoderm Desmid genus, varying greatly in size and shape of cell. Most of them, however, can be readily identified by the polar notch. On the face of the semicell is a protrusion which bears granules and in which there is often a mucilage pore. In some species there are several protrusions or swellings. The walls are often scrobiculate. In filled or living specimens the facial wall features are difficult to see and the specimen must be rolled so that it can be viewed from the top and side. Most of the species of *Euastrum* are limited to an acid habitat.

162b Cells without a notch in the apex of the semicell............163

**163a Apex of the cell extended into 2 or more arms or lobes, the arms usually extending radiately so that the cells are star-shaped or triangular when seen from the top (end view). Fig. 126.......
....STAURASTRUM**

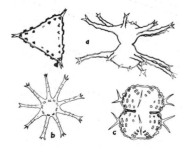

Fig. 126. (a) *Staurastrum rotula* Nordst., front view; (b) end view; (c) *St. cornutum* Arch.; (d) end view.

This is a large Placoderm genus with several hundred species which vary in shape of semicell and type of wall decoration. The chief distinguishing characteristic is the extension of lobes or arms in at least 3 planes so that the cell appears radiate when seen from the top. Many species appear like *Cosmarium* (Fig. 128) when seen in front view and one needs to change the plane of focus to see the lobes of the semicell extending up toward the observer, or down as the case may be. A few species have arms in 1 plane only and these are retained in the genus by virtue of the fact that the shape of the semicells (especially the arms) and the decorations (spines, verrucae, etc.) are those of *Staurastrum*. Some species are definitely euplanktonic and have long arms which give them buoyancy, whereas others are tychoplanktonic and are intermingled with other Desmids in acid swamps.

163b Apex of semicell not extended into arms, or if with arms these not radiating in 3 planes.................................164

164a Semicells with 2 extended arms at their apices as seen in front view, narrowly elliptic when seen from the top. Fig. 127.......
....*STAURASTRUM*

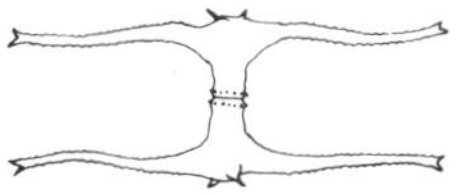

Fig. 127. *Staurastrum leptocladum* Nordst.

164b Cells without radiating arms, semicells compressed or rounded when seen from the top or side...........................165

165a Margin of cell furnished with spines......................166

165b Margin of cell without spines, although many species are granular, sometimes sharp or conical. Fig. 128.........*COSMARIUM*

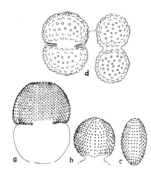

Like the genus *Staurastrum* (Fig. 126) *Cosmarium* includes several hundred species with considerable variations in shape of semicell and manner of wall decoration (granules, teeth, scrobiculations). Nearly all are compressed or rounded when seen from the side or top, regardless of their shape when seen from the front or broad side.

Fig. 128. (a) *Cosmarium panamense* Presc., (b) side view, (c) top view; (d) *C. margaritatum* (Lund.) Roy & Biss., front and side view.

166a Face of semicell with protuberances, or with the wall thickened in the midregion (best seen when the cell is rolled to a lateral view position)..167

166b Face of semicell without swellings or protuberances. Fig. 129..
.... *ARTHRODESMUS*

This genus has compressed cells like *Cosmarium* (narrower in side or end view than in front view). The angles of the semicell bear spines and the cell wall is smooth and undecorated, there being no granules, swellings or pits. Most species occur in acid habitats, intermingled with other Desmids.

Fig. 129. *Arthro-desmus incus* (Bréb.) Hass.

167a Apex of semicell furnished with prominent spines; facial protu-berance (if any) one large low swelling, the wall thickened here and often pitted or punctate. Fig. 130..........*XANTHIDIUM*

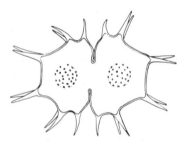

This genus too, like *Arthrodesmus* (Fig. 129) has cells that are compressed so that they are narrow when seen from the side or top. There is usually a facial swelling in the center of the semicell and all angles bear stout spines or short arms that are tipped with spines. There is less variation in the shape of the semicell in this genus than in some of the other Placoderm Desmids.

Fig. 130. *Xanthidium cristatum* var. *uncinatum* Hass.

167b Apex without spines, or with a short tooth-like spine at either side of the polar lobe. (See Fig. 125.)..............*EUASTRUM*

168a (160) Cells spherical, inclosed by a spindle-shaped envelope which has longitudinal ridges. (See Fig. 111.).......*DESMATRACTUM*

168b Cells not inclosed in such an envelope.....................169

169a Cells oval, ovoid, spherical or ellipsoid.....................170

169b Cells angular, pyramidal, trapeziform, or polygonal..........198

170a Cells subcylindrical or ovoid, small, less than 4.5 μ in diameter, with a parietal, plate-like chloroplast at one or both ends. Fig. 131 . . . . *NANNOCHLORIS*

Fig. 131. *Nanno-chloris bacillaris* Naum.

These tiny cells are solitary and are without a gelatinous sheath. They are able to undergo cell division in vegetative reproduction and hence are assignable to the Coccomyxaceae along with *Elakatothrix* (Fig. 45) and *Dactylothece* (Fig. 54). It is a frequenter of laboratory cultures. See *Coccomyxa* (Fig. 46).

170b Cells different in size and shape, or with a different type of chloroplast 171

171a Cells bearing spines or decorated with ridges 172

171b Cells without spines or decorations 179

172a Spine length greater than the diameter of the cell 173

172b Spine length less than the diameter of the cell; wall usually decorated with a network of thickenings 177

173a Spines not tapering from base to apex (with parallel margins but pointed at the tip), long and slender 175

173b Spines tapering from base to apex, long and slender, or short and stout 174

174a Spines stout, broad at the base and tapering to a sharp point. Fig. 132 . . . . *ECHINOSPHAERELLA*

Fig. 132. *Echino-sphaerella limnetica* G. M. Smith.

This is a relatively rare plant from the euplankton. In making identification care should be used to distinguish the single parietal chloroplast by which the plant may be differentiated from some of the spiny zygospores of Desmids (in which the cell content appears dark and massive, with no definitely shaped chloroplast distinguishable).

174b Spines long and slender, gradually tapering in the basal part for a short distance and then abruptly narrowed to a needle. Fig. 133.....................................ACANTHOSPHAERA

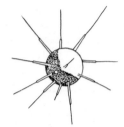

This plant can be distinguished from *Echinosphaerella* (Fig. 132) because the spines are somewhat needle-like, arising from a base which is decidedly thicker than in the apical section. There is a parietal, plate-like chloroplast.

Fig. 133. *Acantho-sphaera Zachariasi* Lemm.

175a (173) Cells round. (See Fig. 95.).................GOLENKINIA

175b Cells oval or ellipsoid.....................................176

**176a Spines at the poles or at the equator of the cell. Fig. 134......
....LAGERHEIMIA
(Chodatella)**

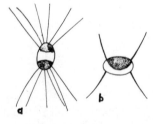

Unlike *Franceia* (Fig. 84) cells of this genus have long, needle-like spines confined to the poles or to the poles and the equator. There are about 12 species reported from this country which are differentiated on the basis of cell-shape and arrangement of spines. All are fairly common in the euplankton, and widely distributed.

Fig. 134. (a) *Lagerheimia longiseta* (Lemm.) Printz.; (b) *L. quadriseta* (Lemm.) G. M. Smith.

176b Spines distributed over the cell wall. (See Fig. 84.)..FRANCEIA

177b Cells oval. Fig. 135..............................*BOHLINIA*

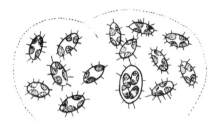

Fig. 135. *Bohlinia echidna* (Bohlin) Lemm.

This rather unique species (the only one in the genus) appears in amorphous, gelatinous masses. Reproduction is by internal cell division to form autospores. Although older cells are characteristically spiny, recently formed individuals may be smooth-walled. The observer should examine the plant mass for the remains of the old cell walls which will show evidence of the spinescence.

178a Cells with bluntly pointed protuberances when mature (smooth-walled when young), pale green (sometimes almost colorless), inhabiting snow fields. Fig. 136..........*MYCANTHOCOCCUS*

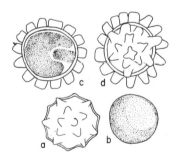

Fig. 136. *Mycanthococcus antarcticus* Wille. (a) cell showing thick, spiny cyst-like wall; (b) chloroplast; (c), (d) a species from the Olympic Mountain snowfields.

This is one of several genera of unicellular algae which occur in banks of permanent snow. There is a light green, parietal chloroplast. The wall is smooth when the cells are young, but becomes thickened and bears blunt protuberances in age, thus showing a resemblance to certain species of *Trochiscia* (Fig. 137). The species illustrated here has been found in the snows of Yellowstone National Park and in the Olympic Mts.

The author believes that this may be an encysted stage of a motile organism.

178b Cells decorated otherwise with ridges, reticulations, sharp spines or with rounded protuberances; chloroplast definite, green; (some species sometimes found in snow). Fig. 137.......*TROCHISCIA*

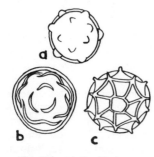

There are about 12 species of this genus, all solitary cells, which are differentiated by the type of wall decoration. It is a little-understood genus and some of the described species are doubtless the zygospores of other algae or their encysted or resting stages. In making identification of plants with the outward characteristics of *Trochiscia* care should be used to identify the several disc-like chloroplasts.

Fig. 137. (a) *Trochiscia granulata* (Reinsch) Hansg.; (b) *T. obtusa* (Reinsch) Hansg.; (c) *T. reticularis* (Reinsch) Hansg.

179a (171) Cells associated with fungi to form lichens. Fig. 138......
...*TREBOUXIA*

This species is an inhabitor of lichens and apparently occurs nowhere else. The cells are spherical and contain an axial rather than a parietal chloroplast characteristic of most members of the Chlorococcales.

Fig. 138. *Trebouxia Cladoniae* (Chod.) G. M. Smith.

179b Cells not associated with fungi...........................180

180a Chloroplast 1, central, with radiating lobes extending to the wall...181

180b Chloroplast not axial, or more than 1 in a cell, without radiating lobes...182

181a Chloroplast definitely star-shaped, with a central pyrenoid; cells spherical. (See Fig. 59.)....................*ASTEROCOCCUS*

181b Chloroplast irregularly lobed, not symmetrically radiate, without a pyrenoid; cells pyriform. Fig. 139...............*MYRMECIA*

Figure 122

Fig. 139. Myrme-
cia aquatica G. M.
Smith. (Redrawn from
Smith.)

These cells are either subspherical or somewhat pear-shaped and usually show a thickening of the wall at one side, giving them an unsymmetrical shape. Although the genus was originally described from aerial situations, specimens in this country have been collected from aquatic habitats.

182a (180) Cells spherical..183

182b Cells oval or ellipsoid.....................................189

183a Cells large (up to 300 μ or more), wall thin; chloroplasts numerous, irregular in shape and lumpy with starch grains, arranged in radiating strands from the center of the cell, and also parietal. Fig. 140.....................................*EREMOSPHAERA*

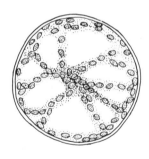

This is one of the largest spherical cells (up to 300 μ, rarely 800 μ in diameter) encountered among the unicellular algae. Although usually solitary it may appear in clusters of 4 within the old mother-cell wall. There is one other rare species (with oblate-spheroidal cells) but the plant illustrated is more common, occurring in desmid habitats. The numerous disc-like chloroplasts are often lumpy and irregular in shape because of the starch grains which collect about them.

Fig. 140. Eremosphaera
viridis De Bary.

183b Cells not as above..184

184a Cells enclosed by a mucilaginous sheath..................185

184b Cells not enclosed by a sheath..........................186

185a Cells eccentrically placed in a sheath which has numerous lamellations (layers); pyrenoid lacking. Fig. 141......*UROCOCCUS*

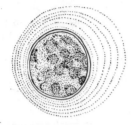

Although holding a place in the Tetrasporales according to original classification, this reddish-colored cell has been shown to be an encysted stage of one of the motile Dinoflagellates (Pyrrhophyta). Unless other species are shown to be separable and distinctive, the genus may be transferred.

Fig. 141. *Urococcus insignis* (Hass.) Kuetz.

185b Cells centrally placed in a sheath which has few or no lamellations; pyrenoid present; usually colonial but sometimes solitary. (See Fig. 48.)................................*GLOEOCYSTIS*

186a (184) Chloroplast 1; cells solitary (but often gregarious)......187

186b Chloroplasts more than 1; cells usually ellipsoid in a gregarious association, but sometimes round. Fig. 142...*PALMELLOCOCCUS*

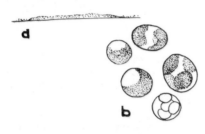

These oval or spherical cells usually occur as films on moist substrates (rock, cement walls, *etc.*). There are 1 to several chloroplasts without pyrenoids. Reproduction is by the formation of autospores characteristic of the Chlorococcales. Identification is difficult unless the organisms are cultured because there are so many minute, green cells which might be confused with this genus.

Fig. 142. *Palmellococcus miniatus* (Kuetz.) Chodat. (a) habit of colony; (b) portion of colony showing cells with *Chlamydomonas*-like chloroplast.

187a Cells associated to form an extended stratum on trees, wood, stones. (See Fig. 77.)........................*PROTOCOCCUS* (*Pleurococcus*)

187b Cells not forming such a stratum........................188

188a Chloroplast a thin layer along the wall; pyrenoid usually lacking; free-living or in tissues of animals (sponges, *etc.*), reproduction by autospores (replicas of the adult cell). (See Fig. 103.)... ....*CHLORELLA* (*Zoochlorella*)

188b Chloroplast a massive cup with a pyrenoid; occurring on damp aerial substrates; reproducing by zoospores. (See Fig. 49.).....
....*CHLOROCOCCUM*

189a (182) Cells oval, ovate, or irregularly globose, with thick-layered walls bearing knobs and protrusions.......................190

189b Cells without thick walls and knob-like protrusions..........191

190a Chloroplasts numerous, parietal, cone-shaped. Fig. 143........
....*EXCENTROSPHAERA*

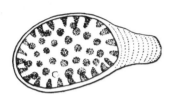

This is the only species reported for the genus. It is found in the water or in very wet soil and is identified by its irregular shape produced by a lamellated thickening of the wall in 1 or more places. The chloroplasts are cone-shaped and all are directed inwardly from their parietal position along the wall.

Fig. 143. *Excentrosphaera viridis* G. T. Moore.

190b Chloroplast a massive, axial body with processes which are flattened against the wall. Fig. 144...........*KENTROSPHAERA*

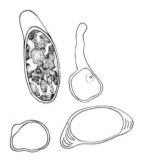

There are 2 or 3 species of this genus (sometimes included in the genus *Chlorochytrium* (Fig. 107) but only *K. Bristolae* has been found in the United States. The cells are similar in shape to *Chlorochytrium* but have a free-living habit, usually occurring on damp soil; *K. facciolae* Borzi has been found in Antarctica.

Fig. 144. *Kentrosphaera Bristolae* G. M. Smith.

191a (189) Cells with spines....................................192

191b Cells without spines......................................194

192a Spines distributed over the cell wall.....................193

192b Spines localized at the poles or at the midregion of the cell. (See Fig. 134)..*LAGERHEIMIA*
(*Chodatella*)

193a Spines shorter than the diameter of the cell. (See Fig. 135.)....
....*BOHLINIA*

193b Spines needle-like, as long as or longer than the diameter of the cell; cell solitary or in 2's. (See Fig. 84)............*FRANCEIA*

194a (191) Cells with spiral, longitudinal ribs on the walls. Fig. 145..
....*SCOTIELLA*

Fig. 145. *Scotiella nivalis* (Chod.) Fritsch.

This genus contains a number of species, most of which have been collected in the flora of red snow at high altitudes. Differences lie in the shape of the cell and the type of ridged decorations on the wall. Occasionally *Scotiella* species are collected in the tychoplankton at low altitudes. Some authorities place this genus in the Volvocales because of the type of chloroplast and the evidence of basal-distal differentiation in the cell; whereas others include it with the Chlorococcales.

194b Cells without longitudinal ribs.............................195

195a Cells small, less than 4.5 μ long, with a plate-like chloroplast at one end. (See Fig. 131.)..................*NANNOCHLORIS*

195b Cells relatively large, without such a chloroplast arrangement..
....196

196a Two or more masses of dark mucilage appearing at either end or on either side of the cell; usually 2 or 4 cells in a common investment, but often found solitary. (See Fig. 94.)...........
....*GLOEOTAENIUM*

196b Without dark masses of mucilage about the cells...........197

197a Cells oval, often solitary but usually gregarious, forming an expanse on moist, aerial substrates. (See Fig. 142).............
....*PALMELLOCOCCUS*

197b Cells lemon-shaped, oval, or ellipsoid (usually several together in old mother-cell wall, but may occur solitary); aquatic. (See Fig. 96.)...*OOCYSTIS*

198a (169) Cell body actually spherical but with 4 long, narrow, brown, arm-like appendages radiating from it. Fig. 146.. *PACHYCLADON*

This rare plant (1 species only in the genus) occurs in the euplankton of lakes. The long, darkly colored appendages from a relatively small, subspherical cell body make it certain of identification.

Fig. 146. *Pachycladon umbrinus* G. M. Smith. (Redrawn from Smith.)

198b Cells shaped differently, or not with such appendages......199

199a With several long spines forming a tuft at the angles of the cell. (See *Polyedriopsis quadrispina,* **however.) Fig. 147............**
....*POLYEDRIOPSIS*

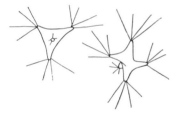

There are 2 species in this genus, both of which are euplanktonic. They are rectangular or polyhedral in shape with from 1 to 4 long spines at each angle. *P. quadrispina* G. M. Smith has but 1 stout spine at the angles; is quadrate in shape.

Fig. 147. *Polyedriopsis spinulosa* G. M. Smith.

199b With 1, 2, or 3 spines, or without spine at the angles of the cell 200

200a Without spines...201

200b With 1 to 3 spines at the angles........................202

201a Body of the cell gradually narrowed at the angles to form horn-like, twisted processes. Fig. 148................ *CERASTERIAS*

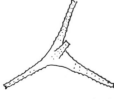

There is apparently only 1 good species in this genus which is characterized by having irregularly pyramidal cells with twisted processes. Thus far the plant has been reported only from lakes in mid-America. It should be compared with *Tetraedron* spp. (Fig. 149).

Fig. 148. *Cerasterias irregulare* G. M. Smith.

201b Body of the cell abruptly narrowed to form horn-like processes. Fig. 149...*TETRAEDRON*

Fig. 149. (a) *Tetraedron limneticum* Borge; (b) *T. asymmetricum* Presc.; (c) *T. lobulatum* var. *crassum* Presc.; (d) *T. regulare* var. *granulatum* Presc., showing chloroplast; (e) showing granular wall; (f) *T. regulare* var. *bifurcatum* Wille.

This genus contains a large number of species which vary considerably in their shape and in the number of arms and spines. Whereas some are simple and have rounded angles, others are trapeziform or polyhedral in shape and have lobes and lobules at the angles. They occur in both eu- and tychoplankton.

202a (200) Cells with 1 spine at each angle...................203

202b Cells with 2 or 3 spines at the angles. (See Fig. 149.).........
....*TETRAEDRON*

203a Spines slender and needle-like. (See Fig. 147)..*POLYEDRIOPSIS*

203b Spines broader at the base, and stout, decidedly tapering. Fig. 150...*TREUBARIA*

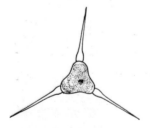

This free-floating plant is similar to *Pachycladon* (Fig. 146) but the processes are not darkly colored and are not toothed at the tip.

Fig. 150. *Treubaria crassispina* G. M. Smith.

204a (42) Plant a microscopic (habit of the plant and parts not visible without a microscope) unbranched filament, attached or free-floating, or a macroscopic (form of the plant determinable without a microscope) thallus in the form of an expanded sheet, a tube, or an arbuscular (tree-like) gelatinous and beaded growth..
.... 205

Fig. 151. *Onychonema laeve* var. *latum* W. & G. S. West.

There are 5 species of this filamentous Desmid genus, 2 rather common. *O. filiforme* (Ehr.) Roy & Biss. has the lateral angles of the semicells furnished with a spine and the polar processes are relatively long. *O. laeve* Nordst. has cells without lateral spines and appears like a small *Cosmarium* (Fig. 128) in a filament, the cells adjoined by short (sometimes scarcely evident) polar processes.

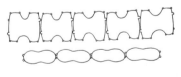

Fig. 152. *Sphaerozosma excavata* Ralfs.

This is a filamentous Desmid in which the cells are adjoined by the interlocking of the polar processes themselves. None of the species bear spines but they usually have minute granules at the angles of the semicell, or forming transverse bands across the semicell. The genus usually occurs in soft water lakes and acid bogs, intermingled with other Desmids.

209a (206) Semicells transversely elliptic or oval, the median incision of the cell deep. Fig. 153 .... *SPONDYLOSIUM*

Fig. 153. *Spondylosium planum* (Wolle) W. & G. S. West.

Although this genus can have cells that are triangular in end view, most species have cells that are compressed and are somewhat like *Cosmarium* (see Fig. 128) in a filament. One species which is rather rare is *S. pulchrum* (Bail.) Archer. It has semicells which are much extended laterally so that the cell is much wider than long. The apices of the cells in this species are furnished with a protrusion which adjoins that of the adjacent cells in the filament. The walls are smooth and undecorated.

209b Cells not transversely elliptic; median incision not deep, sometimes only a slight concavity of the lateral wall 210

210a Cells cylindrical, subcylindrical, or barrel-shaped 211

210b Cells quadrate or angular, usually with the margins conspicuously lobed. (See Fig. 156b, *Desmidium Baileyi* however.) 212

211a Cells barrel-shaped, with a slight notch-like median incision in the broadest part of the cell where it is somewhat bulged. Fig. 154 .... *BAMBUSINA*

Fig. 154. *Bambusina Brebissonii* Kuetz. (*Gymnozyga moniliformis* Ehr.)

There are 5 species of this genus in the United States, differentiated mostly on the size and proportions of the cell, but none is as common as the one illustrated. This species occurs sometimes almost pure in pools within *Sphagnum* bogs.

211b Cells cylindrical or somewhat rectangular, with a broad and shallow emargination rather than an incision in the midregion. Fig. 155 .... *HYALOTHECA*

Fig. 155. *Hyalotheca dissiliens* (Smith) Bréb.

There are 3 or 4 common species in this genus of 10, differentiated by cell shape and proportion, some being short and nearly quadrate whereas others are cylindrical. In some individuals the constriction of the cell occurs only as a shallow invagination in the midregion. In *Sphagnum* bogs small pockets of water or pools in the mat may be densely green with a pure growth of *H. mucosa* (Dill.) Ehr., a species which has a conspicuous gelatinous sheath.

212a (210) Cells wider than long or as wide as long, without a median incision or with but a slight median notch; walls at the poles of young semicells infolded or replicate. Fig. 156.....*DESMIDIUM*

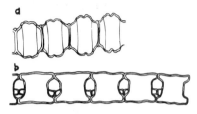

Fig. 156. (a) *Desmidium Grevillii* (Kuetz.) De Bary; (b) *D. Baileyi* (Ralfs) Nordst.

Cells of this filamentous Desmid genus vary much in shape. Some are oval and moniliform when seen in end view, some are triangular, and some are quadrangular. The shape of the cell may be determined by careful focusing up and down through the depth of a specimen. A characteristic habit of some species is to show a spiral twisting of the cell arrangement so that in any one view they do not have their processes in the same plane throughout the length of the filament. *Desmidium* usually occurs in the same habitats with *Hyalotheca*.

212b Cells a little longer than wide, rectangular, with a narrow median incision; 4-lobed in end view; poles of young cells infolded. Fig. 157 ....*PHYMATODOCIS*

Fig. 157. *Phymatodocis Nordstedtiana* Wolle.

Although rarely found this filamentous Desmid may be the dominant form in some habitats that are especially favorable for the growth of Desmids. The cells appear somewhat quadrangular when seen in front view (as they occur in the filament) but are quadrilaterally symmetrical and are 4-lobed as seen in end view.

213a (205) Chloroplast parietal, of various shapes, net-like, ring-like, or plate-like, with pads and thin areas (Fig. 158); or if axial, plants in the form of a macroscopic thallus as in Fig. 173 225

Fig. 158. Three types of parietal chloroplasts; a complete parietal ring; an incomplete ring; a parietal network.

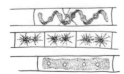

213b Chloroplast axial, a broad band, or star-shaped; if parietal, in the form of a rib-bon as in Fig. 159; microscopic......214

Fig. 159. Types of chloroplasts: a parietal ribbon (*Spirogyra*); axial stellate (*Zygnema*); axial band or plate (*Mougeotia*).

214a Chloroplast 1, or 2 in a cell; stellate, with radiating processes from a central core which includes a pyrenoid...........215

214b Chloroplasts other shapes.................................218

215a Cells quadrate, with 1 star-shaped chloroplast containing a single pyrenoid. Fig. 160...........................*SCHIZOGONIUM*

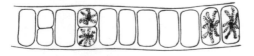

Fig. 160. *Schizogonium murale* Kuetz.

This species and 2 others are found in the United States, growing on dripping rocks or wet soil. *S. crenulatum* (Kuetz.) Gay has short, crinkly filaments.. The basically filamentous habit may become expanded so that a frond-like thallus is produced. This genus, together with *Prasiola* (Fig. 173) have sufficient structural and reproductive characteristics to warrant placing them in a separate family (Schizogoniaceae) and order (Shizogoniales). The star-shaped chloroplast is helpful in making determinations.

215b Cells mostly longer than wide; 2 chloroplasts..............216

216a Chloroplasts 2-6, relatively small and biscuit-shaped, or star-shaped, connected in the midregion of the cell by a strand of cytoplasm inclosing the nucleus; conjugating cells becoming filled with layers of pectic substances; zygospores cushion-shaped, compressed spheroid, or subquadrangular. Fig. 161..ZYGNEMOPSIS

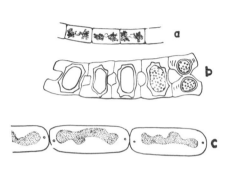

Fig. 161. (a) *Zygnemopsis decussata* (Trans.) Trans., vegetative cells with cushion-like, axial chloroplasts; (b) conjugation to form zygospores; (c) *Z. desmidioides* (W. & G. S. West) Trans.

The differences between this genus and *Zygnema* (Fig. 162) occur mostly within the reproductive habit and details; hence determination of plants in the vegetative condition cannot be certain, but in *Zygnema* the chloroplasts are definitely star-shaped, often with long rays, whereas in *Zygnemopsis* they are more like pads with irregular margins and short radiating processes. *Zygnema* is much more common than the former genus.

216b Chloroplasts different in shape, or if star-shaped, larger than above, and always 2; conjugating cells not becoming filled with pectic substances; zygospores globose, compressed-globose, or oval...217

217a Chloroplasts 2, definitely star-shaped, each containing a large central pyrenoid; aquatic. Fig. 162.................ZYGNEMA

Fig. 162. *Zygnema pectinatum* (Vauch.) C. A. Agardh, vegetative cells showing star-shaped, axial chloroplasts.

There are numerous species of *Zygnema*, differentiated on the basis of zygospore morphology. The paired, star-shaped chloroplasts in each cell make identification of the genus reasonably certain. Frequently the cells are so densely packed with starch grains and cytoplasmic granules that the shape of the chloroplast is difficult of determination. Application of an iodine solution often facilitates observation, or if one examines several lengths of filaments under low magnification the stellate form of the chloroplasts will become apparent. A few species have a conspicuous gelatinous sheath and a very thick wall. The filaments of *Zygnema* form green clumps but not the large, balloon-like or 'cloud' masses as does *Spirogyra*.

217b Chloroplast axial as above but with radiating processes much reduced, sometimes bridged so as to form a dumb-bell-shaped mass; terrestrial or subaerial. Fig. 163.........ZYGOGONIUM

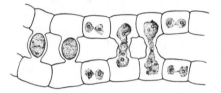

Fig. 163. *Zygogonium ericetorum* Kuetz.

These filaments are somewhat irregular because the cell walls are unevenly thickened and usually are invested by a layer of mucilaginous substance. The cells have the habit of putting out rhizoidal protrusions rather frequently. Sometimes the p r o t r u s i o n s are branched. Occasionally the conjugation tubes, when they fail to meet another tube, will continue to grow as rhizoidal processes. The plant usually is found in subaerial habitats, sometimes in the water on submerged stumps, *etc.*

218a (214) Cell sap purplish....................................219

218b Cell sap not purplish....................................220

219a With 2 disc-like chloroplasts. Fig. 164.......PLEURODISCUS

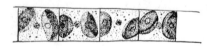

Fig. 164. *Pleurodiscus purpureus* (Wolle.) Lag., showing disc-like chloroplasts.

There is but 1 species of this genus reported thus far from the United States. It is a plant easily identified by its unique curved, plate-like chloroplasts and purple cell-sap.

219b With 1 band-like chloroplast. Fig. 165..........MOUGEOTIA

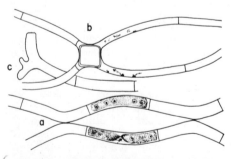

Fig. 165. (a) *Mougeotia genuflexa* (Dillw.) C. A. Agardh, showing geniculate or 'knee-bending' type of conjugation and the plate-like, axial chloroplast; (b) *M. elegantula* Wittr., zygospore with residues in conjugating cells; (c) *M. sp.*, showing rhizoidal branches.

Like *Spirogyra* (Fig. 167) there are many species of *Mougeotia* separable by zygospore shape and wall markings. Most species have a relatively wide, band-like, axial chloroplast containing a row of large pyrenoids. The chloroplast is capable of rotating within the cell so that when seen on edge it appears as a narrow ribbon. The shifting of the chloroplast is thought to be a favorable response to the direction of light.

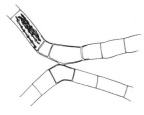

This genus is differentiated from *Spirogyra* (Fig. 167) by the shape and arrangement (nearly straight and parallel) of the ribbon-like chloroplasts, and (in reproduction) by the absence of a conjugation tube between the cells of adjoined filaments. There is geniculation of filaments to bring the conjugating cells into juxtaposition.

Fig. 166. *Sirogonium sticticum* (Engl. Bot.) Kuetz., showing parallel, ribbon-like chloroplasts.

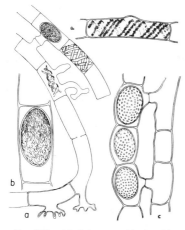

This is the most commonly found member of the entire order of Zygnematales. There are numerous species differentiated by shape and wall features of the zygospores, and by size of the vegetative cells, some of which have replicate cross walls. Species cannot be identified unless observed in the reproductive condition. *Spirogyra* forms green 'clouds' of cottony growths, usually in quiet water. Rarely the filaments are attached by short rhizoidal branches. When in the reproductive state the plants appear at the surface of the water, forming cottony mats (pond silks) and become brown or 'dirty'-colored as the plants lose their green color and form zygospores. Conjugation may be lateral or scalariform.

Fig. 167. (a) *Spirogyra rhizobrachiales* Jao, showing rhizoidal branches and conjugation; (b) zygospore; (c) *S. aequinoctialis* G. S. West; (d) cell showing chloroplasts and numerous pyrenoids.

223a (220) Chloroplasts with pyrenoids. Fig. 168....*MOUGEOTIOPSIS*

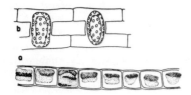

Fig. 168. *Mougeotiopsis calospora* Palla. (a) vegetative cells with plate-like chloroplasts (without pyrenoid); (b) zygospores.

There is only 1 species of this genus reported from the United States, and it is very rare. It is possible to make tentative identification of the species in the vegetative state because the chloroplast is much like that of *Mougeotia* but without pyrenoids. The cells are characteristically very short cylindric. In reproduction it is similar to *Debarya* (Fig. 169) in that the entire contents of the conjugating cells become fused to form the zygospore.

223b Chloroplasts with 2 to several pyrenoids...................224

224a Filaments slender, mostly under 12 μ in diameter (rarely as much as 30 μ or 42 μ); chloroplast a parietal plate, usually not filling the cell; conjugating cells becoming filled with pectic substances; granular residues not found in the emptied reproductive cells; plants relatively rare. Fig. 169......................*DEBARYA*

Fig. 169. *Debarya* sp., showing formation of zygospores and the lamellated substance deposited in the conjugating cells.

This genus, named for DeBary the famous botanist, has filaments that resemble slender species of *Mougeotia* (Fig. 165), and cannot be positively identified in the vegetative condition. The cells are more delicate and the chloroplast is a relatively small, usually twisted plate. *Debarya* is much less frequently collected than *Mougeotia*. In reproduction all of the contents of the conjugating cells enter into the formation of the zygospores and the space once occupied by the protoplasts becomes filled with lamellated substance which is light refractive.

224b Filaments usually wider; chloroplast a broad, axial band with conspicuous pyrenoids, filling the cell laterally (in most species) but not in length; conjugating cells not filled with pectic substances; granular residues present in the emptied reproductive cells; plants common. (See Fig. 165.).............*MOUGEOTIA*

225a (213) Plant a tuft of short, erect filaments (usually branched but sometimes appears unbranched when young); some species forming attached discs. Fig. 170 .... COLEOCHAETE

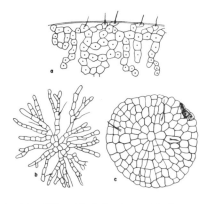

Fig. 170. (a) *Coleochaete Nitellarum* Jost; (b) *C. soluta* (Bréb.) Pringsh.; (c) *C. orbicularis* Pringsh.

There are 6 or 7 species of this which are found commonly in the United States. They are differentiated by habit of growth (prostrate and disc-like, or in cushion-like tufts), and by size of cells. One species, *C. Nitellarum* Jost, occurs only in the walls of *Nitella* (Fig. 3), which is nearly always found with the endophyte. *Coleochaete* appears conspicuously when *Nitella* is allowed to age in the laboratory. The sheathed seta which characterize *Coleochaete* arises from a granule (the blepharoplast) within the cell and emerges through a pore in the wall. The disc-like thallus formed by some species of *Coleochaete* is frequently found on the sides of glass aquaria. In nature they occur on other algae or on submerged stems of cattail, or on submerged glass and crockery.

225b Thallus not in the form of a cushion of erect filaments 226

226a Thallus a macroscopic expanded sheet, 1 cell in thickness (usually in salt water, but also in brackish and fresh water, especially in cold streams); attached. Fig. 171 .... MONOSTROMA

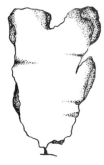

Fig. 171. *Monostroma latissimum* (Kuetz.) Wittr.

In salt water this genus includes species which form relatively large, sheet-like or foliose thalli, several centimeters long and wide, whereas in freshwater the plants are no longer than 5 or 6 centimeters. Salt water species are sometimes carried inland and become distributed on oyster shells. One of the three species found in fresh water occurs in cold, running water, usually at high altitudes.

Like *Monostroma* (Fig. 171) *Enteromorpha* is primarily a marine alga but becomes adapted rather easily to fresh-water habitats. The long, hollow tubes are frequently branched, forming slender threads or crinkled, elongate sacks. The plants are always attached to submerged plant stems, or to stones, especially in flowing water. There are 8 species known from fresh-water or brackish situations. One species is common in the far western part of the United States where it often occurs in troublesome abundance in irrigation ditches.

Fig. 172. *Enteromorpha intestinalis* (L.) Grev., (a) habit of branched thallus; (b) cells showing parietal position of chloroplasts.

Eight species of *Prasiola* have beeen reported from the United States, mostly from alpine and subalpine stations, whereas in the Arctic the plant is common on soil rich in nitrogenous wastes and on bones. The thalli are foliose when fully developed but may be filamentous and ribbon-like when young. This genus and *Schizogonium* comprise the Schizogoniaceae, a family with star-shaped, axial chloroplasts.

Fig. 173. *Prasiola crispa* (Lightf.) Menegh. (a) several forms of thallus; (b) diagram to show cells in 4's.

229b A gelatinous strand, or a tube, or a plant which includes a gelatinous tube that may or may not have cross partitions......230

230a Thallus a stout, tube-like strand, sometimes forked, containing many transverse lamellations (layers); cells at the tips of the strands. Fig. 174...............................HORMOTILA

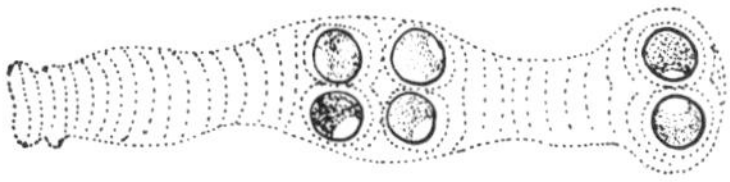

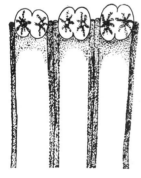

Fig. 174. *Hormotila mucigena* Borzi.

This curious plant is a branched, colonial form by virtue of the fact that as the cells divide they secrete mucilage and construct gelatinous strands that branch and rebranch, the cells always occurring at the distal ends of the strands. The plant (1 species only being known) is classed near *Gloeocystis* (Fig. 48) in the Tetrasporales, family Palmellaceae.

230b Thallus not as above....................................231

231a Cells located at the ends of undivided tubes, the cell bearing a seta with a sheathed base. (See Fig. 73.)..................
......................................CHAETOSPHAERIDIUM

231b Cells without setae......................................232

232a Cells constricted in the middle; occurring at the ends of parallel tubes which are united in colonies and are impregnated with lime. Fig. 175...............................OOCARDIUM

This is a very rare Desmid, or at least it has been reported but few times, probably because it is overlooked by collectors. The *Cosmarium*-like cells occur in colonies at the ends of tubes and are inclosed in a firm encrustation of lime. They are to be sought in limestone and in streams flowing over calcareous rocks. In some hardwater streams every stick and stone may be encrusted with the limey concretions of *Oocardium*.

Fig. 175. *Oocardium stratum* Naeg.

232b Cells not constricted in the midregion; not arranged as above...
....233

233a Cells in tubes which are attached to microfauna. (See Fig. 75.)
....*COLACIUM*

233b Cells not attached to microfauna........................234

234a Cells elongate-oval; brackish water or marine. Fig. 176.......
....*PRASINOCLADUS*

Although essentially marine, this species has been known to occur in brackish water and possibly may be found in fresh-water near coasts. It is an attached, branching tube composed of a series of compartments, forming a tree-like thallus in which the oval protoplasts occur only at the tips of the branches. There is 1 chloroplast at the forward end of the cell which actually is the posterior pole because like some of its relatives (*Malleochloris*, Fig. 109) the cells are in an inverted position with the anterior end downward. The genus belongs to the Chlorangiaceae in the Tetrasporales.

Fig. 176. *Prasinocladus lubricus* Kuck.

234b Cells round, not in brackish water habitats................235

235a Cells in 1 series or in several irregular series within simple or branched tubes; chloroplasts 2, laminate. (See Fig. 52.)........
....*PALMODICTYON*

235b Cells in several series, arranged in clusters of 4 in an irregularly shaped, elongate strand of mucilage; chloroplast 1, a parietal cup. (See Fig. 42.)...............................*TETRASPORA*

236a (229) Filament of cells in 1 series, at least in the basal portion..237

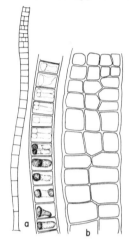

There are but 2 species in this genus, one which is uncommon but widely distributed over the world. The filaments are relatively large when fully developed and rather coarse. They occur in dark green clumps in standing water and have the macroscopic appearance of *Spirogyra* (Fig. 167) or of some large *Ulothrix* (Fig. 188). But unlike these genera, *Schizomeris* filaments separate easily and can be seen individually within the tuft. There is some evidence that the plant favors water rich in nitrogenous matter and is to be looked for in shallow water of lakes near the entrance of drains, effluent of sewage treatments plants, etc.

Fig. 177. *Schizomeris Leibleinii* Kuetz. (a) base of filament and uniseriate portion; (b) multiseriate upper portion of filament.

239a Cells cylindrical, usually many times their diameter in length (sometimes only 3 times longer than wide); wall thick, sometimes lamellated. Fig. 178.....................*RHIZOCLONIUM*

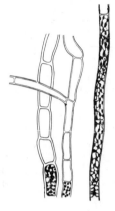

Fig. 178. *Rhizoclonium Hookeri* Kuetz.

The species belonging to this genus are all coarse, wiry and but very little (if at all) branched. The filaments are composed of relatively long, cylindrical coenocytic cells, or if somewhat shorter cells, with lateral walls slightly convex and irregular. The walls are frequently lamellated in the large species, especially near the cross walls. There are numerous chloroplasts, often compactly arranged and difficult of determination in respect to shape and organization. The chloroplasts are sometimes adjoined to form a close network, with pyrenoids in the interconnections or in the chloroplasts. The branches of the filament are usually short and mostly at right angles to the main axis, and irregular in plan. When the branches are long, as in some species, the plants intergrade with some forms of *Cladophora* (Fig. 218) in which the regular plan of branching has been reduced or lost. *Rhizoclonium* forms dense, tangled mats in standing water, or long, stringy, sometimes rope-like strands in flowing water. *R. hieroglyphicum (Ag.)* Kuetz. is the most common species, one which has rather uniformly cylindrical cells with relatively thin walls, and does not branch.

239b Cells not cylindrical, slightly larger at the anterior end, or practically cylindrical in some species, but in any event with at least 1 ring-like scar on the wall at the anterior end just below the cross wall (often with several such annular scars). Fig. 179....
....*OEDOGONIUM*

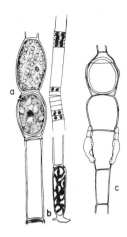

Fig. 179. (a) *Oedogonium crispum* K u e t z., portion of filament with one fertilized and an unfertilized egg; (b) basal hold-fast cell and portion of a filament containing antheridia and antherozoids; (c) *Oe. Westii* Tiffany, s h o w i n g dwarf male filaments epiphytic on the female plant.

There are over 300 species in this large genus which belongs to the family Oedogoniaceae that includes 2 other genera. (*Bulbochaete*, Fig. 221; *Oedocladium*, Fig. 197). Species are differentiated and are identified when in the reproductive condition by the size, shape and morphology of the sex organs and the mature oospore. Whereas some species have the male organs (antheridia) in filaments the same size as those which bear the female (oogonia), others possess dwarf male plants which grow as epiphytes on or near the oogonium. *Oedogonium* plants begin as attached filaments and may remain so throughout life, or they may become free-floating and form cottony masses near the surface of the water, usually becoming pale yellow-green or cream-colored in age. Often these masses are so dense that if left to dry by the evaporation of habitat water they form what is known as "algal paper." Very common habitats are on overhanging grass leaves or the culms of rushes, old cattail stalks, *etc.*

240a (238) Chloroplast a parietal plate, a ring, or a band which incompletely encircles the cell.....................................241

240b Chloroplast massive and dense (difficult of determination), or a parietal sheet of thick and thin areas (padded appearance), or a branched, beaded thread (see *Microspora*). Fig. 180..253

Fig. 180. Beaded (left) and padded parietal chloroplasts as found in *Microspora*.

241a Filaments composed of long, cylindrical, multinucleate units; chloroplast in the form of several parietal rings in each unit. Fig. 181..*SPHAEROPLEA*

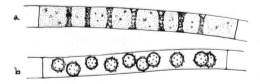

Fig. 181. *Sphaeroplea annulina* (Roth) Ag.; (a) vegetative cell with ring-like chloroplasts; (b) one cell containing fertilized eggs.

Two species of this genus are known from the United States, but *S. annulina* is the one most frequently seen, although it actually is a rather rare plant. Wherever it occurs it is likely to be in abundance. The characteristic long, cylindrical 'cells' may be mistaken for species of *Rhizoclonium* (Fig. 178), especially in the examination of preserved material. It is to be expected in shallow water of marshes and bays in lakes.

241b Filaments not composed of long, multinucleate units; chloroplasts otherwise, usually 1 in each cell..........................242

242a Filaments prostrate, creeping on larger filamentous algae. Fig. 182...*APHANOCHAETE*

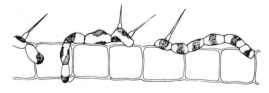

Fig. 182. *Aphanochaete repens* A. Br.

There are 3 species of this genus which are very common but are often overlooked because of their small size and their habit of creeping on the walls of larger filaments. The simple setae, with swollen bases, extending from the cell wall are helpful in making identification, *A. polychaete* (Hansg.) Fritsch is characterized by having several such setae on each cell. *A. repens* A. Br. often has the habit of a minute measuring worm.

242b Filaments not creeping on algae; floating, or if prostrate, with cells in discontinuous series................................243

243a Filaments very short (up to 20 cells); often in interrupted series 244

243b Filaments longer, in continuous series of cells..............245

244a Chloroplast a parietal plate extended over but a small part of the wall; usually subaerial. Fig. 183.......STICHOCOCCUS

Fig. 183. Stichococcus bacillaris Naeg.

The difference between *Stichococcus* and the small filaments characteristic of *Hormidium* (Fig. 190) is difficult to define. In the former genus the filaments are usually relatively short (10 to 20, or 40 cells) and have a tendency to break into short segments intermittently. Of the 6 species which occur in the United States most are found on the bark of trees, old boards, or on damp soil. The species illustrated is the most common, often occurring with *Protococcus* (Fig. 77) in subaerial habitats, the short filaments twisted and contorted, or coiled in 1 plane.

244b Chloroplast a broad plate extended over most of the cell wall; aquatic. Fig. 184.............................HORMIDIOPSIS

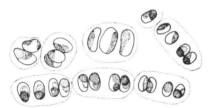

Fig. 184. Hormidiopsis ellipsoideum Presc.

This is the only species reported from this country and possibly cannot be differentiated from *Hormidium* (Fig. 190) except that the filaments are frequently interrupted and are decidedly constricted at the cross walls, the cells being oblong or oval rather than cylindrical. Characteristically, the chloroplast extends only part way around the cell wall.

245a (243) Filament composed of units which include 2 oval or subspherical protoplasts; the space between the protoplasts and the walls filled with layered (lamellose) material. Fig. 185........
...BINUCLEARIA

Fig. 185. Binuclearia tatrana Wittr., one filament showing a gelatinous sheath.

This is the only species of *Binuclearia* reported from the United States; occurs intermingled with other filamentous algae, especially in mixtures taken from bogs. The paired protoplasts within each cylindrical unit of the filament make it certain of identification.

a

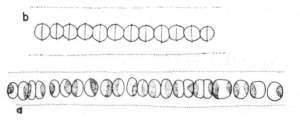

b

These are filamentous plants which have cylindrical or broadly oval cells encased in a wide sheath of mucilage. The cells may be adjoined, or rather evenly spaced one-half to 2 cell lengths apart. Like *Hormidium*

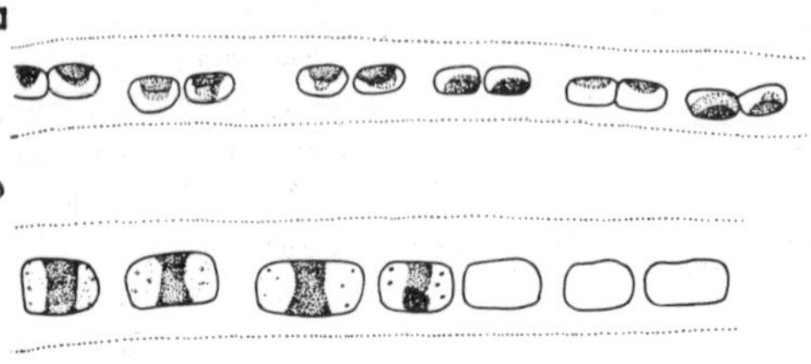

Fig. 186. (a) *Geminella interrupta* (Turp.) Lag.; (b) *G. mutabilis* (Bréb.) Wille.

(Fig. 190) the chloroplast covers but a small portion of the wall.

248a Cells quadrate or cylindrical; wall in 1 piece..............249

248b Cells globose, subglobose, or ellipsoid; wall usually of 2 overlapping pieces that meet in the midregion of the cell and which form short, lateral projections (resulting from a rim about the cell in the midregion). Fig. 187...................*RADIOFILUM*

b

d

Fig. 187. (a) *Radiofilum flavescens* G. S. West; (b) *R. conjunctivum* Schmidle.

The globose or subglobose cells of these filaments help to separate them from *Geminella* (Fig. 186) which also possesses a gelatinous sheath. Some species, *R. conjunctivum* Schm., e.g. have the wall in 2 sections which form a rather conspicuous overlapping in the midregion. There are 5 species in the United States, differentiated by shape and size of the cells.

114

249a Choroplast a parital band or ring which encircles the cell in 1 species and nearly so in others. Fig. 188.........ULOTHRIX

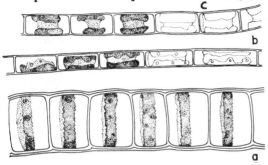

Species of this genus have short or long cylindrical cells, but vary greatly in size. In some the cells are actually shorter than wide. The most familiar species and the largest is U. zonata (Fig. 188a) which has a basal hold-fast cell and chloroplasts which completely

Fig. 188. (a) *Ulothrix zonata* (Weber & Mohr) Kuetz. with ring-like chloroplasts; (b) *U. cylindricum* Presc.; (c) *U. aequalis* Kuetz.

encircle the cell wall. Others have a chloroplast that forms two-thirds or three-fourths of a circle. Usually there are 1 or more conspicuous pyrenoids. Whereas most species occur in standing water, *U. zonata* is commonly found attached to stones and pebbles in flowing, often cold water. Reproduction is by quadriflagellate zoospores, formed 4 or 8 in a cell, or by biflagellate isogametes produced 16 to 64 in a cell.

249b Chloroplast a laminate plate lying over a small portion of the wall and not encircling it. (See Fig. 186.).........GEMINELLA

250a (246) Filaments not showing a basal-distal differentiation....251

250b Filaments with a basal hold-fast.........................252

251a Filaments short, 2 to 6 cells long, tapered at both ends. Fig. 189 .... RAPHIDONEMA

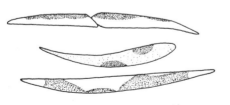

This genus is scarcely a filament, consisting of no more than 6 fusiform cells in a series. The filaments taper at each end. Very frequently the cells occur solitary, especially in snow banks at high altitudes.

Fig. 189. *Raphidonema nivale* Lag.

251b Filaments longer, not tapered at either end. Fig. 190........
...*HORMIDIUM*

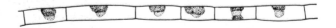

Fig. 190. *Hormidium Klebsii* G. M. Smith.

This genus includes several species of simple, unbranched filaments of cylindrical cells which are characterized by having chloroplasts which extend only part way around the cell and which are only
about one-half the cell in length.

252a (250) Cells elongate-cylindrical, the apical cell unsymmetrically
pointed. Fig. 191....................................*URONEMA*

Fig. 191. *Uronema elongatum* Hodgetts.

There are 2 species
in this genus of ques-
tionable position. The
cells are long and cy-
lindrical with a *Ulo-*
thrix-like chloroplast. Usually the filament is only a few cells in length.
The unsymmetrically pointed apical cell is the chief identifying character. Younger stages in the development of *Stigeoclonium* (Fig. 200)
plants should be kept in mind when identification of *Uronema* is made.

252b Cells short-cylindric, apical cell not tapering. (See Fig. 188.)....
...*ULOTHRIX*

253a (240) Cells quadrate or oval to sub-globose, inclosed in a strati-
fied, gelatinous sheath. Fig. 192.............*CYLINDROCAPSA*

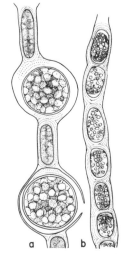

Although filaments of this genus begin as attached plants they soon become free-floating and are found intermingled with other filamentous algae, especially in soft water or acid lakes and bogs. The choloroplasts are so dense and the cell contents include so much food storage material that few structural characteristics can be determined. The female reproductive organ (oogonium) is globular and greatly swollen to several times the diameter of the vegetative cells. The oogonium contents, especially after the egg has been fertilized, are red, as are the antheridia which occur as a single or double series of small cells.

Fig. 192. *Cylindrocapsa geminella* var. *minor* Hansg. (a) portion of filament with oogonia; (b) vegetative cells.

253b Filaments formed otherwise...............................254

254a Cells orange or golden-red because of haematochrome; plants aerial on trees and rocks; chloroplast dense and indeterminate of shape. Fig. 193............................*TRENTEPOHLIA*

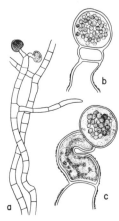

The species illustrated here and *T. aurea* Mart. are the 2 which are the most common of the 14 which have been reported from the United States. They grow on moist stones, dripping cliffs, and on the moist bark of trees. The characteristic orange color makes this plant conspicuous, especially when it forms extensive patches, sometimes forming a felty-mat over large areas of rocky cliffs. In southern United States the moist sides of trees throughout extensive areas of the country side are colored reddish by these algae. In humid situations of the tropics and subtropics the filaments become infested with a fungus to form the lichen, *Coenogonium*. The haematochrome pigment appears in the cell as a reaction to intense illumination.

Fig. 193. *Trentepohlia lolithus* (L.) Wallroth. (a) filament with 2 terminal sporangia; (b), (c) sporangia in detail.

117

254b Cells without haematochrome; plants aquatic; chloroplast a perforated and padded sheet or a branched, beaded ribbon. Fig. 194 . . . . *MICROSPORA*

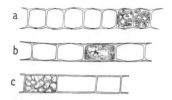

Fig. 194. (a) *Microspora Loefgrenii* (Nordst.) Lag.; (b) *M. Willeana* Lag.; (c) *M. floccosa* (Vauch.) Thur.

In this genus the simple, unbranched filaments have chloroplasts that vary greatly in respect to the degree with which they cover the wall. There are 15 or 16 species, differentiated by cell size and proportions, and by thickness of the wall. Some species show the 2-parted character of the wall, especially at the ends of the filaments where the line of separation, having occurred in the midregion of the cell rather than at the juncture of 2 cells, forms characteristic H-shaped pieces.

255a (236) Plants macroscopic, gelatinous, arbuscular thalli; appearing beaded to the unaided eye (usually) . . . . : 256

255b Plants microscopic, or if macroscopic, not appearing beaded . . 257

256a Branches whorled (beaded effect); when mature with dense clusters of spores (carpospores) formed around the base of the female sex organ (carpogonium) as a result of fertilization. Fig. 195. (B. Dillenii not beaded) . . . . *BATRACHOSPERMUM*

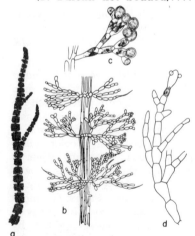

Fig. 195. (a) *Batrachospermum moniliforme* Roth, habit of plant; (b) portion of thallus showing small antheridial cells at tips of branches; (c) *B. vagum* (Roth) Ag., antheridial branch in detail; (d) *B. Boryanum* Sirod., carpogonial branch with 2 male cells attached to trichogyne of the carpogonium (female organ).

This genus belongs to the red algae (Rhodophyta) although it shows none of the red color characteristic of this group of the algae as they occur in the ocean. The macroscopic thalli, highly branched and beaded in appearance, encased in copious mucilage render these plants easy of identification. The thallus may be gray-green or blue-green, or olive in color. *B. vagum* is perhaps the most common species in the country, occurring in large patches over stones in flowing water. Some species prefer quiet water and are to be sought in *Sphagnum* bog pools. Microscopically *Batrachospermum* is one of the most elegant of freshwater algae. Species are differentiated by the morphology of the carpogonium and the shape of its extension, the trichogyne which receives the male gamete in sexual reproduction. (See Fig. 195d.)

256b Thallus similar to above; carpospores solitary or in small clumps, produced on wandering filaments (gonimoblast filaments) which develop from the carpogonium after fertilization of the female gamete. Fig. 196 . . . .*SIRODOTIA*

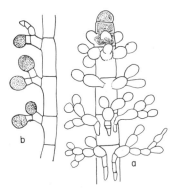

These plants occur in the same type of habitat as *Batrachospermum* (Fig. 195), and look much like that genus macroscopically. The chief difference is that the zygote in *Sirodotia* develops filaments (gonimoblast filaments) that grow through the thallus, cutting off clusters of spores, 2 or 3 together, here and there. In *Batrachospermum* the spores are produced in dense clumps ('cabbage heads') in the immediate vicinity of the fertilized egg.

Fig. 196. *Sirodotia suecica* Kylin, (a) apex of filament with branches; (b) carpospores in detail; borne on gonimoblast filament which develops from carpogonium.

257a (255) Filaments uniseriate below, becoming multiseriate in the upper section, with cells brick-like in shape and arrangement; cells adjoined. (See Fig. 177.) . . . .*SCHIZOMERIS*

257b Filaments multiseriate throughout; cells not adjoined but arranged in irregular series within a gelatinous strand to form a false filament. (See Fig. 52.) . . . .*PALMODICTYON*

258a (204) Plants composed of cellular units; cross walls present . .259

258b Plants multinucleate filaments (coenocytic), without cross walls (except when reproductive structures are developed and separated by a cross partition from the main filament) 302

259a **Plants growing on moist soil with rhizoidal branches composed of long, narrow cells; apical cell usually with a cap (thimble). Fig. 197** . . . . *OEDOCLADIUM*

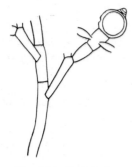

The branched, filamentous plants in this genus have been found only on damp soil. There are 7 species known from the United States, but probably there are many more which have been overlooked. In nature the plants greatly resemble moss protonema. Like other members of the Oedogoniaceae the cells are slightly larger at the anterior end. The female organ (oogonium) is distinctly enlarged, whereas the antheridium is produced in a dwarf male plant that grows as an epiphyte on or near the oogonium.

Fig. 197. *Oedocladium Hazenii* Lewis, portion of branched filament with an oogonium and 2 epiphytic male plants.

259b **Plants aquatic, or, epiphytic or parasitic on higher plants; or if terrestrial, without long, narrow, rhizoidal branches and without a terminal cap** 260

260a **Plants prostrate, growing horizontally; mostly epiphytic or endophytic and forming discs or flat expansions; upright branches present in some forms** 261

260b **Plants erect (not growing horizontal on a substrate but sometimes a thallus with some horizontal growth at the base of the erect portion); free-floating or attached; epiphytic or parasitic on higher plants; sometimes perforating wood or shells** 273

261a **Thallus a freely and openly branched filament; cells usually bearing setae or spine-shaped hairs** 262

261b **Thallus not freely branched, but forming a disc, cushion (pseudoparenchymatous), or a flat expanse of cells** 268

262a **Endophytic in walls of other algae** 263

262b **Not endophytic in the walls of other algae** 264

263a **Thallus irregularly branched; angular cells lying within or under the walls of *Nitella*; cells bearing setae (sometimes very scarce) which are sheathed at the base. (See Fig. 170a)** . . . .*COLEOCHAETE NITELLARUM*

Some species of *Nitella* especially, invariably are found with this species of *Coleochaete* growing just within the wall of the internodal cells. A strong light is often necessary to render the endophyte visible. The sheathed hairs extend through the wall of *Nitella* cells.

263b Cells not angular; short, branched chains of cells; never bearing
setae. Fig. 198.................................*ENTOCLADIA*

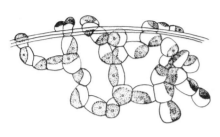

This genus includes only 3
known species in the United
States. Although probably very
common it is easily overlooked
because the thalli are small
and grow inconspicuously within the walls of larger algae.
The filaments are short and irregularly branched; have a
parietal, *Ulothrix*-like chloroplast.

Fig. 198. *Entocladia polymorpha* (G. S.
West) G. M. Smith.

264a (262) Some cell walls bearing setae with a sheathed base; terminal cells of branches not tapering to form setae. (See Fig.
170.) ....*COLEOCHAETE*

264b Cells with setae not sheathed at the base, or if without setae, ends
of branches tapering to hairs or spine-like extensions.......265

265a Setae and terminal hairs multicellular.....................266

265b Setae one-celled...267

266a Multicellular setae in the form of especially slender branches
arising from lateral walls of cells. Fig. 199.....*PSEUDOCHAETE*

The species illustrated is rarely found.
It grows partly prostrate, partly erect
on submerged plants and other substrates. The branched filaments taper
at both ends. Some of the branches
form long, narrow and finely tapering
hairs. Some students of the algae regard *Pseudochaete* as a growth form of
Stigeoclonium (Fig. 200).

Fig. 199. *Pseudochaete gracilis*
W. & G. S. West.

121

266b Multicellular hairs resulting from the apical tapering of branches. Fig. 200 . . . . *STIGEOCLONIUM*
(Most species have erect, branched filaments, but some in young stages show a predominating prostrate portion with a few erect branches.)

There are several species of this genus, differentiated by size, by the plan of branching, and by the morphology of the thallus as a whole. Some form long, graceful tufts; others bunched growths with part of the thallus prostrate.

Fig. 200. *Stigeoclunium flagelliferum* Kuetz., (a) portion of thallus showing tapering branches; (b) cell showing laminate chloroplast and pyrenoid.

267a (265) Growing in the mucilage of other algae. Fig. 201 . . . .
. . . . *CHAETONEMA*

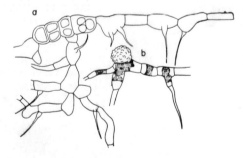

There are only 2 species of this genus known. It is rather rarely seen because its habitat is the gelatinous matrix of highly branched algae such as *Chaetophora* (Fig. 222) and *Batrachospermum* (Fig. 195) where it is camouflaged.

Fig. 201. *Chaetonema irregulare* Nowak. (a) branches containing antheridial cells; (b) oogonium.

267b Growing in a 'creeping' fashion on the walls of larger algae. (See Fig. 182.)..............................APHANOCHAETE

268a (261) Cells bearing setae with sheathed bases. (See Fig. 170.)...
....COLEOCHAETE

268b Cells without setae, or if setae present, without sheathed bases..
....269

269a Endophytic in the walls of other algae. (See Fig. 198.)........
....ENTOCLADIA

269b Not endophytic in the walls of other algae.................270

270a Some cells bearing setae. Fig. 202............CHAETOPELTIS

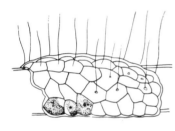

This plant forms relatively small, circular discs composed of indistinctly radiate filaments which grow closely side by side. It should be compared with *Coleochaete* (Fig. 170). Almost every cell in the thallus bears a long, very slender, hair-like seta.

Fig. 202. *Chaetopeltis orbicularis* Berth.

270b Setae lacking..271

271a Thallus a thin expansion, 1 cell in thickness; a circular disc or with a somewhat irregular margin. Fig. 203...PROTODERMA

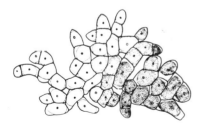

This prostrate plant forms a cushion-like thallus 1 cell in thickness at the margin and one which shows very irregular branching of short filaments. It is to be found growing on the stems of submerged aquatic plants.

Fig. 203. *Protoderma viride* Kuetz.

271b Thallus cushion-like, several cells in thickness in the midregion..
....272

272a Cells with several chloroplasts; thallus inclosed in a mucilage; disc several cells thick in the midregion, 1 cell in thickness at the margin. Fig. 204.......................... PSEUDULVELLA

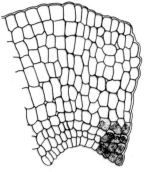

The protrate disc-like thalli of this plant are relatively large. The entire thallus is covered by a gelatinous sheath through which an occasional seta projects from the cell walls, but setae are rarely found.

Fig. 204. *Pseudulvella americana* (Snow) Wille.

272b Cells with but 1 chloroplast; thallus not inclosed in a sheath. Fig. 205 .... ULVELLA

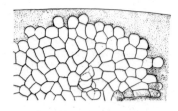

This plant forms irregular, disc-like or cushion-like growths which are several cells in thickness when mature. They grow on submerged aquatic plants, sometimes on animals; do not possess setae.

Fig. 205. *Ulvella involens* (Savi) Schmidle *(Dermatophyton),* diagram of attached colony showing arrangement of cells.

273a (260) Plant a sparsely-branched filament growing erect from the walls of other algae; cells bearing 1 to 3 setae with inflated bases. Fig. 206..............................*THAMNIOCHAETE*

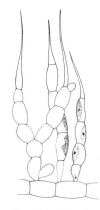

The species of *Thamniochate* illustrated consists of cylindrical or pyriform cells which are arranged in short filaments. The cells, especially near the apex, bear 1 to 3 long spines. The plants grow as erect epiphytes on other algae.

Fig. 206. *Thamniochaete Huberi* Gay, filaments growing erect from algal host.

273b Plant not as above......................................274

274a Filaments irregularly branched, composed of moniliform cells, mostly erect but sprawling and prostrate (in part) on tree trunks and leaves of higher plants. Fig. 207...........*PHYSOLINUM*

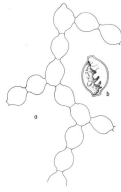

This plant consists of lemon-shaped cells adjoined to form branched chains without any definite central axis. The thallus is mostly prostrate as an epiphyte on higher plants. The cells divide by producing a 'bud' which enlarges and constricts, after which a cross wall is formed separating the new cell from the old. There is one parietal chloroplast, often with projections, or the chloroplast may become divided into 2 or 3 disc-like bodies, but always without pyrenoids.

Fig. 207. *Physolinum monilia* (de Wildm.) Printz, (a) prostrate and erect filaments; (b) cell with chloroplast.

274b Plants not as above...................................275

275a Plants parasitizing leaves of terrestrial plants, living partly within and partly on the surface of leaves or fruits (Magnolia, tea, banana). Fig. 208.............................*CEPHALEUROS*

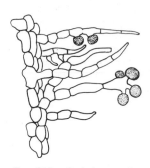

Fig. 208. *Cephaleuros virescens* Kunze, diagram of thallus as it grows under leaf epidermis of host plant, with erect branches bearing sporangia.

This species occurs in tropical and subtropical parts of the world, especially in areas where there is an optimum humidity so that the leaves of the plants on which the alga is parasitic are moist. The host may be *Magnolia*, *Thea*, citrus fruits or *Rhododendron*. Because of the discoloration and degeneration of host tissue in the vicinity of the parasite some damage is caused by this alga and a certain amount of economic loss results, especially in tea plantations. Although the parasitized areas appear gray-green in color, individual filaments of the cushion-like thallus of the alga are usually reddish because of the pigment haematochrome.

275b Plants not parasitizing leaves of higher plants..............276

276a Cells without setae; filaments not tapering to hair-like tips...277

276b Cells bearing setae or with branches tapering to hair-like tips, or fine points...296

277a Branches short, irregular and rhizoidal, often formed only near one end of the filament..................................278

277b Branches long, multicellular, usually forming a definite pattern of growth, opposite or alternate on the main axis............280

278a Chloroplast a spiral ribbon. (See Fig. 167).......*SPIROGYRA*

278b Chloroplast not a spiral ribbon...........................279

279a Chloroplast an axial plate or band. See Fig. 165...*MOUGEOTIA*

279b Chloroplast a parietal network of thickenings and thin strands. (See Fig. 178.)................................*RHIZOCLONIUM*

280a (277) Growing in wood, shells, or within limestone. Fig. 209....
....*GOMONTIA*

Fig. 209. *Gomontia Holdenii* Collins, habit of the thallus showing erect branches.

These plants must be sought within old wood, shells or in limey concretions. The thallus occurs as a cushion-like, irregularly tangled mass of short filaments from which some elements grow downward to form rhizoidal, penetrating threads. Reproductive structures (sporangia) are borne on the upper part of the thallus or on the ends of short erect branches. Akinetes are also produced. In germination these often form aplanospores. Most species are marine. The walls of the cells are relatively thick and often lamellate. The chloroplast is a dense plate or meshwork containing pyrenoids.

280b Not growing in wood nor in shells........................281

281a Growing on trees or moist rocks; many or all cells showing an abundance of orange or reddish-yellow pigment (haematochrome). (See Fig. 193.)................................*TRENTEPOHLIA*

281b Plants growing elsewhere; not containing haematochrome...282

282a Thallus encrusted with lime..............................283

282b Thallus not encrusted with lime.........................284

283a Thallus in the form of a cushion, giving rise to compactly arranged, upright branches; cells broadest near the tip of the filament; growing on wood or shells (sometimes on other plants in the water). Fig. 210...........................*GONGROSIRA*

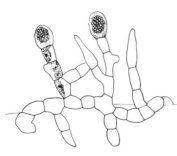

Fig. 210. *Gongrosira Debaryana* Rab., horizontal and erect branches with terminal sporangia.

Like *Gomontia* (Fig. 209) these plants grow on shells and submerged wood, or on aquatic plants, but form external thalli rather than penetrating the substrate. Plants are sometimes encrusted with lime. The erect, branched portion of the thallus is more extensively developed than in *Gomontia*. The chloroplast is parietal and more definite in outline than that of *Gomontia* which may be padded and irregularly netted.

127

283b Thallus composed of loosely branched filaments, the branches arising unilaterally. Fig. 211..................*CHLOROTYLIUM*

The attached, lime-encrusted thalli of this branched filamentous plant are usually found in flowing water. The filaments present a distinctive appearance when seen microscopically because pairs of short, green cells (often with a reddish tinge) alternate with a more elongate and sometimes nearly colorless cell.

Fig. 211. *Chlorotylium cataractum* Kuetz., portion of plant showing characteristic habit of branch development.

284a (282) Thallus a tuft of dichotomously branched, radiating, yellow-green filaments. Fig. 212...........................*LEPTOSIRA*

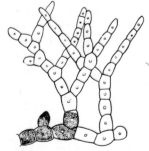

This species is known only from Massachusetts and Kentucky in the United States. Filaments occur in yellowish tufts and are usually attached to substrates. The irregularly branched filaments of bead-like or barrel-shaped cells arising from a prostrate portion of the thallus help in making identificaiton.

Fig. 212. *Leptosira Mediciana* Borzi, portion of plant showing horizontal and erect branching systems.

284b Thallus not a dense tuft of yellow-green filaments...........285

285a Bearing enlarged, thick-walled akinetes (vegetative spores) interspersed among the cylindrical cells of the filament, or with such spores at the ends of branches...........................286

285b Without akinetes...287

286a Akinetes globular. Fig. 213..................... _CTENOCLADUS_

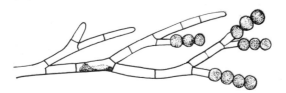

Fig. 213. _Ctenocladus circinnatus_ Borzi, showing a terminal series of akinetes.

This is a branched, filamentous genus, grownig epiphytically on angiospermous plants in brackish water. The chains of globular akinetes at the ends of branches make it distinctive, although the habit of growth is somewhat like _Gongrosira_ (Fig. 210).

286b Akinetes barrel-shaped or oval. Fig. 214........ _PITHOPHORA_

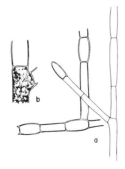

There are 8 species of this irregularly branched, filamentous genus in the United States, differentiated by dimensions of the filament and by size and shape of the much-swollen akinetes that are formed intermittently throughout the plant. The cells are coenocytic. When occurring in laboratory aquaria, usually having been brought in on material obtained from biological supply houses, the filaments often fail to develop akinetes, the cells becoming exceedingly long and losing some of the appearance by which they are usually identified.

Fig. 214. (a) _Pithophora Mooreana_ Collins; (b) _P. Oedogonia_ (Mont.) Wittr., showing a sample of the chloroplast.

287a (285) Growing on submerged wood and stones, with a prostrate, cushion-like mass of branches from which vertical branches arise. (See Fig. 210.)...................................... _GONGROSIRA_

287b Thallus formed differently................................. 288

288a Plants growing on shells of turtles (rarely on submerged bricks or rough stones); branches arising only from the extreme base of the main filament. Fig. 215 . . . . *BASICLADIA*

This and 1 other species (differentiated mostly by size) comprise the genus which is distinctive in that the plants occur almost entirely on the shells of turtles, especially the snapper. Old turtles are usually "mossy" with the tufted growths of filaments which characteristically branch so close to the base that the branching habit is easily overlooked. Cells may be as much as 120 μ in diameter, but a millimeter or two in length.

Fig. 215. Basicladia Chelonum (Collins) Hoffman & Tilden; (a) cells at base of filament; (b) branching habit; (c) series of sporangia formed in upper portion of filament.

288b Plant not growing on turtles, or with other types of branching . . 289

289a Plants showing basal-distal differentiation, usually attached (floating in age); branching usually arbuscular (tree-like or bush-like) 290

289b Plants not forming bushy tufts 294

290a Cells with haematochrome (reddish color masking the chloroplast green). (See Fig. 193.) . . . . *TRENTEPOHLIA*

290b Cells without haematochrome 291

291a Plants stout; walls thick and lamellate; chloroplast a dense reticulum with many pyrenoids 293

291b Plants slender, wall thin, cross walls of branches above the level of branch origin on the main axis; filamentous thallus of either adjoined cells or with cells interrupted or separated from each other; apical cells pointed.................................292

(Color pale green. Indications are that the two following genera are members of the yellow-green algae (Chrysophyta).)

292a Thallus arbuscular; minute, sometimes densely tufted, attached plants. Fig. 216.............................MICROTHAMNION

This species and its relative *M. Kuetzingianum* Naeg. are easily overlooked in collections because the attached branched filaments are so minute and the chloroplast so pale and inconspicuous. They occur on larger filaments of other algae or on aquatic plants, but usually break away and are found free-floating at maturity, intermingled with other algae.

Fig. 216. *Mi-crothamnion stric-tissimum* Rab.

292b Thallus gelatinous, free-floating or entangled among other algae, with radiating series of irregularly dissociated cells; branching scarce and incidental. Fig. 217...............HETEROCOCCUS

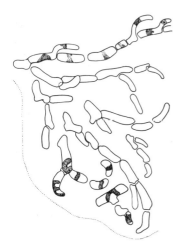

The thallus of this genus consists of irregularly radiating series of dissociated cells, or with 2 or 3 cells adjoined. Branches form from near the apex of a cell, the new cell soon becoming dissociated. The apical cells are tapered or thorn-like and curved. The chloroplast is a parietal plate covering part of the cell wall. The thallus is embedded in rather firm mucilage.

Fig. 217. *Heterococcus arcticus* Pres., habit of branching and radiate arrangement of pseudofilaments.

293a (291) Branching open and spreading; cells mostly cylindrical (sometimes irregularly so). Fig. 218 . . . . .CLADOPHORA

Fig. 218. *Clado-phora* sp., (a) cell showing *parietal*, net-like or discontinuous chloroplast; (b) habit of branching.

There are numerous species of this genus both in fresh and in salt water. They are differentiated by the diameter of the filaments, by the shape of cells, and by the habit of branching. The plan of branching varies, however, according to habitat. Identification and differentiation of species are often difficult. The cell walls are relatively thick. Chloroplasts are discs but may be adjoined in a mesh work. Some plants exist over winter in lakes and become wave-washed and lose their original appearance. Other species in lakes become free-floating and by wave action become rolled over and over with the result that "*Cladophora*-balls" are produced. These appear as densely branched and entangled growths, with the cells very irregular in shape. Perhaps the most characteristic habitat of *Cladophora* is on rocks in flowing water, especially on dams and waterfalls.

293b Branching close and entangled, often dichotomous; downward projecting, rhizoidal branches common; cells irregularly swollen. Fig. 219 . . . . .AEGAGROPILA

This species is more irregularly branched than *Cladophora* and has downward directed, rhizoidal branches. The upper filaments are densely entangled and the cells are more irregular in shape. As the species name suggests, it is found growing on the bottom of lakes at depths up to 200 feet (especially in clear water). Some authorities include *Aegagropila* under *Cladophora*.

Fig. 219. *Aegagropila profunda* (Brand) Nordst.

294a (289) Vegetative cells very long and cylindrical, somewhat regularly interrupted by swollen, thick-walled spores (akinetes). (See Fig. 214.)......................................*PITHOPHORA*

294b Akinetes lacking; cells all cylindrical or nearly so..........295

295a Branches scarce and short, or wanting altogether; if branches present, without repeated branching. (See Fig. 178.)............
....*RHIZOCLONIUM*

295b Branches many-celled, bearing secondary branches which arise irregularly so that the arbuscular habit is almost lost. (See Fig. 218.) Wave-washed and winter forms of........*CLADOPHORA*

296a (276) Setae without cross walls at the base, formed by lateral extensions of cells just below the anterior cross partition of the cell. Fig. 220......................................*FRIDAEA*

This is a very rare species (the only one known for the genus) but is readily identified by the long, cylindrical cells which bear thread-like extensions that are given off laterally just below the anterior cross wall. The filaments occur in compact tufts and are usually yellowish-green in color. The chloroplast is parietal and laminate, but often so dense that the organization is difficult of determination. Zoosporangia are elongate, sac-like, produced laterally on the filaments.

Fig. 220. *Fridaea torrenticola* Schmidle.

296b Setae formed otherwise..................................297

297a Setae bulb-like at the base. Fig. 221. . . . .*BULBOCHAETE*

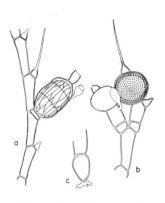

Like its close relative *Oedogonium* (Fig. 179) this genus contains numerous species which are likewise differentiated by dimensions and characteristics of the sex organs and the oospore. They cannot be identified in the vegetative condition. The branched filaments are attached (at least when young) and are readily identified by the bulbous-based, unicellular setae that develop at the anterior end of the cell. The plants are to be sought on overhanging grass, or on the culms of rushes, submerged plants, *etc.* Most species have dwarf male plants that grow epiphytically on the female sex organ (oogonium).

Fig. 221. (a) *Bulbochaete insignis* Pringsh., showing oogonium with oospore, and an attached dwarf male plant; (b) *B. congener* Hirn; (c) hold-fast cell.

297b Setae shaped otherwise. 298
298a Setae sheathed at the base. (See Fig. 170.). . . . .*COLEOCHAETE*
298b Setae not sheathed at the base. 299
299a Thallus not embedded in mucilage, or if so, inclosed in a very soft, watery mucilage without definite shape. 300
299b Thallus inclosed in a firm mucilaginous matrix of definite shape, globular or somewhat elongate and irregularly arbuscular (sometimes strands are 4 to 15 cm. in length). Fig. 222. . . . .
. . . . .*CHAETOPHORA*

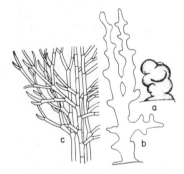

Microscopically, species of this genus are delicately and gracefully branched filaments that occur in macroscopic tufts or gelatinous balls. One, *C. incrassata* (Huds.) Hazen, is composed of cables of elongate cells which give off laterally dense tufts of dichotomous branches. The resulting growth produces bush-like or arbuscular thalli which may become as much as 14 cm. long. Other species form spherical or irregularly globose balls, 1 or 2 mm. in diameter on submerged leaves (especially in cold water), on wood, or on cattail stems and other aquatic plants. The colonies are often gre-

Fig. 222. (a) *Chaetophora elegans* (Roth) C. A. Ag., habit of thallus; (b) *C. incrassata* (Huds.) Hazen, habit of thallus; (c) portion of thallus showing longitudinal filaments with out-turned branches.

garious and form extensive patches. The firmness of the mucilage in which the plants are encased macroscopically differentiates *Chaetophora* and *Draparnaldia* (Fig. 224) and *Stigeoclonium* (Fig. 200).

300a Thallus composed of slender, repeatedly branched filaments; cells all about the same size but tapering to fine points or setae. (See Fig. 200.).................................. *STIGEOCLONIUM*

300b Thallus consisting of main filaments of large cells from which arise tufts of branches composed of much smaller cells......301

301a (300) Main axis consisting of cells of 2 sizes, cylindrical and short rectangular, the tufts of branches arising opposite only from the short cells. Fig. 223.....................*DRAPARNALDIOPSIS*

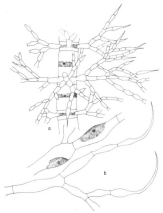

This genus is similar to *Draparnaldia* (Fig. 224) but the main axis cells are of two sizes, the longer cells alternating with short ones. The branches are somewhat dichotomous and rather stiff in appearance.

Fig. 223. *Draparnaldiopsis salishensis* Presc., (a) portion of main axis with branch tufts; (b) sample of branch showing shapes of cells.

301b Main axis composed of cylindrical or barrel-shaped cells all the same size; branches arising opposite, alternate, or in whorls. Fig. 224....................................*DRAPARNALDIA*

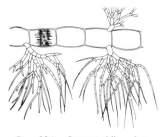

The genus is strikingly characterized by having a filament of large cells forming an axis from which tufted plumes of branches of smaller cell size arise. Different species vary in size and shape of the branching tufts. The thallus is inclosed in amorphous mucilage, soft and watery, and occurs mostly in cold water, trickles from springs, *etc.* Macroscopically the plants appear as pale yellow gelatinous strands that easily slip through the fingers when gathered.

Fig. 224. *Draparnaldia glomerata* (Vauch.) Ag., showing tufts of lateral branches, with barrel-shaped axial cells containing band-like chloroplasts.

302a (258) Parasitic in higher plants such as *Arisaema* (Indian Turnip). (See Fig. 105.)..............................*PHYLLOSIPHON*

302b Not parasitic 303

303a Filaments repeatedly, dichotomously branched, regularly constricted at the base of the forkings. Fig. 225................
....*DICHOTOMOSIPHON*

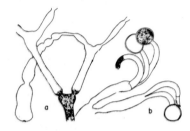

Fig. 225. *Dichotomosiphon tuberosus* (Braun) Ernst.

.. This species (the only one in the genus) occurs in dense, entangled tufts or mats, usually on the bottom of lakes, although occasionally on damp soil and in seeps. There are downward growing, rhizoidal branches and upward directed vegetative and sex organ-bearing branches. The oogonia when mature are so large that they can be discerned with the naked eye. The plants seem to reproduce sexually only when growing in relatively shallow water (up to 4 feet) but may form extensive mats on the bottoms of lakes, without reproducing, up to 60 feet deep. The filaments are siphonous, coenocytic tubes. The chloroplasts are numerous parietal discs or ovals and starch is produced as a food reserve.

303b Filaments not dichotomously branched; without constrictions. Fig. 226 ....*VAUCHERIA*

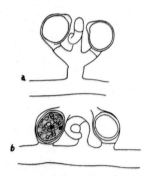

Fig. 226. (a) *Vaucheria geminata* (Vauch.) De Cand., sex organs on a short pedicel; (b) *V. sessilis* (Vauch.) De Cand.

Vaucheria usually forms dark green, velvety mats on damp soil, on rocks in flowing water, or occasionally wooly mats floating at the surface of ponds, having broken away from their substrates. At maturity the growths are 'dirty' green in color. The siphonous filaments are large enough to be seen individually with the unaided eye. Several species are common in fresh water, differentiated by shape and position of the sex organs. Many have brackish and salt water habitats. The mats harbor a veritable zoological garden of small animals. Long considered to be a member of the Chlorophyta, this genus is now classed with the Xanthophyceae in the Chrysophyta; food reserve is oil rather than starch and the zoospores have flagella of unequal length.

304a (5) Chromatophores violet, gray-green, or bluish-green, often appearing brownish in mass; mostly macroscopic Rhodophyta . . 305

304b Chromatophores some other color than above, or yellowish-green, carotin predominating 313

305a Thallus macroscopic, spine-like or spur-like, with node-like swellings, relatively stiff and cartilaginous; thallus usually simple and unbranched (but composed of a complex of filaments which are branched). Fig. 227 . . . . *LEMANEA*

Fig. 227. *Lemanea annulata* Kuetz, habit of plant.

This genus is a member of the Rhodophyta, but like other fresh-water red algae it is some other color, being gray- or olive-green. The thalli are cartilaginous and stand erect from an attached base (but are bent flat in swiftly flowing water). The slender, spine-like growths (up to 20 cm. in length), devoid of branching make the plant easily recognizable. Species are differentiated mostly on details of the reproductive structures. The plants are to be sought on the brink of dams and in waterfalls.

305b Thallus otherwise 306

306a Plant a uniseriate filament, branched or unbranched (cells in 1 series); microscopic 312

306b Plant a multiseriate filament or thallus; macroscopic 307

307a Thallus embedded in soft mucilage, consisting of an axial filament with corticating, overlying cells and with whorls of branches (In *Batrachospermum Dillenii*, however, the branches are not in evident whorls.) 308

307b Thallus otherwise 309

308a Mature plants bearing dense clusters of carpospores which develop around the base of the carpogonium (female organ) after fertilization of the egg. (See Fig. 195.) . . . . . *BATRACHOSPERMUM*

308b Mature plants with carpospores borne mostly singly along filaments which have developed from the fertilized egg and which wander through the thallus. (See Fig. 196) . . . . *SIRODOTIA*

309a (307) **Thallus consisting of multiaxial filaments (strands of filaments) with numerous feathery branchings; without definite nodes and internodes (without whorls of branches). Fig. 228..** *THOREA*

This is a feathery thallus macroscopically; microscopically composed of a multiaxial cable of filaments with short, compactly arranged, out-turned branches. They may be as much as 50 cm. in length. The genus is of infrequent occurrence but abundant in habitats where it does appear. Sexual reproductive stages have not been observed as yet.

Fig. 228. *Thorea ramossisima* Bory.

309b **Thallus otherwise**......................................310

310a **Thallus cartilaginous and irregularly dichotomously branched; composed of a complex of central filaments from which a thick cortex of superficial cells develops (examine lightly crushed tips of branches to determine the structural plan of the thallus). Fig. 229** ....*TUOMEYA*

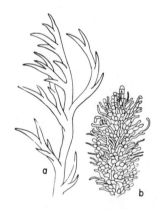

This rather rigid and cartilaginous member of the Rhodophyta is identified by the complex dichotomous or antler-like habit of branching of the thallus which is composed of multiaxial series of filaments and corticating cells. There are but 2 species. Male and female reproducitve cells are produced on the same thallus. Thus far the plant has been found only in the eastern section of the United States.

Fig. 229. *Tuomeya fluviatilis* Harvey. (a) habit of thallus; (b) apical portion of branch.

310b **Thallus composed otherwise, not cartilaginous**..............311

311a Thallus rather regularly branched, arbuscular, composed of a monaxial filament which is inclosed and surrounded by a cortex of compactly arranged and appressed polygonal cells which form and develop just behind the apex (examine tips of branches). Fig. 230.....................................COMPSOPOGON

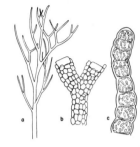

Fig. 230. *Compsopogon coeruleus* (Balbis) Mont. (a) habit of thallus; (b) portion of axis showing corticating cells; (c) apical portion of uncorticated branch showing chromatophores.

This is a member of the Rhodophyta which occurs sometimes in brackish situations, attached to submerged stems of woody plants and stones. *C. coeruleus* (Balb.) Mont. is the most common species; has been found in irrigation ditches in the far western United States. Although essentially filamentous, the thallus is macroscopic in proportions and appears as a rather delicately branched, tufted or bushy growth, blue- or gray- to violet-green in color. It is primarily a tropical and subtropical genus. Sexual reproduction is unknown.

311b Thallus irregularly dichotomously branched; multiaxial (several associated filaments), and corticated; thallus partly prostrate and somewhat dorsiventrally differentiated, with the concave side down, the branches tending to curl at the tips; somewhat tufted, dark gray to blackish-green in color. Fig. 231....*BOSTRYCHIA*

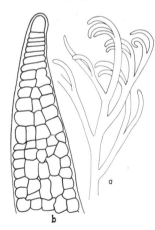

Fig. 231. *Bostrychia scorpioides* (Gmel.) Mont. (a) habit of branching; (b) apex of branch showing development of cortex.

This genus is mostly marine growing on mangrove but at least one species grows in brackish water and in estuaries. *B. scorpioides* occurs in the locks of the Panama Canal and on *Typha* in the adjacent lakes. The thallus is a dichotomously branched somewhat flattened thallus with enrolled margins and with the segments curled at the tips.

139

312a (306) Filaments attached, uniseriate, branched; chromatophore somewhat indefinite, irregularly axial and radiate, or spirally twisted. Fig. 232.............................*AUDOUINELLA*

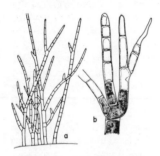

Fig. 232. *Audouinella viola-cea* (Kuetz.) Hamel. (a) habit of thallus; (b) branches in detail.

A member of the Rhodophyta, this species is nevertheless violet- or gray-green. The loosely branched filaments are microscopic but may appear in tufts of macroscopic proportions. The main axial cells have disc-like or short ribbon-like chromatophores. In size, form and habit of growth the plants are easily mistaken for juvenile stages of *Batrachospermum* and if that genus is present in the habitat it could be assumed that *Audouinella*-like plants are the immature or so-called "*Chantransia* - stages" of *Batrachospermum*. There is but 1 species clearly defined for the United States and there is a disposition on the part of some authorities to classify it under the genus *Acrochaetium* which is mostly marine. *Audouinella* has a simple carpogonium and antheridial cells.

312b Filaments attached, uniseriate, unbranched. Fig. 233....*BANGIA*

Fig. 233. *Bangia fuscopurpurea* (Dillw.) Lyngb.

This is a simple, unbranched member of the Rhodophyta, greenish or purplish in color. Filaments occur in tufts, sometimes dense, attached to submerged stones and wood. Although most species of the genus occur in salt water, the one illustrated is known from brackish or from nearby fresh-water habitats. It may be expected in estuaries. The lower cells of the filament develop rhizoidal, downward projecting elongations.

313a (304) Chromatophores yellow, yellow-brown, or dark golden-brown, rarely blue; plants motile or non-motile.....................366

313b Chromatophores not yellow-brown or golden-brown..........314

314a Chromatophores pale yellow-green with xanthophyll predominating; iodine test for starch negative; cell contents often with leucosin showing a metallic lustre. Phylum Chrysophyta. (This group of the algae is difficult of separation on the basis of color of the chromatophore alone inasmuch as the shades of green cannot be clearly distinguished from those of the Chlorophyta. In addition to the iodine test for starch (which ordinarily is confirmative in determining that an alga is not a member of the Chlorophyta) heating plants in concentrated sulphuric acid (when the specimens lend themselves to such treatment) provides a helpful differentiation. The yellow-green algae (Heterokontae or Xanthophyceae) become blue-green in acid, whereas Chlorophyta remain unchanged in color.....................................324

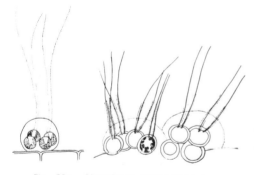

This is an anomalous organism, the morphology and physiology of which are interpreted as that of symbiotism involving a colorless member of the *Tetraspora* family (Figs. 42, 62) and a blue-green or cyanophyceous endophyte. The protoplast is a parietal cup similar to

Fig. 234. *Gloeochaete Wittrockiana* Lag.

the chloroplast of many of the green algae. The long, slender gelatinous hairs make this species easy of identification. Cells occur in clumps (rarely solitary) attached to filamentous algae.

317a A linear series of globular or oblong cells within a mucilaginous matrix; chromatophores star-shaped. Fig. 235...*ASTEROCYSTIS*

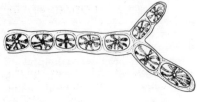

Fig. 235. *Asterocystis smaragdina* (Reinsch) Forti.

The bright blue-green, star-shaped chromatophores of this species (the globose or oval cells being inclosed in a wide gelatinous sheath) help in the identification. It is a simple or incidentally branched filament in the 'lower' Rhodophyta. It occurs mostly as an epiphyte on larger filamentous algae, but may appear in mixtures of free-floating forms.

317b Two to 4 or 8 globose or oval cells contained within an enlarged mother-cell wall; chromatophore-like bodies vermiform (few and long, or many and short). Fig. 236...........*GLAUCOCYSTIS*

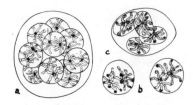

Fig. 236. (a), (b) *Glaucocystis duplex* Presc.; (c) *G. Nostochinearum* Itz.

There are 5 species of this genus which, like *Gloeochaete* (Fig. 234), involve an endophytic blue-green alga and a colorless member of the Oocystaceae (Fig. 96) in the Chlorophyta. The protoplasts are bright blue-green and occur in different shapes and arrangements within either globose or oval cells, according to species. The plants are free-floating in the tychoplankton near shore or in shallow water habitats of swamps and bogs.

318a (315) Cells in compact, irregularly shaped colonies, appearing brown or orange-colored because of dark mucilage. (See Fig. 56.) ....*BOTRYOCOCCUS*

318b Cells not in opaque or orange-colored colonies as above; contents red, violet-red, or green with a red tinge..............319

319a Living in snow in alpine regions (red snow). (See Fig. 31.).... .... *CHLAMYDOMONAS*

319b Not living in snow.......................................320

320a A colony of oval or globose cells inclosed in a layered sheath. (See Fig. 48.)...................................*GLOEOCYSTIS*

320b Cells not in colonies; sheath not layered..................321

321a Cells irregular in shape; living as an endophyte in higher plants. (See Fig. 106.)............................*RHODOCHYTRIUM*

321b Cells not endophytic..................................322

322a Cells spherical, solitary or gregarious, in thin, mucilaginous strands, terrestrial, forming dark red patches on damp soil (common in green houses). Fig. 237..............*PORPHYRIDIUM*

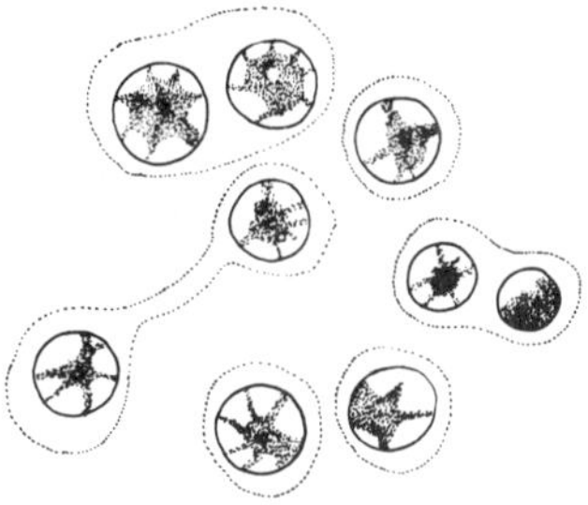

Fig. 237. *Porphyridium cruentum* Naeg.

On the damp soil of green houses or on wet brick walls this plant often forms purple, or wine-red gelatinous films. It is a unicellular member of the Rhodophyta which has a star-shaped chromatophore.

322b Cells round, ellipsoid or fusiform, not arranged as above; not terrestrial (or rarely so)....................................323

323a Cells fusiform; haematochrome coloring the green cell red; with 1 flagellum. (See Fig. 9.)..........................*EUGLENA*

323b Cells round or ellipsoid; protoplast with a wide wall which appears as a gelatinous sheath; flagella 2, but usually not showing when cells are in an encysted condition at which time they exhibit a red color. (See Fig. 21.).........*HAEMATOCOCCUS**

*Also see *Urococcus*, Fig. 141.

324a (314) Plants filamentous....................................325

324b Plants not filamentous....................................329

325a Filaments false; cells not adjoined in continuous series......326

325b Plant a true filament; cells in continuous series..............327

326a A false filament consisting of branched tubes, or of short tubes in chains, with 1 or 2 spherical cells at the distal ends. Fig. 238 ....*MISCHOCOCCUS*

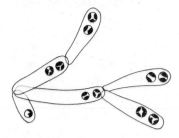

The globose, yellow-green cells of this species occur at the ends of repeatedly branched gelatinous stalks, attached to filamentous algae. Only 1 species is known from the United States. The cells have 2 or 4 parietal chromatophores.

Fig. 238. *Mischococcus confervi-cola* Naeg.

326b Thallus consisting of a floating, gelatinous mass in which short, interrupted series of cells radiate. (See Fig. 217.)...........
....*HETEROCOCCUS*

327a (325) Filament branched. Fig. 239.................*MONOCILIA*

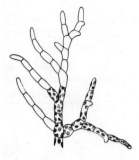

This and another species, *M. flavescens* Gerneck, are the only ones reported from the United States, the former being more common. It occurs as an irregularly and indefinitely branched filament in soil. A member of the Chrysophyta, the disc-like chromatophores are yellow-green or yellow in color, and the food reserve is in the form of oil; starch test negative.

Fig. 239. *Monocilia viridis* Gerneck.

327b Filament not branched....................................328

328a Cells long-cylindric; wall of cells in 2 pieces which overlap at the midregion, the overlapping usually evident when empty cells are viewed; filaments showing H-shaped pieces upon fragmentation; cells with parallel or convex lateral walls. Fig. 240. .
. . . .*TRIBONEMA*

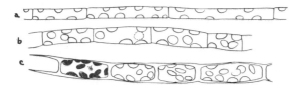

Fig. 240. (a) *Tribonema bombycinum* var. *tenue* Hazen; (b) *T. bombycinum* (Ag.) Derbes & Solier; (c) *T. utriculosum* (Kuetz.) Hazen.

There are several species of this simple, unbranched filamentous member of the Heterokontae, differentiated by proportions of the cell and by the number and shape of the chromatophores. Like *Microspora* (Fig. 194) in the Chlorophyta, the cell walls are composed of 2 sections which adjoin and overlap in the midregion of the cell. Hence when the filaments fragment the typical H-shaped sections are seen. By careful focusing the overlapping of the wall sections can be seen in the unfragmented portions of the filament, especially in some species which have a relatively thick wall. The chromatophores are pale green or yellowish and occur as parietal discs or folded plates. In northern latitudes *Tribonema* is the first alga to appear in ditches after ice thaw.

328b Cells short-cylindric or quadrate; overlapping of wall sections not apparent but visible at the ends of broken filaments; lateral margins of the cells strictly parallel. Fig. 241 . . . . *BUMILLERIA*

Fig. 241. *Bumilleria sicula* Borzi.

There are 2 species known from the United States, *B. exilis* Klebs being much smaller (6 μ in diameter) than the one figured. The unbranched filaments are similar to *Tribonema* (Fig. 240) but the cells are more nearly rectangular in optical section, with parallel lateral walls. Sometimes external overlapping H-shaped sections of thicker wall layers, brownish in color, occur intermittently along the filament.

329a (324) Plant a small (1-2 mm. diam.) green vesicle, balloon-shaped; terrestrial. Fig. 242.................................*BOTRYDIUM*

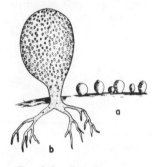

Fig. 242. *Botrydium granulatum* (L.) Grev.

These tiny, green, balloon-like algae appear on damp soil in green houses or on mud at the margins of lakes, especially where water has receded. *Botrydium* is a member of the Heterokontae (Chrysophyta). The thallus is siphonaceous and coenocytic, with underground, rhizoidal branches in which resting spores may be formed. The plants can be seen easily with the unaided eye. Although dark green in color the plant has the physiology and the pigments of the Chrysophyta. Like *Vaucheria*, the chromatophores are numerous and disc-shaped. Oil rather than starch is produced as a food reserve, and zoospores have paired flagella of unequal length. There is another species, *B. Wallrothii* Kuetz. which has a thick, wrinkled, lamellate wall.

329b Plant not a green vesicle; aquatic..........................330

330a Cells solitary or incidentally clustered.....................331

330b Cells in colonies, definite or indefinite in shape and arrangement, sometimes forming stalked colonies.........................358

331a Cells attached, sessile, or on a stalk.....................332

331b Cells free-floating or swimming..........................339

332a Cells sessile...333

332b Cells on a short or long stalk............................335

333a Cell membrane in 2 sections, the upper lifting off at maturity to allow escape of aplanospores (small globular spores); cells oval or short-cylindric. Fig. 243............*CHLOROTHECIUM*

This cylindrical plant with parietal, yellow-green chromatophores is attached by a short stalk and a disc to submerged plants, including larger algae. It is rather rare (only 1 species reported from United States) and is easily overlooked because it occurs in dense mixtures of algae from bogs.

Fig. 243. *Chlorothecium Pirottae* Borzi.

333b Cell membrane not in 2 sections........................**334**

334a Cells globose or subglobose; cytoplasm reticulate. Fig. 244....
....*PERONE*

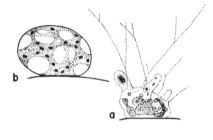

There is a freely moving, amoeboid stage and an attached or epiphytic, encysted stage in the life history of this organism. In the resting stage the cell is to be found in *Sphagnum* or other moss leaves, with a highly reticulated, faintly pigmented protoplast. The chromatophores occur as several small discs.

Fig. 244. *Perone dimorpha* Pascher. (a) rhizoidal stage; (b) vegetative cell.

334b Cells shaped otherwise; cytoplasm not highly reticulated nor alveolar. Fig. 245.............................*CHARACIOPSIS*

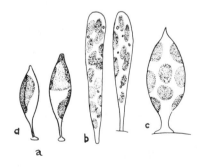

There are several fairly common species of this genus which occur as epiphytes on filamentous algae. They vary in shape and in length of attaching stalk. Unlike the genus *Characium* (Fig. 98), some species of which are very similar in shape, oil is formed rather than starch as a food reserve, and the chromatophores are pale yellow-green. The starch-iodide test must be used to differentiate the two genera. *Chara-*

Fig. 245. (a) *Characiopsis acuta* (Braun) Borzi; (b) *C. cylindrica* (Lambert) Lemm.; (c) *C. spinifer* Printz.

ciopsis often shows 1 to several spherical droplets of oil (?)

147

335a (332) Cells with a vase-like, pitcher-shaped or globose lorica (envelope) with a neck and a terminal opening. Fig. 246.......
...STIPITOCOCCUS

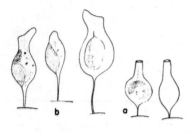

There are 5 or 6 species of this genus of rather uncommon occurrence, although in particular habitats the various species are relatively abundant and filamentous algae may be densely overgrown with the epiphytes. S. urceolatus West & West is perhaps more frequently seen than others and is easily identified because of its distinctive, pitcher-shaped lorica.

Fig. 246. (a) *Stipitococcus vasiformis* Tiffany; (b) *S. urceolatus* W. & G. S. West.

335b Cells without a lorica....................................336

336a Cells cylindrical, straight or curved, sometimes with a spine at one or both ends. Fig. 247....................OPHIOCYTIUM

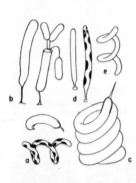

The factors which determine the distribution of this genus are unknown, but there seems to be good evidence that highly refined chemical qualities of water are critical. Several species always occur in the same habitat, along with other genera of the Xanthophyceae (Heterokontae). Species are differentiated by presence or absence of polar spines, and whether free-floating or stalked and epiphytic. They usually occur intermingled with miscellaneous algae in bogs or swamps which are acid. Most species are solitary but attached forms may be incidentally colonial.

Fig. 247. (a), (e) *Ophiocytium parvulum* (Perty) B r a u n ; (b) *O. gracilipes* (Braun) Rab; (c) *O. cochleare* (Eichw.) Braun; (d) *O. desertum* var. *minor* Presc.

336b Cells shaped differently....................................337

337a Cells club-shaped or somewhat pear-shaped; walls in 2 sections, the upper lifting away to permit the escape of spores. (See Fig. 243.)....................................CHLOROTHECIUM

337b Cells spherical, fusiform, or ovoid; wall in 1 piece.........338

338a Stipe slender, thread-like, longer than the cell body. Fig. 248...
.... *PERONIELLA*

Species of this genus occur solitarily or in gregarious clusters on other algae, or are attached in the mucilage of colonial forms. The species illustrated seems to occur no other place but on the filamentous Desmid, *Hyalotheca*. Like other members of the Chrysophyta, the chromatophores are not a grass-green but a pale shade, and there are usually refractive globules of oil or some other kind of food reserve than starch. The chromatophores are parietal plates.

Fig. 248. *Peroniella Hyalothecae* Gobi.

338b Stipe stout, shorter than the cell body in length (or rarely equalling it). (See Fig. 245.)...................... *CHARACIOPSIS*

339a (331) With 2 flagella of unequal length. Fig. 249.............
.... *CHLOROCHROMONAS*
                                              (Ochromonas)

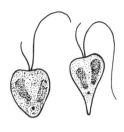

This rare species (probably referrable to *Ochromonas*) is variable in shape from truncately oval to pear-shaped. Care must be used in detecting the 2 flagella of unequal length. Motile, pear-shaped cells in the microscope field, with yellowish chromatophores should be examined for flagella characters. Frequently the cells come to rest and attach themselves to a substrate at the posterior end. Only 1 species has been reported from the United States.

Fig. 249. *Chlorochromonas minuta* Lewis.

339b Without flagella...340

340a Cell wall smooth...341

340b Cell wall sculptured or decorated, sometimes spiny........350

341a Cells spherical, subglobose, or broadly ovate to subpyriform (pear-shaped)...342

341b Cells rectangular, cylindrical, or crescent-shaped..........345

342a Cells contained in a gelatinous envelope. Fig. 250. . . . . :
. . . . *CHLOROBOTRYS*

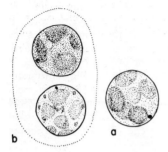

The identifying character of this species is the paired arrangement of the spherical cells inclosed in a mucilaginous sheath. There are several parietal chromatophores and invariably a red spot which is an oil globule. Even though preserved, when some identifying characteristics are lost, the cells retain the dark-colored spot. *Chlorobotrys* is both eu- and tychoplanktonic.

Fig. 250. *Chlorobotrys regularis* (West) Bohlin; (a) single cell; (b) two cells inclosed in common mucilage.

342b Cells not inclosed in a gelatinous envelope 343

343a Cell wall in 2 sections, separating and persisting as membranous sections near the liberated autospores (small replicas of the parent cell). Fig. 251 . . . .*DIACHROS*

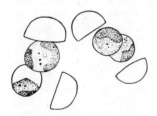

This is the only species reported from the United States. It is somewhat like *Schizochlamys* (Fig. 55) in the Chlorophyta in that the mother-cell wall fragments are retained after new cells (autospores) are released and the pieces persist as hemispherical, transparent cups near the daughter cells.

Fig. 251. *Diachros simplex* Pascher.

343b Cell wall in 1 piece; mother-cell not forming persisting sections but disintegrating to liberate spores 344

344a Cells spherical. Fig. 252 . . . .*BOTRYDIOPSIS*

In the same habitats where *Ophiocytium* (Fig. 247) occurs one may find this species; a solitary free-floating cell which is either spherical or spheroidal. Frequently, however, cells occur in clumps but are closely associated to form definite colonies. Small cells, when young, may contain a single parietal chromatophore, but in age many yellowish-green bodies. Another species, *B. eriensis* Snow, is larger and less commonly seen. Apparently it is a truly planktonic species whereas *B. arhiza* occurs in shallow water tychoplankton.

Fig. 252. *Botrydiopsis arhiza* Borzi.

344b Cells broadly ovoid or pear-shaped. Fig. 253 . . . .*LEUVENIA*

Although essentially unicellular, this species occurs in a dense film at the surface of a quiet pond. Young cells are spherical and have 1 or 2 chromatophores, whereas older cells become pear-shaped or ovate and have numerous yellow-green chromatophores. There is but 1 species in the genus and it seems to be rare, having been reported only from California in the United States.

Fig. 253. *Leuvenia natans* Gardner. (Redrawn from Smith.)

345a (341) Cells rectangular, with a spine at each corner. Fig. 254 . . .
. . . .*PSEUDOTETRAEDRON*

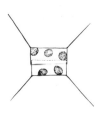

This rectangular cell with a slender spine at each corner clearly shows the chrysophycean character in its 2-parted wall, the sections over-lapping in the midregion of the cell. This can be seen only when the cells are turned on their 'side.' In end view the cells are narrowly elliptic. There are several yellow-green chromatophores and oil bodies as food reserve. The only species has been reported but rarely from the United States.

Fig. 254. *Pseudotetraedron neglectum* Pascher.

345b Cells cylindrical or crescent-shaped **346**

346a Cells elongate-cylindric, coiled or S-shaped, equally rounded at both poles. (See Fig. 247.) . . . .*OPHIOCYTIUM*

346b Cells oblong, sides convex, short-cylindric, or fusiform, sometimes not equally rounded at both poles; curved but not coiled nor twisted 347

347a Cells short-cylindric, 1½-2 times as long as broad; poles symmetrically rounded. Fig. 255 .... *MONALLANTUS*

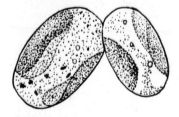

The species illustrated is the only one reported from the United States. It occurs in the same habitats with *Ophiocytium* (Fig. 247) and *Bumilleriopsis* (Fig. 256). There are 2, thin, folded parietal plate-like chromatophores.

Fig. 255. *Monallantus brevicylindrus* Pascher.

347b Cells fusiform or cylindric only in part; poles sometimes unsymmetrical 348

348a Cells fusiform or sickle-shaped 349

348b Cells irregularly cylindrical; poles unsymmetrical. Fig. 256 ....
.... *BUMILLERIOPSIS*

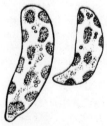

Cells in this genus have yellow-green chromatophores and occur in colonial clusters. The irregularly curved cylinders (rarely somewhat fusiform) with the poles of the cells unlike one another in shape, help to identify this genus.

n

Fig. 256. *Bumilleriopsis brevis* Pascher.

349a Cells broadly fusiform, abruptly narrowed at the poles. Fig. 257
....*PLEUROGASTER*

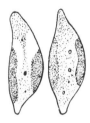

Fig. 257. *Pleur-ogaster lunaris* Pascher.

The chief difference between this group and *Bumilleriopsis* (Fig. 256) is the definitely fusiform shape, the poles of the cells symmetrical. There are 2 species, differentiated by size and variation in shape, reported from the United States, but like many of the Chrysophyta genera, they are rare and never occur in pure growths. There are 2 parietal chromatophores and several refractive globules.

349b Cells narrowly fusiform, spindle-shaped or sickle-shaped. Fig. 258 ....*CHLOROCLOSTER*

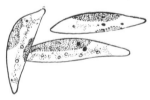

Fig. 258. *Chlorocloster pyreniger* Pascher.

In this genus the cells are narrowly spindle-shaped and usually are distinctly curved or even sickle-shaped. They are found intermingled sparingly among algal mixtures from shallow water of open bogs, and apparently only where the water is acid. Only 1 species has been reported from the United States.

350a (340) Cells elongate-cylindric, with a spine at one or both poles..
....**351**

350b Cells short-cylindric, spherical or angular..................352

351a Cells nearly straight or only slightly bent. Fig. 259...........
....*CENTRITRACTUS*

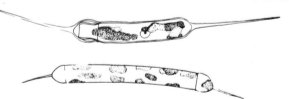

Fig. 259. *Centritractus belonophorus* Lemm.

There are 3 species of the genus reported from the United States, differentiated by size, proportions, and curvature of the cell. Whereas some are very short, and elliptic when young, others are very long indeed, and straight or slightly curved. It is the straight form that can be used to separate this genus from *Ophiocytium* (Fig. 247), some species of which it resembles in respect to the overlapping sections of the wall, color of chromatophores, *etc*. Often the sections of the wall form a cup at either end of the cylindrical cell.

351b Cells coiled, S-shaped, or hooked at one end. (See Fig. 247.)...
....*OPHIOCYTIUM*

352a (350) Cells spherical......................................353

352b Cells some other shape...............................354

353a Cell wall serrate at the margin, the surface of the cell showing broad depressions (sometimes faintly seen). Fig. 260........
....*ARACHNOCHLORIS*

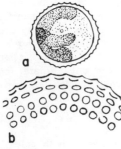

These round cells show the characteristic depressions of the wall at the margin where it appears that the cell is covered with short, sharp spines. These are the tops of ridges formed by slight depressions in the wall that sometimes scarcely can be seen when the cell is viewed at the center. There is but 1 species reported from the United States.

Fig. 260. *Arachnochloris minor* Pascher; (a) cell showing chromatophores; (b) sample of wall showing circular, thin areas.

353b Cell wall bearing curved or straight spines. Fig. 261........
....*MERINGOSPHAERA*

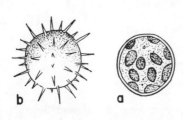

In this genus the wall bears long, or short spines, or cylindrical, thread-like outgrowths. *M. spinosa* questionably has been assigned to this genus from freshwater ponds, although the genus is marine. There are several to many disc-like, yellow-green chromatophores. See *Echinosphaerella* (Fig. 132) in the Chlorophyta.

Fig. 261. *Meringosphaera spinosa* Presc. (a) optical section of cell showing chromatophores; (b) exterior of cell showing spines on wall.

354a (352)) Cells broadly fusiform or subtriangular, narrowed abruptly at one or both poles to form spine-like projections. (See Fig. 257.)..*PLEUROGASTER*

354b Cells some other shape...................................355

355a Cells oblong to subcylindric; surface of wall with rows of depressions. Fig. 262.........................*CHLORALLANTUS*

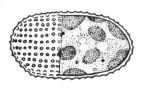

The very regular rows of depressions (forming teeth at the cell margin) help in the identification of *Chlorallantus*. The cells are capsule-like in shape and are found scattered about among other algae in open bogs. Only 1 species has been reported from the United States. There are several disc-like chromatophores and brightly shining refractive globules in the cytoplasm.

Fig. 262. *Chlorallantus oblongus* Pascher, represented with portion of wall removed to show chromatophores.

355b Cells with other shapes..................................356

356a Cells oval or biconvex. Fig. 263............*TRACHYCHLORON*

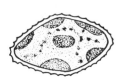

Cells of this genus, like *Chlorallantus* (Fig. 262) have depressions in the wall. They are broadly elliptic, oval, or fusiform in shape and contain a gracefully curved chromatophore. Only 1 species has been reported from the United States.

Fig. 263. *Trachychloron biconnicum* Pascher.

356b Cells triangular, pyramidal or tetragonal...................357

357a Cells pyramidal or tetragonal. Fig. 264.......*TETRAGONIELLA*

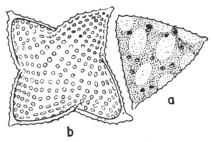

The cells in this genus are beautifully sculptured by regularly arranged rows of depressions. According to position the cells show different shapes, triangles, tetragonal, or cushion-shaped. One species is reported from mixtures of algae taken from bogs in northcentral United States.

Fig. 264. *Tetragoniella gigas* Pascher; (a) optical section showing chromatophores and reticular nature of the protoplast; (b) exterior of cell showing scrobiculate wall.

155

357b Cells flattened, appearing triangular in 'face' view, fusiform in side view. Fig. 265..........................*GONIOCHLORIS*

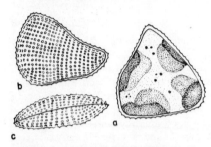

The cells in this genus are triangular in one view but elliptic when seen from the side. In the latter view the overlapping of the 2 pieces of the cell wall can be discerned. The wall is sculptured with rectilinear rows of circular pits. There are 3 or 4 curved, parietal, plate-like chromatophores.

Fig. 265. *Goniochloris sculpta* Geitler; (a) optical section showing chromatophores; (b) exterior, showing regularly arranged depressions in the wall; (c) lateral view showing the junction of the 2 wall sections (sometimes discerned with difficulty).

358a (330) Cells attached by a stipe..........................359

358b Cells without a stipe.....................................360

359a Cells inclosed in a globular lorica (envelope) which has an anterior opening. (See Fig. 248.)....................*PERONIELLA*

359b Cells not inclosed in a lorica. (See Fig. 247.)....*OPHIOCYTIUM*

360a (358)With a mucilaginous sheath..........................361

360b Without a sheath..364

361a Cells oval, many in a globular, macroscopic, free-floating colony. Fig. 266.....................................*CHLOROSACCUS*

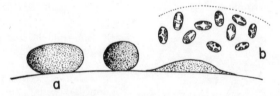

Fig. 266. *Chlorosaccus fluidus* Luther *(Gloeochloris Smithiana* Pascher); (a) diagram of colony shapes; (b) cells in mucilage.

This rare alga occurs as macroscopic gelatinous balls (up to 20 mm. in diameter) on the stems of submerged plants (including *Chara);* occasionally may be found free-floating. The colony is composed of irregularly arranged oval cells containing 2 to 6 parietal chromatophores which are yellow-green. There is but 1 species known.

361b Cells shaped or arranged otherwise........................362

362a Cells solitary or in pairs at the ends of branched gelatinous tubes. (See Fig. 238.) ....*MISCHOCOCCUS*

362b Cells arranged otherwise..................................363

363a Cells spherical, 2 within a globular envelope. (See Fig. 250.)... ....*CHLOROBOTRYS*

363b Cells spherical, many within a gelatinous matrix. Fig. 267.... ....*GLOEOBOTRYS*

The chief difference between this genus and *Chlorobotrys* (Fig. 250) is the presence of a definite mucilaginous sheath about the cells to form colonies. The species illustrated was assigned at one time to *Chlorobotrys;* described from open water lake plankton.

Fig. 267. *Gloeobotrys limneticus* (G. M. Smith) Pascher.

364a (360) Cells forming loose cushions on filamentous algae, in multiples of 2 or 4. Fig. 268..................*CHLORELLIDIOPSIS*

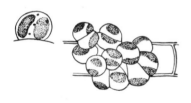

Although cells of the species illustrated are sometimes solitary they usually occur in closely grouped clusters on the walls of other algae. There are 2 parietal chromatophores and at least 1 dark red oil-spot in the mature cells. Only 1 species has been reported from the United States.

Fig. 268. *Chlorellidiopsis separabilis* Pascher.

364b Cells arranged otherwise.................................365

365a Wall in 2 sections which separate to liberate spores (new cells) and which persist nearby; (cells may be incidentally colonial because of gregarious habit). (See Fig. 251.).........*DIACHROS*

365b Wall in 1 piece, breaking down irregularly to liberate spores; (cells incidentally clustered to form colonies). (See Fig. 252.)... ....*BOTRYDIOPSIS*

**366a (313) Plant a branched, feathery, gelatinous thallus, the proto-
plasts crowded in linear series within tough, tubular envelopes.
Fig. 269...*HYDRURUS***

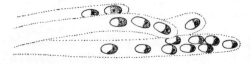

Fig. 269. *Hydrurus foetidus* (Vill.) Trev., cells in mucilaginous tubes.

Usually in high mountain or very cold streams this organism forms stringy, brown, gelatinous masses attached to stones or wood. The bushy, yellow-green or brown tufts contain oval cells arranged in linear series within tube-like strands. Sometimes a small stream actually will be choked with dense growths of *Hydrurus*. The disagreeable odor these plants possess is responsible for the specific name. The cells may change into curiously-shaped, pyramidal zoospores that have but 1 flagellum.

366b Plant not a feathery, gelatinous thallus.....................367

**367a Sparsely branched, sedentary filaments. Fig. 270.............
....*PHAEOTHAMNION***

Fig. 270. *Phaeothamnion confervicola* Lag.

This member of the Chrysophyceae is the only genus in which there is a branched filamentous thallus. The branches scarcely taper at the ends. The plants are relatively small and grow on the walls of larger filamentous algae. Each cell has a parietal, ochre-green to brownish chromatophore.

367b Not a branched filament...................................368

368a A colony of vase-shaped cones (loricas), 1 or 2 cones arising from within the mouth of another and forming forked series. Fig. 271. . . . .*DINOBRYON*

There are several species of this genus, all of which are characterized by having the motile protoplasts inclosed within colorless envelopes. The envelopes are usually contained 1 or 2 within another so that branching chains result. Some species occur solitarily. The genus is one which inhabits mostly hard water lakes in the euplankton; sometimes are very abundant and produce disagreeable odors and tastes in reservoirs.

Fig. 271. Dino-bryon sertularia Ehr.

368b Cells solitary, or arranged otherwise. 369

369a A unicell, consisting of a yellowish protoplast contained in a vase-like envelope. (See Fig. 271.). . . . .*DINOBRYON*

369b Cells shaped otherwise, or located differently; solitary or colonial 370

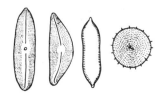

Fig. 272. Samples of Diatom cells, illustrating markings on siliceous walls.

370a Cells solitary, colonial, or filamentous; wall silicious and etched with grooves or rows of puncta which form definite patterns; wall in 2 sections, 1 part (epivalve) forming a lid over a smaller (hypovalve); oil drops usually conspicuous as shiny globules; solitary cells often showing a gliding or jerky movement. Diatoms. Fig. 272. 504

370b Cells without silicious walls thus decorated; wall not in 2 sections; oil droplets lacking or inconspicuous; not showing gliding movements; if motile, equipped with flagella or moving by pseudopodia (amoeboid fashion). 371

371a Unicellular, with flagella but usually not swimming. 372

371b Multicellular or colonial; motile or nonmotile. 404

372a Cell within an envelope of various shapes, with a flagellum opening...373

372b Cell without such an envelope...........................381

373a Envelope cone-shaped, narrowed posteriorly to a blunt or sharp point...374

373b Envelope flask-shaped, globose or pyramidal..............376

374a Lorica pear-shaped, or a much elongated, slender cone; sessile. Fig. 273...*EPIPYXIS*

Species in this genus are sometimes placed in *Dinobryon* (Fig. 271). The cells in cone-shaped loricas are sessile and solitary (never forming colonies (chains).

Fig. 273. *Epipyxis Tabellariae* (Lemm.) G. M. Smith, protoplasts in loricas epiphytic on filamentous algae.

374b Loricas not attached; cones only 3 or 4 times the diameter in length..375

375a Envelope with a smooth or slightly wavy margin. (See Fig. 271.)..
....*DINOBRYON*

375b Envelope with marginal, bristle-like projections caused by transverse growth rings. Fig. 274.....................*HYALOBRYON*

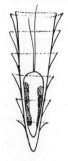

In this genus the cells are solitary and the envelope has margins which have bristles which represent the remains of envelopes of previous generations of cells. Whereas *Dinobryon* (Fig. 271) is freely swimming, this genus is solitary or colonial as an epiphyte on filamentous algae.

Fig. 274. *Hyalobryon mucicola* (Lemm.) Pascher.

376a (373) Lorica globose, smooth-walled; cells swimming by 1 flagellum which emerges through an opening; chromatophore brown; eye-spot present. Fig. 275....................*CHRYSOCOCCUS*

The globular loricas of this genus have a small, often inconspicuous pore through which the flagellum extends from a protoplast that contains 2 golden chromatophores. Curiously the species are all found mostly in the Ohio valley.

Fig. 275. *Chrysococcus rufescens* Klebs.

376b Lorica not as above.......................................377
377a Cells free-floating or free-swimming........................378
377b Cells sedentary...379
378a Cells globular or transversely oval, bearing on each side a long, pointed spine. Fig. 276.............................*DICERAS*

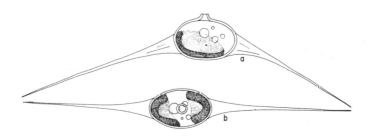

Fig. 276. *Diceras phaseolus* Fott.; (a) front view; (b) top view. (Redrawn from Fott.).

These golden-brown, free-floating cells are inclosed by a close-fitting lorica which bears on either side a long, sharply pointed spine.

The body of the cell is transversely oval. The protoplast has 2 fine strands extending through a low, apical collar.

378b Cells globular, flask-shaped, bearing several scattered, long, needle-like spines which may be forked at the tip. Fig. 277....
....*CHRYSOSTRELLA*

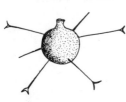

The species illustrated is the only one reported thus far from the United States, occurring either in open-water plankton or intermingled among algae near shore (tychoplanktonic). The test or envelope bears a few, long needle-like setae which are often forked at the tips. The round or oval lorica with a short collar around the flagellum aperture should be compared with *Trachelomonas* (Fig. 5).

Fig. 277. *Chrysostrella paradoxa* Chod.

379a (377) Envelope vase-shaped, transversely oval or pyramidal, the base flattened against the substrate. Fig. 278 .....*LAGYNION*

a

b

Fig. 278. (a) *Lagynion reductum* Presc.; (b) *L. triangularis* var. *pyramidatum* Presc.

There are 6 or 7 species of this genus reported from the United States. They are relatively small organisms, growing epiphytically on filamentous algae and are easily overlooked. The cells are globular, without a neck, or pyramidal with an apical elongation. The lorica contains a globular protoplast in which there is a faintly pigmented, yellowish chromatophore.

379b Envelope shaped otherwise...............................380

380a Epiphytic cells, attached to filamentous algae by two basal prongs which straddle the host cell. Fig. 279....CHRYSOPYXIS

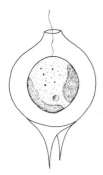

This genus seems to be confined to swamps and *Sphagnum* bog habitats. The cells may be swimming but usually are identified as sedentary in a lorica that is divided posteriorly to form a saddle over filamentous algal cells. The lorica has a broad anterior opening through which a fine pseudopodium extends.

Fig. 279. *Chryso-pyxis bipes* Stein.

380b Cells attached by a simple narrowing of the lorica. Fig. 280....
..DEREPYXIS

The chief difference between this genus and *Lagynion* (Fig. 278) is the presence of a supporting membrane through the lorica upon which the protoplast is suspended. This is the only species reported from the United States, occurring as a minute epiphyte on filamentous algae.

Fig. 280. *Derepyxis dispar* (Stokes) Senn.

381a (372) Cells swimming by 1 flagellum; wall impregnated with variously shaped silicious scales (appearing like chain armor) which bear bristles or needles. Fig. 281.........MALLOMONAS

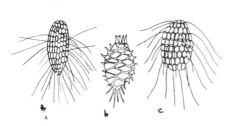

These species occur in open water plankton of mostly hard water lakes, frequently in abundance. They are differentiated from one another by shape and arrangement of the scales in the membrane and by the arrangement of the bristles. Some species occur regularly in lakes in which there

Fig. 281. (a) *Mallomonas caudata* Iwanoff; (b) *M. pseudocoronata* Presc.; (c) *M. acaroides* Perty.

is a high degree of pollution. Although motile, the single flagellum is hardly distinguishable unless the cells are recently collected and viewed under favorable optical conditions. The scales and spines are siliceous .

381b Cells not as above......................................382

382a Cells circular in 'front' view, but strongly compressed; swimming by 3 flagella. Fig. 282................*CHRYSOCHROMULINA*

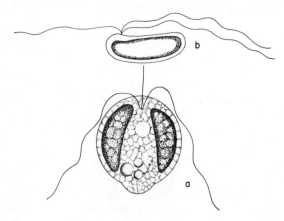

Fig. 282. *Chrysochromulina parva* Lackey; (a) front view; (b) end view. (Redrawn from Lackey.)

The cells in this genus are without a wall; have 3 laterally attached and relatively long flagella. They are broadly rounded in 'front' view but narrow and somewhat reniform when seen from the side. The genus has been reported only from Ohio.

382b Cells either motile or non-motile, or moving by pseudopodia (amoeboid fashion), or by 2 flagella; wall without scales and needles 383

383a Cells amoeboid; protoplast very pale yellow-green or yellow-brown...384

383b Cells swimming by 2 flagella, or sedentary; protoplast deeply pigmented, usually a golden brown or blue...............385

384a Pseudopodia long and needle-like. Fig. 283.....*RHIZOCHRYSIS*

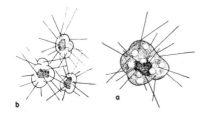

The species illustrated is the only one reported from the United States. The amoeboid member of the Chrysophyta has long, slender, needle-like pseudopodia. Cells are ordinarily solitary but may occur in loose, temporarily united groups.

Fig. 283. *Rhizochrysis limnetica* G. M. Smith; (a) single cell; (b) cells in temporary colonial arrangement.

384b Pseudopodia relatively shorter, tapering from the base to a fine point. Fig. 284................................*CHRYSAMOEBA*

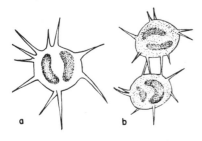

The species illustrated is the only one known for the genus. It occurs much more commonly than does *Rhizochrysis* (Fig. 283). Usually the cells occur in an amoeboid condition, bearing short, sharply pointed pseudopodia, but may change to a condition in which a single flagellum is present as a locomotory organ.

Fig. 284. *Chrysamoeba radians* Klebs.; (a) single cell; (b) temporarily adjoined cells.

385a (383) Cells attached......................................386

385b Cells free-floating or swimming..........................389

386a Cells inversely triangular, or tetrahedral in top view, angles tipped with 1 or 2 spines. Fig. 285.............*TETRADINIUM*

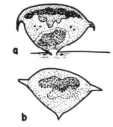

The chromatophores of this sessile member of the dinoflagellates are typically golden brown. The 4 corners of the cell are tipped with 2 short spines. The species illustrated and 1 other, *T. javanicum* Klebs, have been reported as epiphytes on filamentous algae. It should be compared with *Raciborskia* (Fig. 287) in making determinations.

Fig. 285. *Tetradinium simplex* Presc.; (a) side view; (b) vertical view.

165

386b Cells other shapes, or if inversely triangular, then elliptic in vertical view 387

387a Cells pyriform, epizoic, with rhizoidal attaching organs. Fig. 286 ....*OODINIUM*

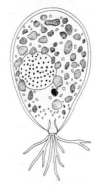

The brown, globular or ovate cells have basal rhizoidal extensions which attach the parasite to fish and to other aquatic animals. In reproduction the cells form 2 dinoflagellate-type zoospores.

Fig. 286. *Oodinium limneticum* Jacobs. (Redrawn from Jacobs.)

387b Cells differently shaped; without rhizoidal holdfasts..........388

388a Cells inversely triangular, elliptic in top view epiphytic. Fig. 287. ....*RACIBORSKIA*

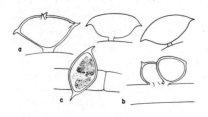

These are elliptical cells, sessile on a short stalk and attached to filamentous algae or aquatic mosses. There is a single spine at each pole of the cell. One species only has been reported from the United States . Compare with *Tetradinium* (Fig. 285) in making determinations.

Fig. 287. *Raciborskia bicornis* Wolosz.; (a) side view showing stipe; (b), (c) end and top views.

388b Cells globular or oval, with an elongate, narrow stipe. Fig. 288.
. . . .*STYLODINIUM*

These globular cells have a relatively long, slender stipe and attaching disc. They occur epiphytically on filamentous algae. The membrane is thick. There are numerous, disc-like chromatophores and a large red globule of oil, characteristic of the dinoflagellates. The cell forms 2 dinoflagellate-type zoospores which escape by rupture of the wall.

Fig. 288. *Stylodinium globosum* Klebs.

389a (385) Cells crescent-shaped, the horns extended to form spine-like tips which are recurved in most species. Fig. 289. . . . .
. . . .*CYSTODINIUM*

The species illustrated and 3 others occur in the United States as free-floating members of the encysted type of Dinoflagellates. They are differentiated on the basis of variations of shape, with the horns twisted at various angles. Several species of *Tetraedron* (Fig. 149) have been described incorrectly from members of the genus *Cystodinium*.

Fig. 289. *Cystodinium cornifax* (Schiller) Klebs.

389b Cells not crescent-shaped 390

390a Cells globular, with usually stellate clusters of chromatophores;
without flagella. Fig. 290........................*HYPNODINIUM*

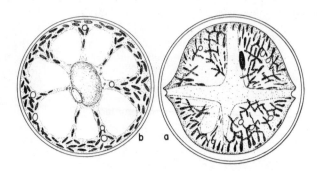

Fig. 290. *Hypnodinium sphaericum* Klebs.; (a) cyst with
dinoflagellate type of daughter cell; (b) cyst. (Redrawn from
Thompson.)

The brown, ellipsoid chromatophores are arranged in numerous
rosettes. The spherical cells are free-floating, without flagella but the
protoplast shows a typical transverse girdle and a red oil globule. The
single species is rare and has been found in the United States only
in Maryland.

390b Cells not as above.......................................391

391a Cells oval, occurring in few-celled clusters within a sheath; cells
with a conspicuous transverse furrow; chromatophores somewhat
radiately arranged but not in clusters. Fig. 291...*GLOEODINIUM*

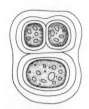

Although these plants exist in a palmelloid, non-
motile state they clearly show their dinoflagellate
affinity by the transverse furrow and the radiately
arranged, golden-brown chromatophores. The cells
are inclosed in a lamellate, gelatinous sheath, 2
to 8 in a clump.

Fig. 291. *Gloeodini-
um* sp., cyst.

391b Cells not as above......................................392

392a Cells motile; flagella 2 but both not directed forward; chromatophores brown..393

392b Cells motile; flagella 2, both directed forward; chromatophores brown..**394**

393a Cells without a transverse furrow; flagella 2, 1 directed forward, the other undulating at right angles. Fig. 292.....*EXUVIAELLA*

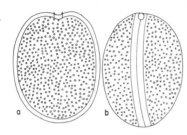

This is an unusual member of the Dinoflagellates in that there is no transverse furrow, and the flagella are apical rather than lateral in attachment. Although marine, at least 1 species has been found in brackish water.

Fig. 292. *Exuviaella compressa* Ostenf.; (a) front view; (b) side view.

393b Cells with a transverse furrow; chromatophores brown; flagella 2, laterally attached; cells globular or top-shaped...........**396**

394a Chromatophores blue or bluish-green; cells without a gullet at the anterior end, but with a slight apical notch. Fig. 293.......
....*CHROOMONAS*

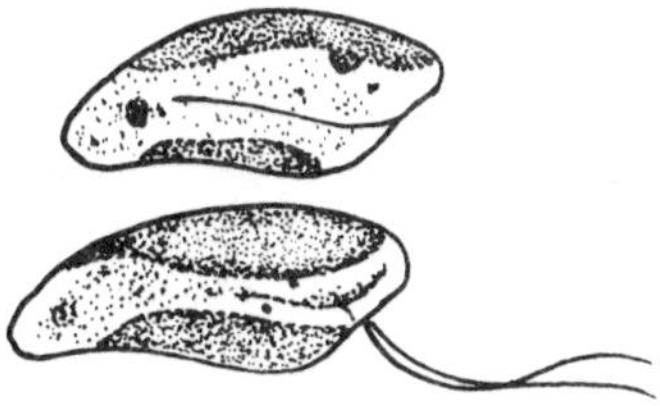

These minute, slipper-shaped organisms have 2 parietal, blue or bluish-brown chromatophores and 2 flagella that are attached just below the apex of the cell. They move rapidly and determinations cannot be made unless some medium is introduced to the mount to retard their action. Use 5% glycerin.

Fig. 293. *Chroomonas Nordstedtii* Hansg.

394b Chromatophores yellow or yellowish-green (rarely brownish)..**395**

395a Cells with a gullet in which 2 equal flagella are attached. Fig. 294..*CRYPTOMONAS*

There are probably several species of this genus but few are reported, probably because they are easily overlooked among dense mixtures of algae. They are fast-moving like *Chroomonas* (Fig. 293). The cells are somewhat pyriform being broader at the anterior end. There are usually

Fig. 294. *Cryptomonas erosa* Ehr.

2 yellowish-green chromatophores, or the 2 may appear as 1 diffuse body. When the organisms are slowed in their movement and under proper optical conditions the characteristic anterior gullet can be discerned, especially when the cell rotates on its axis.

395b Cells without a gullet; flagella 2, of unequal length, attached at the apex. (See Fig. 249.)................CHLOROCHROMONAS
                                                              (Ochromonas)

396a (393) Cells with a long anterior horn and 2 or 3 posterior horns. Fig. 295...CERATIUM

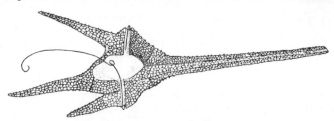

Fig. 295. *Ceratium hirundinella* (O.F.M.) Duj.

This genus possesses such a distinctive shape that it can be unmistakably identified. It occurs either intermingled with other algae, or in open water plankton of lakes, sometimes slow-flowing streams. At times during late summer *Ceratium* may produce a veritable bloom, causing the water to become a gray-brown or coffee color. There is a prominent transverse furrow that divides the cell into an epicone and a hypocone. When seen from the ventral surface the longitudinal sulcus shows. Here the two flagella are attached, one of which trails, the other wound about the cell in the furrow. There are numerous brown chromatophores and a large, red eye-spot. The plates which compose the cell wall are marked with a close reticulation. *Ceratium* is the most common of all the freshwater armored Dinoflagellates.

396b Cells without prominent horns as above....................397

397a Cells without a true wall, but with a membrane which may be either delicate or thick and firm; smooth, without plates......398

397b Cells with a true wall, with a pattern of definitely arranged plates usually evident (in some the boundary lines of the plates are seen with difficulty; reduce or modify illumination); a transverse furrow present, encircling the cell completely or incompletely 401

398a Cells oval; the transverse furrow spirally descending. Fig. 296..
.... *GYRODINIUM*

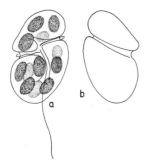

The chromatophores in this genus are relatively large. Identification can be made by the descending, spiral transverse furrow which produces a hypocone much larger than the epicone.

Fig. 296. *Gyrodinium pusillum* (Schilling) Kofoid & Swezy.; (a) ventral view, showing relatively large chromatophores; (b) dorsal view.

398b Cells top-shaped or fusiform; transverse furrow mostly at right angles to the long axis, or occurring as a 'V' near the apex...399

399a Transverse furrow dividing the cell approximately into 2 equal parts (epicone and hypocone). Fig. 297.........*GYMNODINIUM*

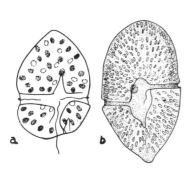

Species of this genus are of wide occurrence but seldom occur in conspicuous numbers. They are intermingled in tychoplanktonic algae, but sometimes appear in open-water plankton hauls. In microscope mounts they are usually swimming actively, rotating on their axes as they go forward. The thin cell membrane (cell wall not present) helps in identifying these species. The transverse furrow extends around the cell in a downward fashion.

Fig. 297. (a) *Gymnodinium palustre* Schilling; (b) *G. fuscum* (Ehr.) Stein.

399b Transverse furrow dividing the cell into a hypocone and epicone unequal in size...400

400a Cells mostly top-shaped, the epicone distinctly larger than the hypocone. Fig. 298 . . . . *MASSARTIA*

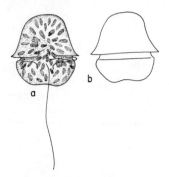

These Dinoflagellate cells, without a cell wall, are broadly oval but truncate at the poles. The transverse furrow divides the cell into an epicone distinctly larger than the hypocone. The brown chromatophores are somewhat radiate in arrangement. Compare with *Gymnodinium* (Fig. 297).

Fig. 298. *Massartia Musei* (Dan.) Schiller; (a) ventral view showing sulcus; (b) dorsal view.

400b Cells subquadrate, the epicone smaller than the hypocone and appearing as an apical lobe of the cell. Fig. 299 . . *AMPHIDINIUM*

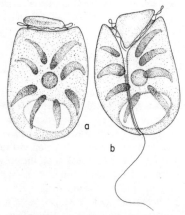

This genus is mostly marine in distribution but may be found in brackish water, or in fresh water near the sea. The chromatophores are large and radiately arranged. The cell is unusual in that the transverse furrow is located near the apex so that the epicone is but a small lobe.

Fig. 299. *Amphidinium Klebsii* Kof.; (a) dorsal view; (b) ventral view.

401a (397) Wall thick; plates easily discerned, with a suture (usually) between the plates; transverse furrow completely encircling the cell. (Thecate Dinoflagellates.) 402

401b Wall thin; plates seen with difficulty (especially in filled and living cells); transverse furrow completely encircling the cell or not 403

402a Wall with 2 antapical plates (the plates at the posterior pole, to be seen in posterior end view); cell slightly flattened dorsiventrally in most species. Figs. 300, 301.) ....*PERIDINIUM*

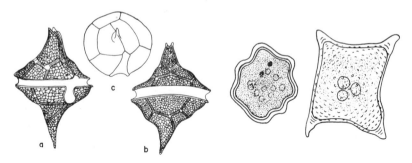

Fig. 300. *Peridinium wisconsinense* Eddy;
(a) ventral view showing longitudinal sulcus;
(b) dorsal view; (c) posterior view showing
2 antapical plates.

Fig. 301. Dinoflagellate cysts.

This genus is represented by more species in fresh water than any of the other Dinoflagellates. They are differentiated by shape and size of the cell and by the number, arrangement and shape of the plates. The 2 posterior or antapical plates can be determined by patiently rolling the cell so that it can be seen from the end. Most species are some variety of top-shape. In most species the plates are marked with a fine reticulation.

402b Wall with 1 antapical plate; cell not flattened dorsiventrally, but round in cross section. Fig. 302 ....*GONYAULAX*

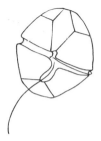

These almost spherical cells are differentiated from *Peridinium* by its single apical plate and by the slightly spiral direction of the transverse furrow. Some authorities regard the species illustrated as belonging to *Peridinium*.

Fig. 302. *Gonyaulax palustre* Lemm.

403a (401) Cells strongly flattened dorsiventrally; plates not evident; transverse furrow not encircling the cell completely, usually located in the posterior part of the cell. Fig. 303.....*HEMIDINIUM*

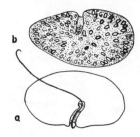

There are several species of this genus reported from the United States. The cells are mostly oval when seen from the broad side, but much flattened in lateral view. The transverse girdle extends only part way around the cell. The species are differentiated by shape and size of the cell and by the pattern of plates which are usually delicate and difficult of determination.

Fig. 303. *Hemidinium nasutum* Stein; (a) ventral view; (b) dorsal view.

403b Cells not at all or but very little flattened dorsiventrally (nearly round in cross section); plates evident, (especially clear in empty cells); transverse furrow completely encircling the cell. Fig. 304.. ....*GLENODINIUM*

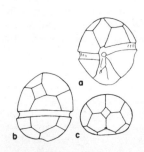

The several species of this genus reported from the United States are differentiated by cell size and shape. Mostly they are broadly oval to nearly round. The plate pattern is much more easily discerned than in *Hemidinium* (Fig. 303) but patience is required in rotating the cell in various positions to determine the pattern. As in other genera, such as with *Peridinium*, e.g., it is desirable to examine empty cells to see the wall characters plainly.

Fig. 304. *Glenodinium Kulczynski* (Wolosz.) Schiller; (a) ventral view showing longitudinal furrow; (b) dorsal view; (c) apical view.

404a (371) Colony motile by flagella............................405

404b Colony non-motile, or if moving, by rhizoidal processes (pseudopodia)..411

405a Colony globose or subglobose (oval); cells ovoid or pear-shaped, compactly arranged or forming a hollow sphere............406

405b Colony not globular; cells shaped otherwise................410

406a Cells bearing 2 long, rigid, rod-like processes at their anterior ends. Fig. 305.........................*CHRYSOSPHAERELLA*

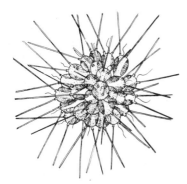

This distinctive organism is easily identified by the curious long rods, borne in pairs, on each cell. The rods have a collar at their bases, with a single flagellum between. The chromatophores are brownish-yellow. Although widely distributed the single species is rare in occurrence.

Fig. 305. *Chrysosphaerella longispina* Lauterb.

406b Cells without such rods.................................407

407a Cells ovoid, at the periphery of an oval, gelatinous colony, attached at the ends of branched, radiating threads. Fig. 306....
....*UROGLENA*

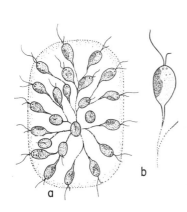

Although rare, *Uroglena volvox*, the only species, is widely distributed in the United States, especially in eutrophic lakes. The elliptic cells, with the posterior portion abruptly narrowed, are arranged at the periphery of a mucilaginous sheath. The cells are attached at the ends of fine, radiating and branched threads which can be seen after the application of a stain. The chromatophore is a parietal, folded plate, golden-yellow in color, but usually faint. The cell bears 2 flagella of unequal length. Identification is aided by the definitely oblong shape of the colony.

Fig. 306. *Uroglena volvox* Ehr.; (a) colony; (b) single cell.

407b Cells shaped otherwise.................................408

408a Cells pear-shaped, arranged relatively compactly within a wide, gelatinous sheath in which conspicuous granular particles occur; flagella of equal length. Fig. 307.................SYNCRYPTA

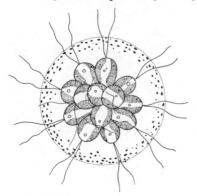

Syncrypta is a motile colony of radiately arranged, pyriform cells inclosed in a gelatinous envelope in which there are numerous, small granular bodies. The chromatophores and the cell-shape are similar to Synura (Fig. 308) but the cell membrane is smooth, without siliceous spicules. The 2 flagella are of equal length.

Fig. 307. *Syncrypta volvox* Ehr., showing pebbled granulations in the colonial mucilage.

408b Cells shaped or arranged otherwise........................409

409a Cells elongate-ellipsoid or elongate-pyriform, rather compactly arranged to form a globular colony which is not inclosed in a gelatinous sheath; cell wall with minute, siliceous scales in the anterior end; flagella 2, of equal length but unlike structurally; chromatophore densely pigmented, brown. Fig. 308....SYNURA

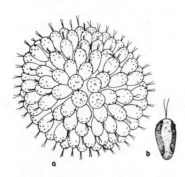

This species is very common in hard water lakes and may be so abundant as to produce disagreeable odors and tastes in water supply reservoirs. The chromatophores are golden brown and mask the small spicules in the walls at the anterior end of the cell. These can be determined by proper focusing on colonies that are quiescent. There is another species with longer and narrower cells, *S. Adamsii* G. M. Smith, that is of more rare occurrence.

Fig. 308. *Synura uvella* Ehr. (a) colony; (b) single cell showing siliceous spicules in membrane.

409b Cells ovoid or pear-shaped, separated and evenly spaced within a colonial envelope; without scales in the wall; flagella 2, of unequal length; chromatophore pale yellow. Fig. 309 . . . .
. . . . *UROGLENOPSIS*

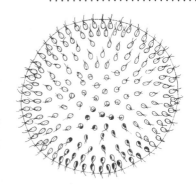

This species frequents bodies of water that are contaminated with nitrogenous wastes. The colonies are large and contain several hundred cells; are sometimes mistaken for *Volvox* (see Fig. 16), but are quickly differentiated by the yellow-brown color of the plate-like (not cup-shaped) chromatophores. It is interesting that this organism is sometimes the dominant member of plankton in arctic lakes.

Fig. 309. *Uroglenopsis americana* (Calkins) Lemm.

410a (405) Cells elongate-ovoid or pear-shaped, compactly arranged side by side in radiate fashion in 1 plane to form a plate with a small central opening; motile by 2 flagella. Fig. 310 . . . .
. . . . *CYCLONEXIS*

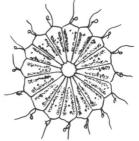

The flat, disc-like colony of compactly arranged, pear-shaped cells is very distinctive. The flagella are relatively coarse and can be seen easily when the colony is quiescent. There are 2 elongate, lightly pigmented chromatophores.

Fig. 310. *Cyclonexis annularis* Stokes. (Redrawn from Stokes.)

410b Cells not as above; contained in a vase-shaped envelope, 1 or 2 such envelopes arising from the mouth of the one below to form a branched series. (See Fig. 271.) . . . . *DINOBRYON*

411a (404) Individuals furnished with pseudopodia (colony sometimes loosely formed and only temporary) 412

411b Individuals not furnished with organs of locomotion; colonies non-motile 414

412a Cells joined together by long, narrow protoplasmic extensions, arranged in a linear series. Fig. 311........*CHRYSIDIASTRUM*

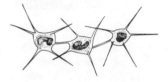

Although this organism may occur singly it is seen frequently adjoined in loose colonies by the interconnecting pseudopodia. There is 1, plate-like or disc-shaped chromatophore, usually faintly pigmented .

Fig. 311. *Chrysidiastrum catenatum* Lauterb. (Redrawn from Smith.)

412b Cells not joined as above.................................413
413a Pseudopodia numerous, radiating needles; colony formation mostly temporary and incidental. (See Fig. 283.)....*RHIZOCHRYSIS*
413b Pseudopodia short, protoplasmic extensions which join individuals to form temporary colonies. (See Fig. 284.).....*CHRYSAMOEBA*
414a (411) Colony consisting of vase-shaped envelopes, 1 or 2 such envelopes arising from the mouth of one below to form forked series (organisms actually motile by flagella, but often appearing quiescent with the flagella completely invisible in microscope mounts). (See Fig. 271.)...........................*DINOBRYON*
414b Individuals not cone-shaped; colony formed otherwise......415
415a Thallus composed of a compact layer of epiphytic cells in rectilinear series; mucilaginous sheath wanting. Fig. 312..........
....*PHAEOPLACA*

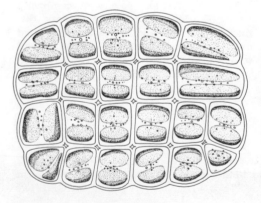

This genus has angular cells with relatively thick walls, compactly arranged to form a subquadrate thallus; the cells in 1 layer. The cells contain 2 yellow-brown chromatophores.

Fig. 312. *Phaeoplaca thallosa* Chod. (Redrawn from Thompson.)

415b Thallus composed of cells arranged otherwise; mucilaginous sheath present...416

416a Thallus a sparsely branched, gelatinous cylinder or a mucilaginous network, with cells arranged in 1 to several irregular series. Fig. 313.....................................PHAEOSPHAERA

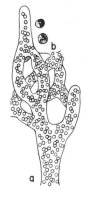

The golden-brown cells of this species occur in gelatinous masses of irregular shape and of macroscopic size. The thallus may be a stringy mass of mucilage occurring in skeins or meshworks. Unlike *Tetraspora* (Fig. 42) with which it might be mistaken, the cells are not arranged in groups of 4 but occur in irregular series throughout the gelatinous strands; neither are there pseudocilia. The plant is widely distributed in the United States, having been found in North Carolina and in arctic Alaska.

Fig. 313. *Phaeosphaera perforata* Whitford. (a) small portion of perforate colony; (b) cells showing chromatophores.

416b Thallus not a branched gelatinous strand or network.......417
417a Cells as many as 150 within an epiphytic gelatinous investment from which a tuft of fine branched hairs extends. Fig. 314....
..NAEGELIELLA

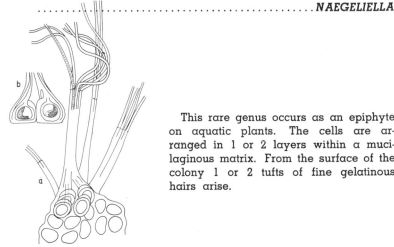

This rare genus occurs as an epiphyte on aquatic plants. The cells are arranged in 1 or 2 layers within a mucilaginous matrix. From the surface of the colony 1 or 2 tufts of fine gelatinous hairs arise.

Fig. 314. (a) *Naegeliella britannica* Godward; (b) *N. flagellifera* Correns. (Redrawn from Correns.)

179

417b Cells arranged otherwise; colony not bearing a tuft of hairs..418

418a Cells in clusters of 2-4-8-16 within an irregularly globose colonial investment. Fig. 315..........................*CHRYSOCAPSA*

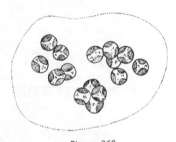

The colonies are globular or nearly so; the mucilage clear and transparent, the cells with brown chromatophores. The species illustrated is the only one which seems to be common, but another one, *C. paludosa* (West & West) Pascher with oval rather than round cells has been recorded. *Chrysocapsa* is usually collected from the euplankton.

Figure 268

Fig. 315. *Chrysocapsa planctonica* (W. & G. S. West) Pascher. (Redrawn from Smith.)

418b Cells 16-32-64 within a wide, flat colonial matrix, the mucilage impregnated with granular substances which appear as shiny bodies. Fig. 316..................*CHRYSOSTEPHANOSPHAERA*

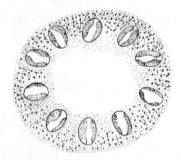

This colony of brown or yellowish-green cells is disc-like. The cells are inclosed by a wide gelatinous matrix which contains dark granules. The cells are oval and are arranged with their long axes directed parallel with the radius of the colony.

Fig. 316. *Chrysostephanosphaera globulifera* Scherff.

419a (4) Plants filamentous, thread-like (the thread of cells called a trichome; trichome and sheath, if present together called a filament) 420

419b Plants not definitely filamentous; cells globular, rod-shaped, or angular from mutual compression; solitary, in floating colonies, or forming cushion-like masses in which a suggestion of filamentous arrangement may be apparent....................472

420a Trichomes coiled or spiralled in a regular fashion.........421

420b Trichomes otherwise, straight or irregularly twisted, not forming a regular spiral (occasionally, however, *Oscillatoria* (Fig. 328) may become twisted about itself in a regular spiral fashion)......**424**

421a Trichome unicellular. Fig. 317....................*SPIRULINA*

Fig. 317. (a) *Spirulina laxissima* G. S. West; (b) *S. princeps* (W. & G. S. West) G. S. West; (c) *S. subsalsa* Oersted.

Although essentially unicellular, this genus is thread-like and is included with the Oscillatoriaceae (a filamentous family of the Cyanophyta). Although some species are solitary they are often found in masses, either by themselves or intermingled with *Oscillatoria* (Fig. 328). Species are differentiated by size and by type of coiling of the cell. The plants usually are in active motion when viewed microscopically. The movement in this and other blue-green genera is accomplished by the extrusion of mucilage and by the flow of mucilage along the trichome.

421b Trichomes multicellular, *i.e.,* with cross walls..............**422**

422a Trichomes composed of bead-like or barrel-shaped cells, with heterocysts present (cells located here and there in the trichome which are larger and sometimes different in shape from the vegetative cells). Fig. 318............................*ANABAENA*

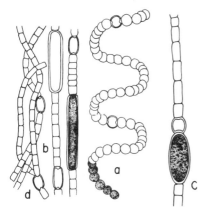

Fig. 318. (a) *Anabaena spiroides* var. *crassa* Lemm; (b) *A. subcylindrica* Borge; (c) *A.* sp., showing oval akinete; (d) *A. subcylindrica* Borge, showing heterocysts.

There are many species of this genus, some solitary and some forming colonial masses of indefinite shape. When colonial they are surrounded by a conspicuous mucilage and sometimes are mistaken for *Nostoc* (Fig. 356). The colonial mass is indefinite in shape and the mucilage soft, however, rather than firm and skin-like as in *Nostoc*. Whereas some forms are truly planktonic, others occur intermingled with algae in shallow water or on moist soil. The planktonic species may form a bloom in lakes of northern latitudes during summer months, but seldom cause disagreeable conditions in lakes or reservoirs because these plants remain suspended throughout the water and do not form surface scums. *Anabaena* spp. are responsible for the death of cattle and other animals that drink water in which the plants have developed profusely, supposedly because of toxic substances given off into the water by the algae.

422b Cells not bead-like but rectangular, usually wider than long, disc-like; heterocysts absent...............................**423**

423a Trichome with a sheath. Fig. 319...................*LYNGBYA*

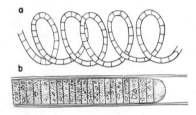

Fig. 319. a() *Lyngbya contorta* Lemm.; (b) *L. Birgei* G. M. Smith.

Most species are straight and rigid, or sometimes curved and entangled; whereas *L. contorta* is regularly spiralled. Trichomes are mostly rounded or conical at the apex; seldom constricted at the joints. Some species are entangled among other algae and occasionally epiphytic, but many are planktonic. The definite, rather firm sheath extending beyond the end of the trichome is characteristic and helps to separate this genus from *Oscillatoria* (Fig. 328). One species, *L. Birgei* is so characteristically a planktonic species of hard water lakes that it can be used as an index organism.

423b Trichomes without a sheath. Fig. 320..........*ARTHROSPIRA*
    The plants in this genus are multicellular but at times the cross

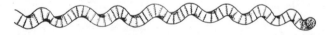

Fig. 320. *Arthrospira Jenneri* (Kuetz.) Stiz.

partitions are difficult to discern and short sections of a trichome may be mistaken for *Spirulina* (Fig. 317). Species are differentiated mostly by size and form of coiling of the trichomes. The plants do not show as active motion as does *Spirulina* (Fig. 317) and *Oscillatoria* (Fig. 328). *Arthrospira* occurs intermingled with *Spirulina;* are in purées of miscellaneous algae in the tychoplankton.

424a (420) Trichomes with cells all alike in shape and size, although the trichome may taper at one or both ends, or the apical cell may be slightly swollen (capitate); heterocysts lacking......**425**

424b Thichomes with differentiated cells; occasional cells larger (hetero-cysts) appearing empty, or with polar plugs of mucilage; others enlarged, with thick walls serving as akinetes (gonidia)......**445**

425a Trichomes tapering at one or both ends...................**426**

425b Trichomes not tapering, the same diameter throughout (or nar-rowed only in the extreme apical portion).................**429**

426a Trichomes tapering from base to apex, without branches, or if with false branches these not 'U'-shaped..................**427**

426b Trichomes tapering at both ends, with 'U'-shaped false branches. Fig. 321......................................*HAMMATOIDEA*

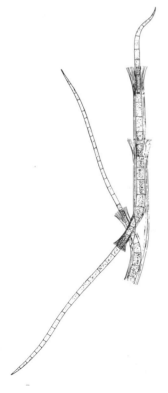

This genus has false branches which form 'U'-shaped loops lateral to the main axis. Like other members of the Rivulariaceae the branches taper toward the apices—but there are no heterocysts. The plants usually occur in the mucilaginous sheath material of other algae.

Fig. 321. *Hammatoidea yellow-stonensis* Copeland. (Redrawn from Copeland.)

427a Trichomes aggregated, tapering from a base which is incorporated in a prostrate cushion of cells. Fig. 322..........*AMPHITHRIX*

Fig. 322. *Amphithrix janthina* (Mont.) Bor. & Flah. (Redrawn from Bornet & Flahault.)

These are tapering filaments, arranged in somewhat parallel fashion to form clusters (but without conspicuous mucilage) attached to substrates. There is a weakly-developed, prostrate expansion of the thallus from which the upright trichomes arise. The lack of heterocysts (see *Anabaena*, Fig. 318) makes this a somewhat anomalous member of the Rivulariaceae which characteristically have this type of cell at the base of the filament.

427b Without a prostrate cushion of cells at the base of the trichome..**428**

428a Trichomes gregarious, parallel in a colonial mass. (See Fig. 322.) ....*AMPHITHRIX*

428b Trichomes solitary or loosely clustered, without parallel arrangement (some species possessing heterocysts). Fig. 323......... ....*CALOTHRIX*

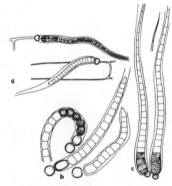

These tapering filaments are solitary or loosely clustered, 2, 3 or 4 together, or in rare instances, gregarious and forming extensive masses. There is a basal heterocyst (sometimes lacking) and in certain species there is an akinete adjacent to the terminal heterocyst. Species are differentiated on the basis of size, presence or absence of akinetes, and by the degree of tapering of the filament, being very abrupt in some.

Fig. 323. (a) *Calothrix epiphytica* W. & G. S. West ;(b) *C. atricha* Fremy; (c) *C. Braunii* Bor. & Flah.

429a (425) Filaments branched...................................**430**

429b Filaments not branched...................................**432**

430a Branching false (a branch formed by proliferation of a broken trichome which pushes off to one side of the main axis, not branching by the lateral division of a cell in the main axis); branching often sparse. Fig. 324.........................PLECTONEMA

Fig. 324. *Plectonema Wollei* Farlow.

The false habit of branching places this genus in the Scytonemataceae, but unlike other members of the family there are no heterocysts. The species illustrated is a common one, occurring in brownish-green or black, cottony masses at or near the surface of the water; is a relatively large species, being up to 50 μ in diameter. Many of the smaller species form clumps, or are intermingled with other algae. Several specimens should be studied throughout the length of a filament in making determinations and to discern the habit of branching. Branching is often scarce.

430b Branching true; the branches formed by lateral division of cells in the main axis of the trichome............................431

431a Filaments with prostrate and erect portions; branching dichotomous; sheaths transversely lamellate. Fig. 325...COLTERONEMA

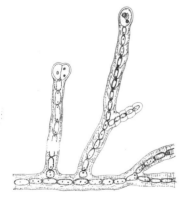

This plant is similar to *Albrightia* (Fig. 326) but the branching is dichotomous. The branches arise vertically from a more or less prostrate axial filament. The rather soft gelatinous sheath has transverse lamellations. There are no heterocysts. There is but 1 species, known only from Yellowstone Park hot springs.

Fig. 325. *Colteronema funebre* Copeland. (Redrawn from Copeland.)

185

431b Filaments without a distinct prostrate and an erect portion; branching irregular and sparse; sheath not transversely striated. Fig. 326..*ALBRIGHTIA*

The branched filaments of this plant resemble strings of sausages inclosed in a relatively firm, colorless sheath. There are no heterocysts, and reproduction occurs only by cell division as far as is known, this occurring in the apical region of the trichome. It has been found only in Yellowstone Park hot springs.

Fig. 326. *Albrightia tortuosa* Copeland. (Redrawn from Copeland.)

432a (429) Trichomes without a sheath..........................433

432b Trichomes with a sheath..................................435

433a Trichomes short, 3 to 10 (20) cells long. Fig. 327........*BORZIA*

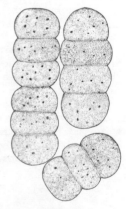

This rare plant occurs as very short, hormogonia-like trichomes of as many as 8 cells. The terminal cells are hemispherical. *Borzia* has been reported only from Indiana in the United States, having been found in lake-bottom debris.

Fig. 327. *Borzia trilocularis* Cohn. (Redrawn from Daily.)

434a Trichomes solitary or intermingled, not lying in parallel bundles, sometimes tapered slightly toward the anterior end, or with the apical cell swollen (capitate). Fig. 328.........*OSCILLATORIA*

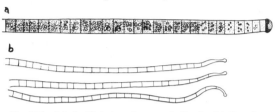

Fig. 328. (a) *Oscillatoria rubescens* DeCand.; (b) *O. splendida* Grev.

The chief characteristic of species in this genus is their lack of a sheath, and another is their active, oscillating movement. A mass of plants left in a shallow laboratory dish will creep up the sides of the container, or spread itself over the bottom. There are numerous species, on the basis of diameter, cell proportions, and upon the morphology of the apex of the trichome. Some species are straight and rigid; others curved or hooked; some taper and may have a capitate apical cell. In some the trichome is constricted at the cross walls which may or may not have a row of granules. *Oscillatoria* occurs both in water and on damp soil or dripping rocks. A few species such as *O. rubescens* is planktonic and at certain times of the year is so abundant as to color a lake red. This is related to light refraction produced by the pseudovacuoles in the cells rather than to pigments.

434b Trichomes not tapered at the anterior end, lying in parallel bundles; apical cell never capitate. Fig. 329......*TRICHODESMIUM*

Fig. 329. *Trichodesmium lacustre* Kleb.

This is a species of uncertain position because it has an *Anabaena*-like filament, but without heterocysts. The filaments are arranged in parallel bundles which form free-floating, dark green flakes. The cells contain numerous pseudovacuoles (gas pockets). *T. erythraceum* Ehr., a marine species, because of the light refraction produced, gives the characteristic color to the Red Sea.

436a Sheath firm and definite, not adhering to sheaths of adjacent filaments...437

436b Sheath soft and sticky, often adhering to sheaths of adjacent plants and intermingling (confluent) with them.............439

437a Sheaths purple or reddish, conspicuously stratified. Fig. 330.... ....*PORPHYROSIPHON*

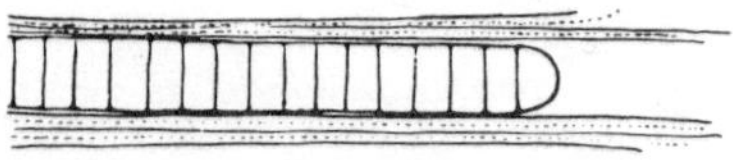

The purple color of the lamellated sheath of this species accounts for the brightly colored patches on damp soil in subtropical sections of the United States. Denuded soil in the South frequently is colonized by *Porphyrosiphon*.

Fig. 330. *Porphyrosiphon Notarisii* (Menegh.) Kuetz.

437b Sheaths colorless or yellowish...........................438

438a Trichomes short, 2 to 20 cells long; sheaths colorless, homogeneous. Fig. 331.......................................*ROMERIA*

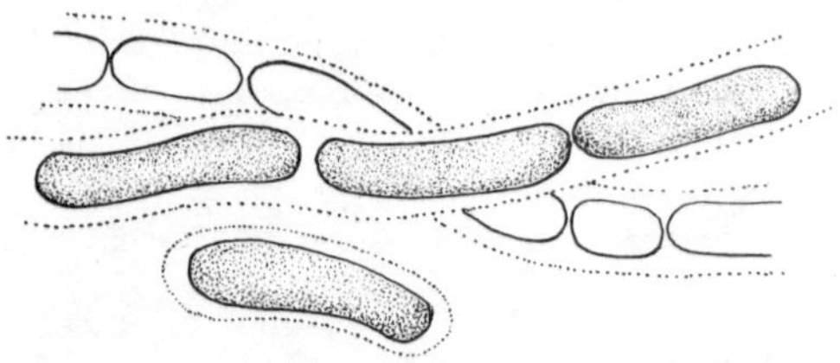

Fig. 331. *Romeria elegans* var. *nivicola* Kol. from Olympic Mt. snowfields.

This genus consists of sausage-shaped or cylindrical cells arranged in short trichomes, usually within a thin sheath. There are neither heterocysts nor akinetes formed as far as is known. In the United States the genus has been found only in snow fields.

438b Trichomes long, composed of many cells; sheath colorless or yellowish, sometimes stratified. (See Fig. 319.).......*LYNGBYA*

439a (436) Filaments forming an expanded plant mass, sometimes developing erect tufts......................................440

439b Filaments not forming an expanded mass or stratum........441

440a Plant mass having erect tufts. Fig. 332............SYMPLOCA

Filaments of this species occur in erect tufts in moist aerial situations. S p e c i e s which have thin, s t i c k y sheaths should be compared with *Phormidium* (Fig. 333) with which they may be confused if seen individually and not in colonial mass.

Fig. 332. *Symploca muscorum* (Ag.) Gom.

440b Plant mass without erect tufts. Fig. 333..........PHORMIDIUM

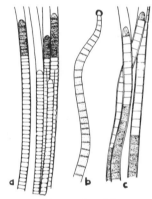

There are numerous species of this genus, differentiated by size and by characteristics of the apical cell . The sheaths are very thin and sticky, hence the plants form rather closely compacted mats that coat over submerged surfaces. Such a mat when handled does not break apart easily (as do somewhat similar-appearing growths of *Oscillatoria* (Fig. 328). The plant masses are blue, or black-green in color and feel slimy or slippery to the touch. Plants should be compared carefully with *Lyngbya*.

Fig. 333(a). *Phormidium ambiguum* Gom.; (b) *P. favosum* (Bory) Gom.; (c) *P. inundatum* Kuetz.

441a (439) Filaments lying parallel in free-floating bundles. (See Fig. 329.)......................................TRICHODESMIUM

441b Filaments irregularly intermingled, not arranged in free-floating bundles. Fig. 334..............................PHORMIDIUM

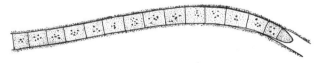

Fig. 334. *Phormidium* sp., isolated filament.

442a (435) Sheaths soft and sticky, without an even or smooth outer boundary **443**

442b Sheaths firm and definite, not mucilaginous **444**

443a Sheath containing 2 or 3 trichomes. Fig. 335....*HYDROCOLEUM*

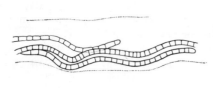

In this genus there are only 3 (sometimes 4) trichomes within a wide, lamellate, gelatinous sheath. The filaments may be solitary or spread in a thin layer on damp soil. *H. oligotrichum* usually is lime-encrusted, whereas *H. homeotrichum* Kuetz. is not.

Fig. 335. *Hydrocoleum oligotrichum* A. Braun.

443b Sheaths containing many trichomes. Fig. 336...*MICROCOLEUS*

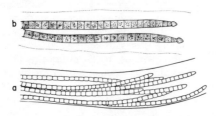

Fig. 336. (a) *Microcoleus vaginatus* (Vauch.) Gom.; (b) *M. lacustris* (Rab.) Farlow.

There are several species of this genus, differentiated by diameter of the trichome and by the characteristics of the apical cell. Unlike *Hydrocoleum* (Fig. 335) there are many intertwined trichomes in each sheath. Usually the trichomes show an active slithering motion over one another, may emerge from the end of the sheath and then retract. The thallus is often of macroscopic size as it grows on damp soil. Some species, however, are more often found on submerged substrates.

444a (442) Sheaths wide, containing 2 or 3 loosely arranged trichomes (often relatively short). Fig. 337 .... *DASYGLOEA*

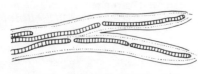

Fig. 337. *Dasygloea amorpha* Berk.

The sheaths of the plants in this genus are rather firm and definite in outline; contain but 1 to 3 trichomes. See *D. amorpha* Berk. The sheaths are usually forked or branched at the ends (as they are also in *Schizothrix*, (Fig. 338), with which it should be compared). Only 1 species has been reported from the United States.

444b Sheaths close, usually containing several crowded trichomes. Fig. 338..*SCHIZOTHRIX*

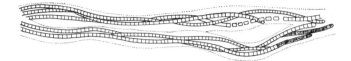

Fig. 338. *Schizothrix tinctoria* Gom.

In this genus there are but few trichomes within a definite and rather firm sheath. The plant masses are of macroscopic size and often form extended films and wefts over submerged vegetation. Several of the species quickly disintegrate when stored in a covered container for a short time without preservative. Under this treatment the plants liberate a copious amount of the pigment phycocyanin. In an aqueous solution the pigment shows a distinct fluorescence. There are at least a dozen species reported from the United States, differentiated by size, by cell proportions and by the characteristics of the sheath, which often is forked.

445a (424) Trichomes definitely tapering at one or both ends......446

445b Trichomes not tapering, or rarely tapering slightly near the apex.. 452

446a Trichomes tapering at both ends, short, 20 cells or less long; heterocysts wanting; akinetes present. Fig. 339...*RAPHIDIOPSIS*

The short trichomes taper at one or usually at both ends. The plants are solitary, curved and twisted, or sigmoid, or sickle-shaped. There are akinetes but no heterocysts. So far the 1 species reported from the United States has been found only in Florida and Ohio.

Fig. 339. *Raphidiopsis curvata* Fritsch & Rich.

446b Trichomes tapering from base to apex, basally-distally differentiated; with a heterocyst and often with an akinete at the base.. 447

447a Filaments inclosed within abundant mucilage, forming a globular or hemispherical body, attached or free-floating...........448

447b Filaments not inclosed by abundant mucilage to form a thallus of definite shape...450

448a Sheath containing 2 or more trichomes. Fig. 340...SACCONEMA

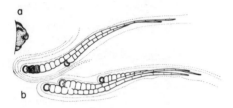

Fig. 340. *Sacconema rupestre* Borzi. (a) habit of colony; (b) filaments from colony.

Trichomes in this genus are tapering from a basal heterocyst as in *Gloeotrichia* (Fig. 341), but there is more than 1 trichome within a sheath and the gelatinous colony is very irregular in shape as it occurs on stones (sometimes in very deep water). The sheaths are wide, lamellate, and are flaring at the outer end.

448b Sheath containing 1 trichome............................449

449a With cylindrical spores adjoining a basal heterocyst; colonial mucilage soft in floating species, firm with attached species which form hemispherical or globular growths 1-3 mm. in diameter. Fig. 341.......................................GLOEOTRICHIA

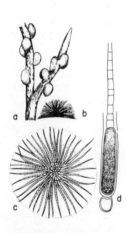

Fig. 341. (a) *Gloeotrichia Pisum* (Ag.) Thur., habit on *Ceratophyllum;* (b) diagram of filament arrangement; (c) *G. echinulata* (J. E. Smith) P. Richter, diagram of filaments in colony; (d) diagram of base of single filament showing heterocyst and spore.

In this genus the tapering trichomes are encased in mucilage which is usually relatively soft, but may be firm and comparatively hard in the attached forms. The filaments are not so closely compacted as in *Rivularia* (Fig. 342). *Gloeotrichia* produces filaments with large akinetes adjoining the basal heterocysts when mature. When immature, plants may be easily mistaken for *Rivularia* which never produces spores. One of the more common species is *G. echinulata* which occurs in abundance in the plankton of hard water lakes. The floating colonies are globular and appear as 'tapioca' grains, making the water buff-colored. When abundant along bathing beaches this plant causes a severe skin irritation among some persons which has been mistaken for 'swimmer's itch.' *G. natans* (Hedw.) Rab. is also fairly common. It begins as an attached plant but late in the growing season it appears at the surface in brown, gelatinous masses, either expanded and flat or irregularly globular. *G. Pisum* forms hard, green or black balls, 1 or 2 mm. in diameter on submerged vegetation, sometimes completely covering the host plant. In the main the filaments are radiately arranged within the colonial mucilage.

449b Spores absent; trichomes embedded in hard mucilage to form globular thalli which may coalesce, thus producing a continuous stratum; trichomes radiate, or more often densely compacted and nearly parallel. Fig. 342..........................RIVULARIA

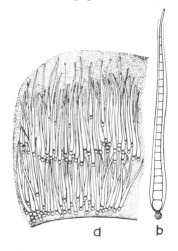

Fig. 342. *Rivularia* sp. (a) diagram of portion of attached colony to show arrangement of filaments; (b) one filament showing basal heterocyst.

There are several species of this genus reported from the United States. They may be differentiated from *Gloeotrichia* (Fig. 341) by the hardness of the colonial mucilage, the compactness of arrangement of the filaments, and by the absence of akinetes. Small globular, dark green to black colonies occur on rocks or submerged logs. Some species grow on moist subaerial surfaces, especially marine forms. *Rivularia* is not found free-floating; whereas *Gloeotrichia* frequently is. See notes under the latter genus.

450a (447) Filaments freely branched, the branches usually lying several within the sheath of the main filament for some distance, then diverging. Fig. 343..........................DICHOTHRIX

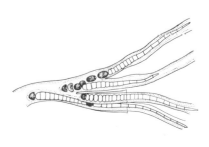

Fig. 343. *Dichothrix gypsophila* (Kuetz.) Bor. & Flah.

In this genus the tapering trichomes are enclosed 2 or 3 together within branching sheaths. Brush-like tufts are produced by their habit of growth and these sometimes attain macroscopic proportions. The species are differentiated by size and sheath characteristics. They are customarily found intermingled with miscellaneous algae; are sometimes attached or at least are adherent to aquatic plants.

450b Filaments not freely branched, if branched the branches not lying within the sheath of the main filament......................451

451a Branching at regular intervals, solitary or in pairs, the branches tapering, heterocysts mostly terminal, but also intercalary. Fig. 344......................................*SCYTONEMATOPSIS*

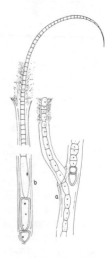

This is the only member of the Rivulariaceae in which the tapering false branches arise at regular intervals. Heterocysts are both basal and intercalary and usually branches, solitary or in pairs, arise just below them. Plants are very similar to *Tolypothrix* (Fig. 359) or *Scytonema (Fig. 358)* except for the tapering of the trichomes.

Fig. 344. *Scytonematopsis hydonoides* Copeland; (a) habit of branching; (b) heterocyst and tapering filament. (Redrawn from Copeland.)

451b Branching absent or scarce and irregular, the heterocysts basal. (See Fig. 323.)......................................*CALOTHRIX*

452a (445) Trichome branches formed by the lateral division of cells in the main axis (true branching)........................453

452b Trichomes unbranched or with false branches (sections of trichomes developing a series of cells to one side of a break in the main axial rows of cells..................................457

453a Individual trichome sheath not apparent; colony of trichomes invested by a mucilage; heterocysts usually on the ends of short branches. Fig. 345...........................*NOSTOCHOPSIS*

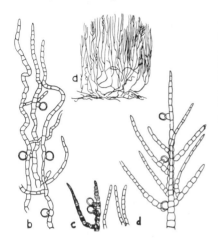

This is the only species reported from the United States. The filaments are composed of *Anabaena*-like cells and bear true branches. The heterocysts are borne laterally along the trichomes or on the ends of short branches (rarely intercalary also). The trichomes are colonial and are inclosed in a firm mucilage in the form of cylinders or hollow tubes which extend vertically from the bottom in quiet water, or lie horizontally in currents. In shallow water the gelatinous tubes may reach the surface and then broaden and flatten horizontally.

Fig. 345. *Nostochopsis lobatus* Wood. (a) diagram of filament arrangement in colony; (b-d) filaments and lateral heterocysts.

453b Individual trichome sheaths evident; heterocysts in the same series with the main axis, or cut off laterally from them but not on the ends of branches...................................454

454a Filaments closely aggregated, forming an attached, gelatinous thallus, 1-2 mm. in diameter. Fig. 346.............*CAPSOSIRA*

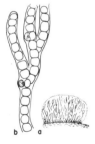

This species builds small bulbous, mucilaginous colonies attached to the substrate. The individual trichomes which bear true branches are surrounded by a definite sheath that is yellowish. Heterocysts are usually lateral, but may be intercalary in the trichomes which do not taper toward the apices. There is but 1 species reported from widely separated stations in the United States.

Fig. 346. *Capsosira Brebissonii* Kuetz. (a) habit of attached colony; (b) portion of filament showing lateral heterocysts. The sheath is thin and soft, without a definite limiting membrane.

195

454b Filaments not forming a definitely shaped gelatinous thallus, but spreading irregularly **455**

455a Filaments with more than 1 series of cells within a wide, gelatinous sheath; heterocysts small, cut off laterally from the vegetative cells. Fig. 347 .... *STIGONEMA*

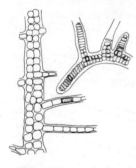

Fig. 347. (a) *Stigonema muscicola* Borzi (*Fischerella muscicola* (Thur.) Gom.); (b) *S. turfaceum* (Berk.) Cook.

Although there are several species reported from the United States, *S. turfaceum* and *S. ocellatum* (Dillw.) Thur. are by far the most common. The latter is one which frequently does not show the multiseriate arrangement of cells. The sheath is wide and mucilaginous and in some species is distinctly lamellate, the cells showing individual sheaths. The heterocysts typically are cut off laterally from a vegetative cell; often are scarce, small and difficult of discernment. Usually they are olive-brown in color. The cells are connected by narrow strands in some species. *Stigonema* forms brownish, olive-green or blue-green growths on submerged reed stems, on exposed roots and other aquatic vegetation or it may occur as velvety growths on moist soil, rocks or concrete. *Stigonema ocellatum* invariably is found in acid-water (Desmid) habitats.

455b Filaments with cells in 1 series; heterocysts within the series of vegetative cells (intercalary), not lateral **456**

456a Branches extending parallel with the main axial trichome. Fig. 348 .... *THALPOPHILA*

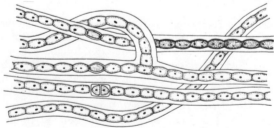

Fig. 348. *Thalpophila imperialis* Copeland. (Redrawn from Copeland.)

As shown in the illustration, *Thalpophila* trichomes have true branching as in *Hapalosiphon* (Fig. 349), but the branches are predominantly unilateral and lie parallel with the main axis. The branching habit produces a cord-like thallus with each trichome within its own sheath. *Thalpophila* has been found only in geyser waters in Yellowstone National Park.

456b Branches arising at right angles to the main filament. Fig. 349...
....*HAPALOSIPHON*

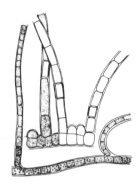

Fig. 349. *Hapalosiphon hibernicus* W. & G. S. West.

This genus is differentiated readily from *Stigonema* (Fig. 347) by the cells being arranged in one series, by the intercalary heterocysts, and by the close, relatively firm sheath. The habit of branching separates it from *Thalpophila* (Fig. 348). Whereas *Stigonema* cells are rounded or oval, and are often interconnected, *Hapalosiphon* cells are mostly rectangular, but may be constricted at the cross walls in some species. The plants mostly sprawl over a substrate, branching and rebranching. The younger branches, especially when growth is vigorous, possess cell characteristics different from the main or primary axial growth and hence in a few instances have led students to identify the outer portions of the thallus as different species. *Hapalosiphon* species occur more frequently in acid (soft) water than in hard; at least 1 common species is terrestrial.

457a (452) Trichomes unbranched...............................**458**

457b Trichomes with false branches...........................**468**

458a Individual trichome sheath firm and definite; heterocyst basal (rarely intercalary heterocysts also). Fig. 350...*MICROCHAETE*

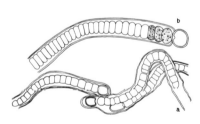

Plants of this genus are mostly epiphytic (or loosely adjoined to a filamentous alga), with part of the filament lying parallel with the substrate, then curving away. The filaments do not taper (or scarcely so) and although there may be intercalary heterocysts they usually are basal, 1-3 in a series. There are 4 species described from the United States, differentiated on size and by habit of growth.

Fig. 350. (a) *Microchaete diplosiphon* Gom.; (b) *M. robusta* Setch. & Gard.

458b Individual sheath soft, often indistinct and confluent with colonial mucilage; heterocysts either all terminal or all intercalary....**459**

459a Heterocysts terminal....................................**460**

459b Heterocysts intercalary..................................**461**

460a Spores adjacent to the heterocysts which are at one end of the trichome (rarely at both ends). Fig. 351....*CYLINDROSPERMUM*

Fig. 351. (a) *Cylindrospermum majus* Kuetz.; (b) *C. marchicum* Lemm.

The chief characteristic of this genus is the location of the heterocysts and spores—always terminal and usually only at one end of the trichome which does not taper at the extremities. The filaments often lie somewhat parallel with the heterocysts all in the same position. The gregarious plants form patches or films over submerged vegetation and are usually bright bluish-green. The akinetes form 1, 2, or 3 immediately behind the terminal heterocyst. Frequently a dense 'nest' of spores will be found where there has been a colony of filaments. Some species are terrestrial.

460b Spores not adjacent to the heterocysts; heterocysts at both ends of the trichomes. Fig. 352.....................*ANABAENOPSIS*

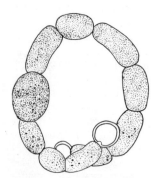

Fig. 352. *Anabaenopsis Elenkinii* Miller. (Redrawn from Smith.)

The trichomes of this genus are usually relatively short (8 to 20 cells), and coiled. The 5 species which have been reported from the United Statest are all euplanktonic.

461a (459) Thallus composed of many trichomes, usually parallel within the colonial mucilage...................................462

461b Plant a solitary trichome, or if aggregated, not parallel but entangled within colonial mucilage...........................464

462a Trichomes inclosed in abundant mucilage, arranged to form a hollow, attached, tubular thallus. Fig. 353............WOLLEA

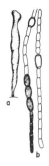

The filaments of this species lie more or less parallel in long, gelatinous, tube-like or sac-like thalli which grow vertically from the bottom of standing water. The cells are barrel-shaped or *Anabaena*-like, and the intercalary heterocysts are cylindrical or nearly so.

Fig. 353. *Wollea saccata* (Wolle) Born. & Flah. (a) habit of colony; (b) trichomes in detail showing heterocysts and akinetes in a series.

462b Thallus not a gelatinous, sac-like tube.....................463

463a Trichomes parallel, forming a free-floating flake-like bundle, each containing near the middle a single heterocyst and an akinete. Fig. 354.................................APHANIZOMENON

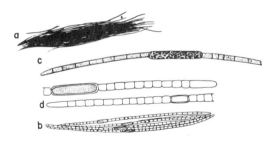

Fig. 354. *Aphanizomenon flos-aquae* (L.) Ralfs. (a) diagram of colony; (b) a few trichomes from the colony; (c-d) trichomes in detail showing medial akinete.

The species illustrated is only one reported from the United States and is very widely distributed in basic lakes which are rich in nitrogen and phosphorous. The trichomes lie in parallel bundles and form flakes of macroscopic size. Because of the gas vacuoles (pseudovacuoles) the plants float high in the water and often form surface scums and mats. Hence they are able to cause serious trouble in lakes and reservoirs used for water supply and pleasure resorts. During the summer months the species may develop a "bloom" condition and be so abundant as to give the water the appearance of "pea soup." Considerable economic loss is suffered as a result of the disturbance caused by *Aphanizomenon* when it leads to the death of fish. It is a plant that usually accompanies human settlement about lakes and rarely is found in any abundance in lakes remote from habitation.

463b Trichomes not parallel, or if so, forming indefinitely shaped flakes or clumps, mostly not macroscopic. (See Fig. 318.) (In part.)....
....*ANABAENA*

464a (461) Trichomes planktonic, solitary........................465

464b Trichomes colonial, in a gelatinous mass....................466

465a Vegetative cells and heterocysts compressed, wider than long, disc-shaped. Fig. 355...........................*NODULARIA*

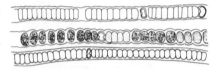

Fig. 355. *Nodularia spumigena* Mert.

Filaments of this species are at once distinguishable by the very short, compressed vegetative cells and heterocysts. The sheath is rather thin and mucilaginous and sometimes is not immediately apparent. The species illustrated is the most common of the 4 that are reported from the United States. Plants of this genus are found usually intermingled with miscellaneous algae from the tychoplankton.

465b Cells globose to cylindric, or barrel-shaped, not compressed as above. (See Fig. 318.).............................*ANABAENA*

466a (464) Plant mass definite in shape, usually globular, bound by a firm, gelatinous tegument, (sometimes forming an expanded gelatinous or rubbery sheet); colonies microscopic or macroscopic. Fig. 356..*NOSTOC*

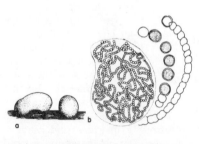

Fig. 356. (a) *Nostoc pruniforme* Ag., showing habit of colonies; (b) *N. linckia* (Roth) Bor. & Flah., with 2 trichomes in detail showing heterocysts and akinetes.

This genus is characterized chiefly by the firm outer tegument of the mucilaginous material in which numerous filaments of bead-like cells are inclosed, thus giving the thallus a definite form. One species, *N. commune* Vauch. builds tough, membranous green or brown layers on the bottoms of pools or in swampy places, sometimes in wet alpine meadows, and commonly on the tundra of the Arctic. *N. pruniforme* is a very common species which forms marble- or acorn-sized colonies on damp soil, often among grasses in marshy places. The globular or oval thalli are mistaken frequently for turtle or some other type of reptilian egg. *N. amplissimum* Gard. is known as Mare's Eggs in the far West where it produces colonies 10 cm. in diameter. *N. parmeloides* forms shelving or bracket-like growths on the down-stream side of stones, usually in mountain brooks. The thallus of this species almost invariably contains the larva of a midge.

466b Plant mass not definite in shape; mucilage soft, not bounded by a firm tegument...467

467a Trichomes forming small bundles within a gelatinous sheath, either entangled or parallel. Fig. 357...............*AULOSIRA*

Fig. 357. *Aulosira laxa* Kirch.

The species illustrated is the only one reported from the United States. The genus is much like *Microchaeta* (Fig. 350) and is sometimes classified with it. Some authorities differentiate it on the basis of the soft sheath, the intercalary heterocysts, and the akinetes which occur intercalary, (approximately the same diameter as the heterocysts).

467b Trichomes not forming bundles. (See Fig. 318.)......*ANABAENA*

468a (457) Branches arising in pairs about midway between 2 heterocysts (branching also rarely solitary). Fig. 358....*SCYTONEMA*

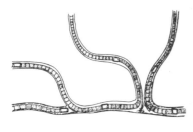

Fig. 358. *Scytonema Archangelii* Born & Flah.

There are several species of this genus which are very common. Although some branch rather seldom, most of them show numerous false branches which arise singly or in pairs between the heterocysts. The sheaths may be thin and rather firm, or wide and lamellate. These are plants of both aquatic and subaerial habitats. Species are differentiated by size, shape of cell, and sheath characters.

468b Branches arising singly just below a heterocyst or a series of them; (branching sometimes rare and not regular, requiring a search through a number of plants to determine this character)..
....**469**

469a Sheath close and firm; 1 trichome in a sheath..............**470**

469b Sheath usually wide and soft; at least more than 1 trichome within a sheath...**471**

470a Branches frequent, arising just below the heterocyst which is always intercalary. Fig. 359.....................*TOLYPOTHRIX*

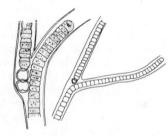

This genus is differentiated from *Scytonema* (Fig. 358) principally by the fact that the false branch always arises below a heterocyst or sometimes from below a series of them. There are several species that are common in the United States, differentiated by size and by sheath characters, some of which are thick and lamellate, others thin and soft.

Fig. 359. *Tolypothrix distorta* Kuetz.

470b Branches rare; heterocysts terminal (rarely intercalary also). (See Fig. 350.)......................................*MICROCHAETE*
(Fremeyella)

471a (469) Trichomes parallel within a fairly wide sheath; plant mass developing bushy tufts; heterocysts basal in the trichome. Fig. 360 ....*DESMONEMA*

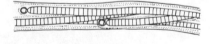

Fig. 360. *Desmonema Wrangelii* (Ag.) Born. & Flah.

The falsely branched filaments of this genus differ from others in the Scytonemataceae by having several trichomes within 1 sheath. The filaments are gregarious and form plant masses of macroscopic size on moist aerial substrates, and usually show erect tufts. This is the only species reported from the United States.

471b Trichomes twisted and entangled in a wide sheath; heterocysts intercalary. Fig. 361.............................DIPLOCOLON

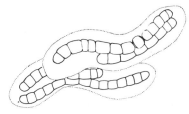

This plant forms an expanse on moist aerial substrates such as dripping rocks and banks. The trichomes are falsely branched, have intercalary heterocysts and are inclosed several together in a wide gelatinous sheath; often form rather short hormogonia.

Fig. 361. *Diplocolon Heppii* Naeg.
(Redrawn from Smith.)

472a (419) Plants attached; cells club-shaped or with other shapes, gregarious, forming cushion-like masses or horizontal expanses, or solitary; epiphytic or growing on shells; cells usually showing endospores (segments of the protoplast rounded up and forming reproductive bodies which are spore-like).................473

472b Plants not attached; cells mostly spherical, hemispherical, or rod-shaped, not forming cushion-like masses or horizontal expanses; cells often incidentally attached to plants or to substrates; endospores lacking...480

473a Cells erect, club-shaped or sub-cylindrical, straight or curved..474

473b Cells some other shape; gregarious, forming horizontal expanses or cushions...475

474a Protoplast dividing by cleavage planes at the apex to form endospores which are cut off successively. Fig. 362..CHAMAESIPHON

These club-shaped or cylindrical plants grow as epiphytes on filamentous algae and whereas they may be solitary they usually occur in gregarious patches. When mature the ends of the protoplasts become cut off, the segments forming endospores which drift away as regenerative elements. A patch of the plants will show many different stages of development from these spores.

Fig. 362. *Chamaesiphon incrustans* Grun.

474b Protoplasts divided throughout its length to form endospores. Fig. 363 . . . . *STICHOSIPHON*

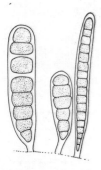

These club-shaped unicells are epiphytic (usually on other algae). They are similar to *Chamaesiphon* (Fig. 362) but the endospores are not cut off successively at the apex but may be formed by simultaneous cleavage throughout the entire protoplast.

Fig. 363. *Stichosiphon regularis* Geitler., showing simultaneous cleavage of entire protoplast to form endospores.

475a (473) Plant mass composed of cells in 1 layer 476

475b Plant mass in the form of a cushion with the cells arranged in vertical rows 478

476a Colony not attached; cells closely arranged in packets. Fig. 364. . . . . *MYXOSARCINA*

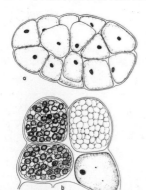

In this genus the plants are essentially unicellular but, by cell division, packets of angular cells are formed which are inclosed in a common mucilage. Some of the cells are usually seen filled with marble-like endospores.

Fig. 364. *Myxosarcina amethystina* Copeland. (Redrawn from Copeland.) (a) colony; (b) cells with endospores.

476b Cells not so arranged; colony sessile.......................477

477a Plant mass composed of a few closely arranged, pyriform cells;
endospores formed by cleavage in 3 planes. Fig. 365..........
....*DERMOCARPA*

Dermocarpa occurs as a solitary cell but often individuals are closely aggregated, forming compact clumps on aquatic plants or other submerged substrates. The cell frequently shows the contents divided into numerous spherical endospores.

Fig. 365. (a) *Dermocarpa r o s t r a t a* Copeland. (Redrawn from Copeland.) (b) *D. prasina* (Reinsch) Bor. & Thur. (Redrawn from Reinsch.)

477b Plant mass a definite colony of many cells; cells round (or angular from mutual compression). Fig. 366..........*XENOCOCCUS*

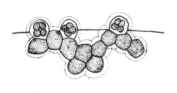

There are at least 4 species of this genus in the fresh waters of the United States, but most forms are marine. They occur as patches of blue-green cells, compactly arranged as epiphytes on filamentous algae. Cells form endospores although they may reproduce actively by fission.

Fig. 366. *Xenococcus Schousbei* Thur.

478a (475) Cells surrounded by a sheath; plant mass thick, cartilaginous, usually macroscopic. Fig. 367...........CHONDROCYSTIS

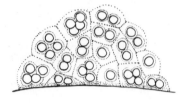

Fig. 367. *Chondrocystis Schauinslandii* Lemm.

The species illustrated here forms extensive, cushion-like masses on exposed surfaces and are heavily encrusted with lime. The colonial mass is inclosed by a tough mucilage in which families of cells are surrounded by individual sheaths. This is the only species in the genus and seems to have been reported but a few times from the United States.

478b Cells not inclosed by a thick sheath; plant mass macroscopic..479

479a Plant mass forming a flat, encrusting layer; cells forming short, erect, unbranched filaments. Fig. 368............PLEUROCAPSA

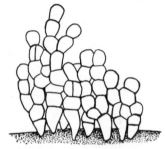

Fig. 368. *Pleurocapsa minor* Hansg.

In this genus the plant mass is essentially filamentous but the cells are so closely appressed that the filamentous, branching habit cannot be determined easily without dissecting the colony. Encrusting thalli are produced with some differentiation between the lower or inner cells and those near the surface which produce the endospores.

479b Plant mass cushion-like; cells forming erect, branched filaments. Fig. 369...ONCOBYRSA

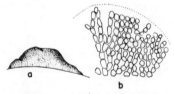

Fig. 369. *Oncobyrsa* sp. (a) habit of colony; (b) diagram of cell arrangement.

Oncobyrsa rivularis is the most common species of this genus. It has compactly arranged series of cells in which the filamentous plan can be determined more easily than in *Pleurocapsa* (Fig. 368). The thallus is a mound of cells, encased in a tough mucilage on filamentous algae. Although the general habit is that of members of Chamaesiphonaceae, there have been no endospores observed.

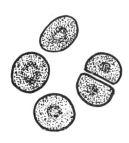

This is a rather rare plant which probably is of more common occurrence than is evidenced by records of it from the United States. There are globular or oval cells, solitary or in pairs, without a mucilaginous sheath being apparent. The densely granular 'central' body of the cells is more complex than for other genera in the Chroococcaceae.

Fig. 370. *Synechocystis aquatilis* Sauv.

207

486a Cells arranged to form a flat plate; cell division in 2 directions in 1 plane. Fig. 371..........................MERISMOPEDIA

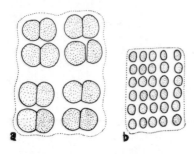

There are several species on record from the United States, differentiated by cell shape and size, color, and by presence of vacuoles. The genus is easily distinguishable by the definite arrangement of the cells in rectilinear series. *M. convoluta* Bréb. is an uncommon species which forms relatively large plates that are enrolled at the margin.

Fig. 371. (a) *Merismopedia elegans* var. *major* G. M. Smith; (b) *M. glauca* (Ehr.) Naeg.

486b Cells arranged to form cubical colonies; cell division in 2 planes. Fig. 372..EUCAPSIS

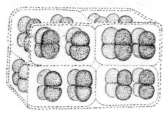

This colonial blue-green alga is regarded by some as being a *Chroococcus* species. But the cubical sarcina arrangement of the cells with sheaths about groups of 8 or 16 individuals distinguish *Eucapsis*. Cell division occurs regularly in 3 planes.

Fig. 372. *Eucapsis alpina* Clements & Shantz.

487a (485) Cells heart-shaped or round, occurring at the ends of short, radiating gelatinous strands of mucilage (focus down into the colony and reduce illumination to detect presence of radiating strands). Fig. 373..........................GOMPHOSPHAERIA

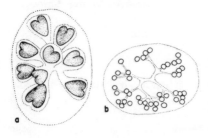

These plants are characterized by having cells in globular or oval colonies, closely or distantly arranged at the ends of mucilaginous strands that radiate from the center of the thallus. *G. lacustris* is frequently found in the euplankton, whereas *G. aponina* occurs mostly in the tychoplankton.

Fig. 373. (a) *Gomphosphaeria aponina* Kuetz.; (b) *G. lacustris* Chod.

488a Groups of many cells inclosed in concentric layers of mucilage; colonial investment intermingling (confluent) with sheaths of other groups and so forming gelatinous masses, mostly on moist substrates; sheaths showing definite concentric rings. Fig. 374....
....*GLOEOCAPSA*

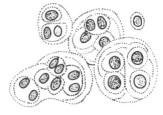

Fig. 374. *Gloeocapsa punctata* Naeg.

This is a genus in which globular cells are inclosed, many 'families' together, within gelatinous masses of considerable size. Common habitats are the surface of moist rocks and cliffs, soil in greenhouses, moist cement work, *etc.* Cells, pairs of cells, or clusters of cells are inclosed in concentric layers of mucilage. Many species, especially when few cells are involved, can scarcely be differentiated from *Chroococcus* (Fig. 375) and there is a disposition among some specialists to place the two genera together.

488b Colonial mucilage not intermingling with that of other colonies; families of few (2 to 8) cells separated from one another, usually free-floating but commonly inhabiting soil and moist surfaces of all kinds; colonial sheath usually not showing concentric layers. Fig. 375................:........................*CHROOCOCCUS*

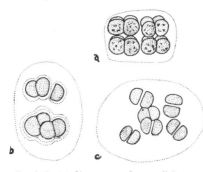

Fig. 375. (a) *Chroococcus Prescottii* Drouet & Daily; (b) *C. limneticus* var. *distans* G. M. Smith; (c) *C. limneticus* Lemm.

There are numerous species in this genus, many of them inadequately described and not clearly differentiated. The genus is separated from *Gloeocapsa* (Fig. 374) mostly on the basis of the fewness of cells involved in a colony and by the fact that 'families' of cells are not all inclosed in a common lamellated, mucilaginous matrix. The colonies are usually composed of not more than 16 cells and more commonly of 2, 4, or 8 cells. A few species are definitely planktonic but others occur attached to aquatic substrates or form films on aerial surfaces. *C. turgidus* (Kuetz.) Naeg. is a large species in which cells occur in 2's and 4's within a stratified envelope and is one that invariably is found in Desmid habitats where the water is acid.

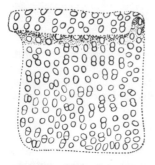

This genus differs from *Merismopedia* by having the cells irregularly arranged within a gelatinous plate. Only the species illustrated has been reported for the genus from the United States.

Fig. 376. *Holopedium irregulare* Lag.

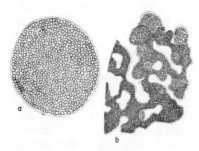

The marble-like cells of this genus are closely compacted and irregularly arranged in definitely shaped but irregular colonies inclosed in mucilage. *M. flos-aquae* has more nearly globular and symmetrically shaped colonies than *M. aeruginosa* which may have clathrations or interstices. The cells often contain pseudovacuoles (gas pockets) and float high in the water. Hence they produce surface scums and like *Aphanizomenon* (Fig. 354) cause a great deal of disturbance in lakes and reservoirs. Dense growths may lead directly or indirectly to the death of fish through suffocation or by poisoning. It is rather curious that where these species occur (especially *M. aeruginosa*) the water is completely

Fig. 377. (a) *Microcystis flos-aquae* (Wittr.) Kirch; (b)*M. aeruginosa* Kuetz. emend. Elenkin.

dominated by the plant to the exclusion of almost all other forms of Cyanophyta. It has been noted often that a lake may be densely overgrown with either *Microcystis* or with *Aphanizomenon*, but not the two together. There are several species of the genus differentiated by size and by details of the sheath structure, and by the form of the colony.

492b Cells not densely crowded but evenly spaced or regularly arranged 493

493a Cells in 1 layer at the periphery of the mucilage. Fig. 378......
....*COELOSPHAERIUM*

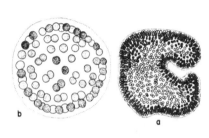

There are 2 common (7) species of this genus which are members of the open water plankton. As the name suggests, the cells are arranged so as to form a hollow colony. *C. Naegelianum* has cells which c o n t a i n pseudovacuoles which are light refractive and the colony appears brownish-purple or even black rather than blue-green when seen microscopically.

Fig. 378. (a) *Coelosphaerium Naegelian-um* Unger; (b) *C. Kuetzingianum* Naeg.

493b Cells distributed throughout the colonial mucilage; cells evenly spaced, often in pairs. Fig. 379...............*APHANOCAPSA*

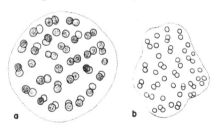

Whereas *Microcystis* (Fig. 377) has cells compactly arranged or crowded, in this genus they are rather evenly spaced throughout the colonial mucilage. The cells are spherical and vary in size in different species, some being not much larger than large bacteria and can be mistaken for them. Cells often appear in pairs; usually do not show pseudovacuoles. There are several species reported from the United States.

Fig. 379. (a) *Aphanocapsa Grevillei* (Hass.) Rab.; (b) *A. elachista* W. & G. S. West.

494a (491) Cells crowded, usually with refractive pseudovacuoles. (See Fig. 377.) ....*MICROCYSTIS*

494b Cells evenly spaced within the mucilage; false vacuoles lacking. (See Fig. 379.)................................*APHANOCAPSA*

495a (480) Cells quadrangular, arranged in flat plates. Fig. 380...... ....*TETRAPEDIA*

Tetrapedia Reinschiana Arch. is a rare and dubious plant that has quadrangular cells arranged in multiples of 4 to form a flat rectangular plate.

Fig. 380. *Tetrapedia Reinschiana,* diagram showing arrangement of rectangular cells.

495b Cells some other shape.................................496

496a Cells solitary or in colonies of few cells....................497

496b Cells numerous within a globular or amorphous, gelatinous matrix. 502

497a Without a gelatinous sheath. Fig. 381......*SYNECHOCOCCUS*

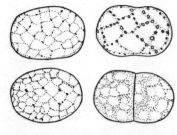

This is a solitary unicell which does not possess a gelatinous sheath. Cells may be in pairs as a result of recent fission. They are relatively large for Cyanophyta of this type (may be up to 35 μ in length) and are often conspicuous in the microscope mount because of their bright blue color.

Fig. 381. *Synechococcus aeruginosus* Naeg.

497b With a gelatinous sheath (sometimes discerned with difficulty), or inclosed by a gelatinous matrix........................498

498a Cells elongate, pointed at the ends. Fig. 382................
.....................................*DACTYLOCOCCOPSIS*

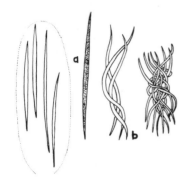

These are fusiform-shaped cells, arranged with their long axes mostly parallel with that of the fusiform-shaped colonial envelope. Five species are known from the United States, occurring in the plankton. Some species are slightly lunate; others are spirally twisted about one another, often do not exhibit a mucilaginous sheath. Compare with *Ankistrodesmus*.

Fig. 382. (a) *Dactylococcopsis acicularis* Lemm.; (b) *D. fascicularis* Lemm.

498b Cells not pointed at the ends...........................499

499a Cells heart-shaped, at the ends of radiating strands of mucilage; colonies globular. (See Fig. 373.).........*GOMPHOSPHAERIA*

499b Cells not at the ends of radiating strands................500

500a Cells radiately disposed. Fig. 383.............*MARSSONIELLA*

In this genus there are pear-shaped cells which are more or less definitely arranged about a common center with the narrow end of the cell directed outward. There is scarcely any evidence of a colonial sheath of mucilage. It is to be looked for in open water plankton.

Fig. 383. *Marssoniella elegans.* Lemm.

500b Cells not radiately disposed..............................501
501a Individual cell sheath distinct. Fig. 384..........*GLOEOTHECE*

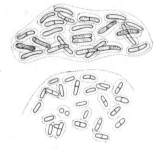

In this genus the cells are elongate cylinders or bacilliform in shape and are inclosed by individual sheaths, all within a common mucilage. There are several species differentiated mostly by cell shape and size. Species should be compared with *Aphanothece* (Fig. 386).

Fig. 384. *Gloeothece linearis* Naeg.

501b Individual cell sheath not apparent. Fig. 385.....*RHABDODERMA*

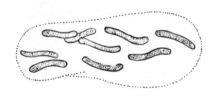

In this genus the cells are elongate and cylindrical, even vermiform and are much like *Gloeothece* (Fig. 384) except that there is no individual cell sheath. The plants occur in small colonies of 4, 8 or 16 in the plankton of lakes; are sometimes in the tychoplankton.

Fig. 385. *Rhabdoderma lineare* Schm. & Lauterb.

502a (496) Cells arranged at the periphery of a gelatinous matrix. (See Fig. 378.).............................*COELOSPHAERIUM*

502b Cells irregularly scattered throughout the colonial mucilage. .503

503a Individual cell sheath not distinct (or wanting). Fig. 386.......
....*APHANOTHECE*

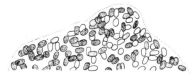

Fig. 386. *Aphanothece Castagnei* (Bréb.) Rab.

Cells are elongate cylinders, or are bacilliform, occurring in large colonies, microscopic or as much as 5 cm. in diameter, and have no individual sheaths. The colonies develop on the bottom of lakes but become free-floating and often are washed into shallow water along shores where they may form a 'soupy' mass of brownish or olive-green (rarely bluish) thalli. Some species form microscopic colonies intermingled in the tychoplankton. Macroscopically the larger colonies appear much like *Nostoc* (Fig. 356) especially if the colonies are young and smooth in outline.

503b Individual cell sheaths distinct. (See Fig. 384.)....*GLOEOTHECE*

504a (370) Frustule (diatom shell)[1] elongate, rod-shaped, boat-shaped, rectangular or wedge-shaped, 2 or more times longer than wide as seen in valve view.......................................517
(See notes, p. 216.)

504b Frustules isodiametric or nearly so; round, triangular, or oval, but less than twice the diameter in length......................505

---

[1]See note on p. 13 for the preparation of diatom mounts.

505a Frustules rectangular in side (girdle)[2] view, joined in chains by interlocking of long, slender, spine-like horns which arise from the corners of the valve; frustules without a raphe; horns hollow or solid. Fig. 387..............................CHAETOCEROS

This genus is well-named because of the long, horn-like processes, one at either pole of the oval cells as seen in valve[2] view. In girdle view the cells are quadrate, with a horn at each angle. The horns of adjacent cells interlock so that filaments are formed. Most species are marine but some may occur in brackish water, such as in Devils Lake, North Dakota.

Fig. 387. *Chaetoceros Elmorei* Boyer, girdle view showing only portions of the very long polar horns. (Redrawn from Boyer.)

---

[2]Diatoms exhibit two general expressions of form and according to a standard classification system there are two Orders. One is the elongate, 'cigar'-shaped, 'boat'-shaped or wedge-shaped cell with bilateral symmetry in the arrangement of wall markings, constituting the Pennales. The other includes round, 'pill-box'-shaped, or nearly isodiametric cells with radiate ornamentation, the Centrales.

The wall or shell of the diatom is called a frustule. It is not a plain, simple envelope but is composed of two sections, one slightly larger and overlapping the smaller much as a box lid. The larger or upper section is called the epitheca, the smaller, inner section the hypotheca. The 'lid' and the 'box' are adjoined by overlapping side pieces, the cingula (singular cingulum). The flattened or broad surface is called a valve and has marginal flanges to which the side pieces, the cingula fit. In some genera there may be supplementary or additional connecting bands, called intercalary bands. When the shell is seen from the top or from the bottom it is said to be in valve view; when seen from the side so that the line shows that is formed by the overlapping of the connecting bands the frustule is said to be in girdle view. The cell may be quite different in appearance in these two views.

The siliceous shells have decorations and markings in an almost endless variety: linear etchings, rows of puncta (dots), costae (ribs), vertical canals (pores). Externally there may be ridges or flanges on the valves; internally, partitions or septations (septa). In certain Pennales genera the valves (or at least one of the two) may contain a longitudinal groove or furrow, the raphe (seen in valve view as a distinct line usually in the mid-region, but it may be sigmoid or to one side of center). Sometimes the raphe lies within a marginal rib or keel. The raphe is not continuous throughout the full length of the valve but is interrupted at the mid point by an internal swell-

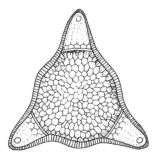

These beautifully ornamented frustules are triangular in valve view, quadrate in girdle view and in cross section are somewhat orbicular. The genus is mostly marine, but species may be found in estuaries and in coastal ponds. *Hydrosera* is regarded as synonymous with *Triceratium* by some diatomists.

Fig. 388. *Hydrosera triquetra* Wall., valve view.

ing on the wall called the central nodule. There may be nodules at either pole of the cell. The central nodule may be large and lobed and referred to as a stauros. A false or pseudoraphe results when the wall decorations form lines (striae) in from the margin but leave a narrow, linear, smooth central region. This 'line' or smooth field may appear on one or on both valves. Care and patience must be used in diatom identification to determine the presence or absence of a raphe or pseudoraphe on one or both valves.

The Centrales which are circular in valve view do not possess a raphe; may have spines or horns. The radiate markings may be evenly disposed or interrupted by smooth zones, or form patterns according to their sizes.

Observations by electronmicroscopists in recent years have disclosed refinements in the decorations and markings of the frustule. Lines under the light microscope actually may be rows of minute puncta, *etc.* These disclosures have necessitated a change in terminology relating to the wall markings. The terms employed in the accompanying key are based on observations made by the customarily used light microscope.

508a Valve with a single, undecorated, mammillate protrusion or thickening just within the margin; (frustules sometimes broadly elliptic or rhomboidal). Fig. 389......................ACTINOCYCLUS

The pill-box frustule (member of the Centrales) has a large pustle-like swelling just within the margin of the epivalve. The puncta or areolae are radiately arranged as in *Coscinodiscus* (Fig. 391) which are usually larger and more conspicuous in the center of the valve. Some species are broadly elliptic in valve view rather than circular. Most members of this genus are marine, but the one illustrated occurs in Lake Erie and presumably throughout the Great Lakes region.

Fig. 389. *Actinocyclus* sp., valve view showing portion of wall decoration.

508b Valve without intramarginal protrusions....................509

509a Valve with an intramarginal zone of costae, smooth or finely punctate within the costal zone; with various markings in the center zone, or smooth. Fig. 390......................CYCLOTELLA

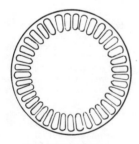

These circular cells (Centrales) are narrowly rectangular in girdle view and often lie parallel with one another to form chains. In valve view there is a zone of radiate costae just within the valve margin and a central, smooth or punctate area. Species are planktonic, often occurring with *Stephanodiscus* (Fig. 392).

Fig. 390. *Cyclotella Meneghiniana* Kuetz., valve view of a species in which the central region is smooth and the marginal region is coarsely striated.

509b Valve marked by rows of puncta radiating from the center to the margin; frustules drum-shaped, rectangular in girdle view....510

510a Valves evenly ornamented, the rows of puncta usually forking, with an intramarginal circle of fine teeth; plants euplanktonic. Fig. 391 .....................................COSCINODISCUS

These are pill-box-shaped frustules, (Centrales) circular in valve view, narrowly rectangular in girdle view. Radiating from the center in valve view are decussating rows of areolae or puncta. Just within the margin in many species is a series of short, sharp spines. There are more than 450 species in the plankton of both marine and fresh waters. This genus and *Stephanodiscus* (Fig. 392) are common within blue-green algal blooms.

Fig. 391. *Coscinodiscus lacustris* Grun., valve view showing radial striae of coarse puncta and minute marginal spines.

510b Valves unevenly ornamented, the radiating rows of puncta separated by clear, smooth, radiating zones; intramarginal circle of coarse spines which extend beyond the edge of the valve; plants euplanktonic or tychoplanktonic. Fig. 392....*STEPHANODISCUS*

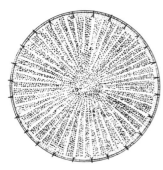

These are relatively large, drum-shaped cells, (Centrales) usually showing a circle of prominent spines just within the margin. In valve view there are radiating rows of costae alternating with clear, smooth zones. The girdle view is smooth and there are no intercalary bands. The species illustrated is very common in hard water basic lakes.

Fig. 392. *Stephanodiscus niagarae* Ehr., valve view; alternating smooth and punctate radial zones; marginal teeth prominent.

511a (507) Frustules broadly elliptic or oval in valve view but commonly short rectangular, the corners protruding and out-turned; no raphe or pseudoraphe. Fig. 393 . . . . *BIDDULPHIA*

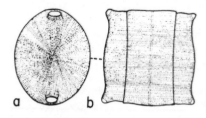

Fig. 393. *Biddulphia laevis* Ehr. (a) valve view; (b) girdle view.

This genus contains variably-shaped cells, mostly rectangular in girdle view, broadly oval in valve view. The chief characteristic is a blunt process extending from the ends of the valves. There is a broad intercalary band. The areolae are in radiating, linear series in valve view and in parallel series in girdle view. Most species are marine, usually solitary but sometimes adjoined in chains.

511b Frustules with a raphe or a pseudoraphe, oval or rhomboidal in valve view 512

512a Frustules rhomboidal to circular in valve view, arched and saddle-shaped in girdle view; pseudoraphe in one valve at right angles to that of the other. Fig. 394 . . . . *CAMPYLODISCUS*

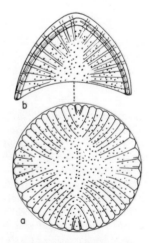

The clear areas are regarded by some diatomists as not being justifiably called pseudoraphes. When seen vertically these cells are circular in outline but are folded or bent to form a saddle when seen from the side. Costae extend inward from the edge of the valve. The raphe is marginal in the valve. In girdle view the cell takes on various shapes according to the angle of observation. The cells occur solitarily; mostly marine but 3 species have been reported from fresh water in the United States.

Fig. 394. *Campylodiscus hibernicus* Ehr. (a) valve view; (b) girdle view, showing marginal keel in which the raphe lies. (Redrawn from Smith.)

512b Frustules oval or broadly elliptic, not bent nor saddle-shaped. .513

513a Frustules broadly elliptic or slipper-shaped, with prominent marginal costae; raphe lateral in a marginal keel...............514

513b Frustules oval or narrowly elliptic, with a pseudoraphe, or with a raphe not in a marginal keel............................515

514a Frustules slipper-shaped, surface of valve transversely undulate, seen when the cell is viewed from the side; transverse striae often faint, occurring in zones or bands across the valve; some species much longer than wide. Fig. 395..............*CYMATOPLEURA*

Fig. 395. *Cymatopleura elliptica* (Bréb.) W. Smith, valve view, the surface undulations represented by clear and shaded areas. (Redrawn from G. M. Smith.)

Although sometimes linear, most species are broadly elliptic or football-shaped in valve view. The cells are rectangular in girdle view but have wavy margins because the valves are transversely undulate. In this view the marginal, often short costae are very prominent. The valve appears zoned or banded when the frustule is seen in valve view. There is a keel along the valve margins in which the raphe lies. A pseudoraphe can be determined in some species. The cells are solitary; are both marine and fresh water.

221

514b Frustules broadly oval, egg-shaped, or slipper-shaped, the surface of the valve not undulate; costae extending inward from the margin showing prominently. Fig. 396.................SURIRELLA

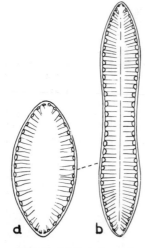

These boat-shaped or oval cells (Pennales) are usually identified readily by the very prominent costae which extend from the margin, with a clear linear area in the axis. Some species are spirally twisted. The raphe is marginal in both valves. The cells, solitary in both eu- and tychoplankton, are relatively large Diatoms.

Fig. 396. (a) *Surirella ovalis* Bréb.?; (b) *S. oblonga* Ehr.

515a (513) Raphe in hypovalve; pseudoraphe in epivalve; with central and polar nodules in the hypovalve; cells epiphytic. Fig. 397.. ....COCCONEIS

The frustules are broadly ovoid-elliptic in valve view. The epivalve shows an axial pseudoraphe whereas the hypovalve shows a raphe, with a central and a polar nodule. The valves have prominent transverse striae. The frustules are epiphytic on filamentous algae or on aquatic plants, sometimes occurring so abundantly as to form a coating over the host substrate.

Fig. 397. *Cocconeis pediculus* Ehr., valve view showing enlarged clear area in the midregion of hypovalve.

515b Raphe in both epi- and hypovalve; frustules oval or variously shaped 516

516a Frustules with transverse septa which show as bands across the cell in valve view; raphe in a canal within a marginal keel; the canal with pores. Fig. 398 . . . . *DENTICULA*

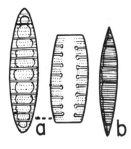

These cells are subrectangular in girdle view but the margins are slightly convex. The girdle is smooth and there are intercalary bands. The transverse septa are seen extending from the margin to the junction of the valves and the girdle. In valve view the frustules are narrowly elliptic with a keel next to one margin. There are transverse septa, and the wall has fine, transverse striae. The cells may be solitary or in short ribbons.

Fig. 398. (a) *Denticula elegans* Kuetz.; (b) *D. tenuis* Kuetz.

516b Frustules without transverse septa; raphe in a central axis of the valve; a prominent central nodule which extends both directions on either side of the raphe; the valve with costae. Fig. 399 . . . .
. . . . *DIPLONEIS*

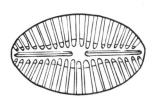

The frustules in this genus are broadly elliptic in valve view; rectangular in girdle view. In some the cells are elongate in valve view and with a median constriction. The central nodule is quadrangular and has elongate projections which extend on either side of the raphe, a feature not clearly evident in the fresh water species. The axial field is enlarged in the mid-region. Across the valve are converging rows of coarse puncta. Free-floating or sedentary.

Fig. 399. *Diploneis elliptica* (Kuetz.) Cl., valve view.

HOW TO KNOW THE FRESH-WATER ALGAE

517a (504) Frustules bilaterally undulate in valve view, the poles capitate; in girdle view triangular, the septa showing as inward projecting processes extending to the intercalary bands. Fig. 400...
....*TERPSINOE*

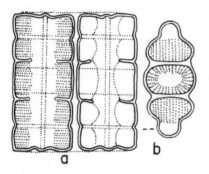

The frustules, although quadrangular in girdle view are conspicuously undulate-elliptic or even triangular in valve view. The septa are evident in valve view as well as in girdle view where they show as perpendicular extensions from the wall. The cells may be solitary or in chains.

Fig. 400. *Terpsinoe americana* (Bailey) Ralfs. (a) girdle view; (b) valve view. (Redrawn from Schmidt.)

517b Frustules shaped otherwise, without septa, or if present, not so arranged..518

518a Frustules usually with 1 or 2 spine-like extensions at the poles.519

518b Frustules without spines at the poles........................521

519a Frustules with intercalary bands; cells solitary..............520

519b Frustules without intercalary bands; cells arranged in filaments. Fig. 401...*MELOSIRA*

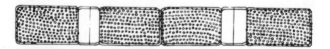

Fig. 401. *Melosira granulata* (Ehr.) Ralfs. (Redrawn from Smith.)

These are capsule-like cells, (Centrales), cylindrical as they lie end to end in relatively long filaments (in girdle view). The valves are either flat or convex in which instance there are teeth at the poles which aid in adjoining cells. In some there is a sulcus in the mid-region, the girdle being smooth. The wall is punctate, coarsely or faintly so. The girdle is also ornamented when there is no sulcus. The plants frequently occur abundantly in the euplankton.

520a Frustules rectangular in girdle view, with 2 spines at each pole. Fig. 402...**ATTHEYA**

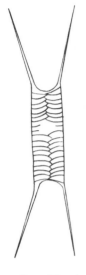

This curiously-shaped genus is remindful of a miniature squid egg-case. The numerous intercalary plates separate the valves so much that a rectangular shape is produced in girdle view—with the 4 corners extended into long, diverging spines. The 2 valves are at either end of the rectangle. In some species there is a horn borne midway between the other two on the valve. Compare with *Rhizosolenia* (Fig. 403).

Fig. 402. *Attheya Zachariasi* Brun. (Redrawn from Hustedt.)

520b Frustules extended into a single spine at each pole; wall markings usually lacking. Fig. 403.................**RHIZOSOLENIA**

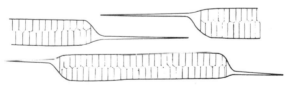

Fig. 403. *Rhizosolenia eriensis* H. L. Smith. (Redrawn from G. M. Smith.)

In this genus the cylindrical cells lie in girdle view with the 2 valves widely separated by intercalary bands. The valves are mostly cap-like in this view and terminate in a long, slender spine. The walls are not decorated but the imbricate intercalary bands form a pattern. The walls are delicate and do not withstand the usual (especially acid) cleaning treatment by which diatom frustules are clarified.

521a (518) Frustules cylndrical in girdle view (quinine capsule-shaped), attached end to end in filaments; polar margins often with denticulations. (See Fig. 401.)..............................*MELOSIRA*

521b Frustules not cylindrical, not attached in filaments..........522

522a Frustules triangularly divided (3-parted) with a pseudoraphe in each valve; frustules non-septate. (Questionably a diatom). Fig. 404 ....*CENTRONELLA*

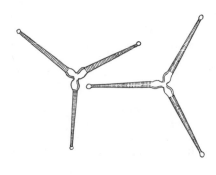

These uniquely shaped cells have tri-radiate, branched valves. The apices of the valve lobes are slightly capitate. The midregion is smooth but on either side of the pseudoraphe are fine, transverse striae. The frustules are non-septate. Apparently this little-understood "diatom" has been reported only from Europe.

Fig. 404. *Centronella Reichelti* Voigt., valve view. (Redrawn from Schoenfelt.)

522b Frustules not triangularly divided.........................523

523a Frustules without a raphe; pseudoraphe showing in both valves.. 524

523b Frustules with a raphe in at least 1 valve.................533

524a Frustules in girdle view elongate-rectangular, forming a circular colony in which the cells radiate from a common center like spokes of a wheel, the frustules slightly enlarged at the poles. Fig. 405.....................................*ASTERIONELLA*

These species are planktonic and are readily identified by the spoke-like arrangement of the rectangular frustules about a common center. The poles are enlarged, more so at the adjoined than at the free (outer) ends. Some species may form a bloom in favorable habitats and often are involved in the spoilage of water. The common species are usually found in hard water lakes.

Fig. 405. *Asterionella formosa* Hass., colonial arrangement of cells in girdle view.

524b Frustules shaped and arranged otherwise..................525

525a Frustules wedge-shaped in girdle view, adjoined side by side to form flat, circular, semicircular or fan-shaped colonies (sometimes forming spiral bands). Fig. 406.....................*MERIDION*

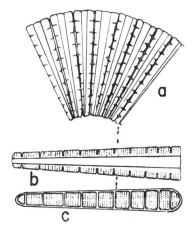

The wedge-shaped cells in this genus have 1 or 2 intercalary bands between the girdles. The frustules lie in girdle view, side by side in a complete or incomplete circular plate. In valve view they are cuneate and show (usually) transverse septa. The species illustrated is common in waters which support a luxuriant blue-green algal flora, but is found also in temporary pools, sometimes coating the bottom of ditches and trickles of water with a brown scum.

Fig. 406. *Meridion circulare* (Grev.) Ag. (a) part of a colony; (b) girdle view; (c) valve view.

525b Frustules other shapes, or without fan-like arrangement in circular plates...526

526a Frustules slightly arcuate or bent in the long axis...........527

526b Frustules not arcuate....................................528

527a Central smooth area present, extending to ventral (concave) margin as seen in valve view, the ventral margin with a slight swelling in the midregion. Fig. 407....................*CERATONEIS*

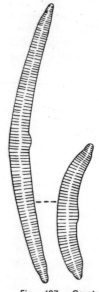

The cells are arched or somewhat boomerang-shaped, with capitate poles in valve view. In the midregion there is an enlargement on the ventral or concave margin. There is a conspicuous pseudoraphe. In girdle view the frustules are narrowly rectangular with truncate ends. Transverse striae on the valves are prominent. Most species have been reported from cold mountain streams.

Fig. 407. *Cerato-neis* spp., valve view of 2 cell shapes.

527b Central smooth area lacking; pseudoraphe narrow throughout length of valve; margins showing pointed undulations in valve view. Fig. 408................................*AMPHICAMPA*

Frustules in this genus are slightly arched (crescent-shaped) and have both margins (as seen in valve view) undulate, or with tooth-like projections. In girdle view the cells are elongate-rectangular. The valves are marked by transverse striae.

Fig. 408. *Am-phicampa eruca* Ehr., valve view. (Redrawn from Ehren-berg.)

528a (526) Frustules attached in zig-zag chains (sometimes semi-stellate or radiate colonies); longitudinal septa present, straight; rows of transverse puncta visible in valve view; frustules not showing transverse costae. Fig. 409.............. *TABELLARIA*

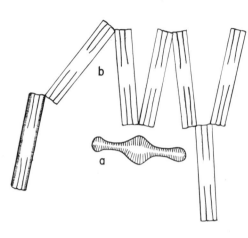

Frustules in this genus are short or elongate rectangles as seen in girdle view. They are attached at the corners to one another, forming chains or wheel-like arrangements. There are longitudinal septa which show in girdle view. In valve view the cells are narrowly elongate, subcylindrical with capitate poles and a median swelling. There is a pseudoraphe bordered by transverse striae. Common in both eu- and tychoplankton.

Fig. 409. (a) *Tabellaria* sp., valve view; (b) *T. fenestrata* (Lyngb.) Kuetz., girdle view in zig-zag chain.

528b Frustules not arranged in zig-zag chains, or if so, with curved septa..529

529a Frustules with curved septa; costae present, appearing as septa; frustules arranged in bands (sometimes in zig-zag chains). Fig. 410... *TETRACYCLUS*

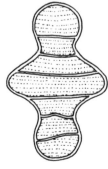

The cells in this genus are rectangular in girdle view, with truncate poles that have rounded corners. The two valves are widely separated by intercalary bands, and appear as caps at ends of the cells. In valve view the cells are oval and show transverse false septa. The wall is not ornamented. Two species are reported from the United States, occurring in the tychoplankton or forming part of the films on submerged substrates.

Fig. 410. *Tetracyclus lacustris* Ralfs., valve view.

529b Frustules without septa.....................................530

530a Frustules with prominent costae in the valves..............531

530b Frustules without prominent costae........................532

531a Valve view symmetrical, usually elliptic or subcylindric, often with subcapitate poles; in valve view with a faint pseudoraphe; girdle view rectangular. Fig. 411....................*DIATOMA*

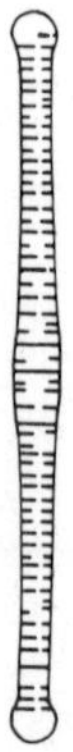

Species in this genus are variously shaped in valve view; oval or elongate, but rectangular in girdle view. There usually are intercalary bands and there are transverse septa. These appear as costae across the valves. The valve and the girdles are finely punctate. In the valves is a narrow pseudoraphe where the wall is not punctate. Frustules usually form zig-zag chains; adjoined by gelatinous pads at the corners of the cells. Compare with *Tabellaria* (Fig. 409).

Fig. 411. *Diatoma vulgare* Bory var., valve view.

531b Valve view symmetrical, egg-shaped; asymmetrical and wedge-shaped in girdle view; transverse costae conspicuous. Fig. 412..*OPEPHORA*

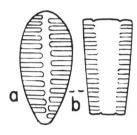

These elliptic or egg-shaped cells in valve view are cuneate and asymmetrical in girdle view. There are prominent, punctate costae on the valves. Elsewhere the wall is smooth. In valve view is a pseudoraphe. Only 2 species have been reported from fresh water in the United States.

Fig. 412. *Opephora Martyi* Herib., (a) valve view; (b) girdle view.

532a (530) **Frustules quadrate or rectangular in girdle view, attached side by side to form ribbons (rarely in chains); valve view fusiform, the poles narrowed from an enlarged central region. Fig. 413** . . . . ***FRAGILARIA***

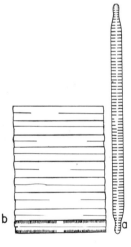

The frustules are narrowly elongate, fusiform in valve view, rectangular in girdle view and usually show intercalary bands. The pseudoraphe is broad and distinct (usually). The most common species form ribbons with the valves attached side by side (rarely in zig-zag chains). A dozen or more species occur in both eu- and tychoplankton.

Fig. 413. (a) *Fragilaria* sp., valve view; (b) *Fragilaria capucina* Desm., diagram to show ribbon-like arrangement in girdle view.

231

532b Frustules elongate and straight (rarely slightly curved), needle-shaped in both views, or with slightly capitate poles; pseudoraphe between transverse striae; frustules solitary or in radiating colonies, attached to substrate, single or in clumps, at one end by short, gelatinous stalks. Fig. 414 . . . .*SYNEDRA*

These needle-like cells are commonly solitary but often form radiately clustered associations, attached or free-floating. In valve view is a pseudoraphe bordered by transverse striae. These are absent in the midregion of the cell in some species. *Synedra* is common in the plankton and in scums on substrates.

Fig. 414. *Synedra* sp., valve view showing absence of striae in midregion.

533a (523) Frustules lunate or slightly curved in valve view; rectangular or boat-shaped in girdle view 534

533b Frustules some other shape in valve view 537

534a Curvature slight (frustules often nearly straight); frustules bearing a keel near the margin of a valve in which the raphe is inclosed, the location of the keel marked by a row of dots; frustule quadrangular in cross section. Fig. 415 . . . .*HANTZSCHIA*

Like *Nitzschia* (Fig. 429) frustules in *Hantzschia* are bean pod-shaped in valve view, rectangular in girdle view. There are fine, transverse striae across the valve. There is a keel along one margin of each valve . Unlike *Nitzschia* the keeled margin of one valve lies opposite that of the other valve. The raphe lies within the keel and from the fissure a row of pores open into the cell cavity, forming "carinal dots." The frustules are rectangular in optical section. There are only 2 or 3 species reported from the fresh water of the United States.

Fig. 415. *Hantzschia amphioxys*

534b Curvature decidedly evident; frustules not bearing a keel on the valve; asymmetrical in longitudinal axis; the raphe usually lying much closer to the ventral (concave) margin.................535
535a Arcuate valve view showing prominent transverse lines of the septa of the frustules (appearing as costae); raphe along the ventral margin and in the midregion bent inwardly to form a 'V' as seen in valve view; frustules epiphytic on filamentous algae and aquatic plants. Fig. 416.......................*EPITHEMIA*

The frustules are slightly bowed with the dorsal (convex) side more strongly curved as seen in valve view. The axial field lies along the concave margin but forms a V-shaped bending in the midregion. The raphe lies in the axial field. The girdle view of the frustule is rectangular. In the valve view there are prominent transverse septa and rows of puncta. There may be a longitudinal septum also. The frustules are commonly found as epiphytes on filamentous algae with the concave side down.

Fig. 416. *Epithemia* sp., valve view showing V-shaped pattern formed by in-bending of smooth axial field.

**535b Frustules without transverse septa (costae) showing in the valve
view** **536**

**536a Axial view expanded in the midregion, forming a clear area in
the valve ornamentation which extends to the ventral margin of
the curved frustule; cells usually with the concave margin against
a substrate. Fig. 417** .... *AMPHORA*

Frustules in this genus are crescent-shaped in valve
view but broadly elliptic with truncate poles in girdle
view. The raphe presents two curved lines near the
ventral margin of the valve, the two curves meeting over
the central nodule which lies next to the ventral margin
of the cell. The cells usually are found lying with the
concave surface of the hypovalve uppermost when
viewed under the microscope, but in nature occurs with
the concave face against the substrate (often filamentous algae).

Fig. 417. *Am-
phora* sp., valve
view showing ex-
centric raphe.

**536b Axial field central and small, not expanded as above; frustules
forming linear colonies in gelatinous tubes, or attached singly at
the end of a gelatinous stalk (often found floating free); lunate,
with a slight swelling in the midregion of the ventral margin.
Fig. 418** .... *CYMBELLA*

These are mostly gracefully curved, crescent-
shaped cells which are slightly tumid along the concave margin in the midregion. The axial field in
which the raphe lies is enlarged in the midregion.
In valve view rows of prominent puncta extend from
the margin in a converging pattern. Although usually free-floating, the frustules are often found at the
ends of branching, gelatinous strands.

Fig. 418. *Cym-
bella cistula*
(Hempr.) Kirch.
(?), valve view,
showing excentric
raphe, bent in-
ward at the poles
toward the con-
cave margin.

537a (533) Frustules 'S'-shaped or sigmoid; wall ornamented with transverse and longitudinal striae which make a pattern of intersections. Fig. 419.................................*GYROSIGMA*

The frustules of *Gyrosigma* are sigmoid in valve view, as in the narrow axial field which is enlarged in the midregion. The valve is marked by intersecting longitudinal and transverse striae. In girdle view the frustules are lanceolate. The cells occur singly. It is reported that 12 species are known from the fresh waters of the United States.

Fig. 419. *Gyrosigma acuminatum* (Kuetz.) Cleve., valve view.

537b Frustules not sigmoid.....................................538

538a Frustules broadly elliptic, slipper-shaped or boat-shaped in valve view, the margins showing prominent, often short costae; surface of valve undulate; in girdle view elongate but with the sides undulate; pseudoraphe often indistinct. (See Fig. 395.)...........
....*CYMATOPLEURA*

Although sometimes linear, most species are broadly elliptic or football-shaped in valve view. The cells are rectangular in girdle view but have wavy margins because the valves are transversely undulate. In valve view the marginal, often short costae are very prominent. There is a keel along the valve margins in which the raphe lies. A pseudoraphe can be determined in some species.

538b Frustules without such costae; not undulate, not showing marginal undulations in girdle view.........................539

539a Raphe along both margins of the valve, located within a keel..540

539b Raphe not marginal; keel present or absent................541

540a Valves sharply bent to form a saddle; pseudoraphe in each valve but at right angles to one another; raphe in a marginal keel. (See Fig. 394.)....................................CAMPYLODISCUS

540b Valve usually twisted, sometimes flat; prominent costae extending from the valve margin toward the smooth, pseudoraphe area. (See Fig. 396.)....................................SURIRELLA

541a (539) Frustule in valve view curved and 'bone'-shaped, one pole distinctly larger than the other; transverse rows of puncta in valve view. Fig. 420.............................ACTINELLA

Cells in this genus are all elongate and sub-cylindric, but the poles are enlarged and unsymmetrically so. In valve view there are numerous transverse rows of puncta. In some species there are fine, intramarginal spines. The raphe lies along the concave margin of the valve, extending diagonally from the polar nodules. The species illustrated is the only one reported from the United States and it is rare.

Fig. 420. Acti-
n e l l a punctata
Lewis, valve view.

541b Frustules some other shape..............................542

542a Valve with "wings," furnished with a sigmoid keel vertical to the face of the valve; boat-shaped in valve view; '8'-shape or hourglass-shaped in girdle view. Fig. 421............AMPHIPRORA

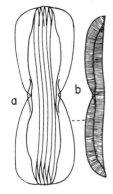

The frustules are elongate boat-shaped in valve view but '8'-shaped or hour-glass-shape in girdle view. The valve has a curious vertical flange or keel which extends in a sigmoid fashion. The raphe extends through the outer margin of this keel. The wall is decorated with longitudinal rows of puncta which form parallel striae. Species may be free-floating or adhere in mucilage on moist substrates.

Fig. 421. Amphi-prora paludosa W. Smith. (a) girdle view; (b) valve view.

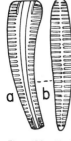

In valve view these cells are elongate-oblanceolate, narrower at one end than the other. The hypovalve shows a raphe and there is a pseudoraphe in the epivalve. In girdle view the cells are curved cuneate. The intercalary bands are not decorated. Coarse transverse striae show in both views. There are 2 longitudinal septa which are parallel to the face of the valve. The species illustrated is the only one reported from the United States; occurs attached by a gelatinous stalk to algae or aquatic plants.

Fig. 422. Rhoi-cosphenia curvata (Kuetz.) Grun. (a) girdle view; (b) valve view. (Re-drawn from Smith.)

545a Frustules broadly elliptic or oval, incompletely septate; appressed valve down to substrate; pseudoraphe in epivalve; raphe in hypovalve. (See Fig. 397.)............................*COCCONEIS*
545b Frustules narrowly elliptic, with smooth or undulate margins in valve view; bent, rectangular or naviculate in girdle view; without septa; attached by stalks to filamentous algae and aquatic plants. Fig. 423...............................*ACHNANTHES*

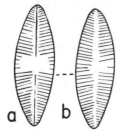

Fig. 423. *Achnanthes lanceolata* (Bréb.) Grun. (a) hypovalve view showing raphe; (b) epivalve view showing pseudoraphe. *A. coarctata* (Bréb.) Grun. is a common species which is on stalks, epiphytizing filamentous algae.

These frustules are symmetrical in valve view but not when seen from the side. They are, in general, elliptic in valve view, undulate-rectangular in girdle view. The epivalve shows a pseudoraphe, the hypovalve a raphe. The cells may be free, or more commonly attached by a gelatinous stalk to various substrates, sometimes forming packets or filaments. There have been about a dozen species reported from the United States.

546a (543) Raphe confined to polar regions.....................547
546b Raphe evident throughout the length of the valve..........548
547a Frustule straight in the apex; margin smooth in valve view; costae on both lateral margins. Fig. 424...................*PERONIA*

Fig. 424. *Peronia (Opephora)* sp., valve views; (b) showing raphe near poles.

These cells are elongate or cigar-shaped with rounded poles. One pole is often larger than the other as seen in valve view. The raphe extends from the poles only about 2/3 of the distance to the midregion and is slightly curved near the inner end. The valves have prominent marginal costae.

547b Frustules bent or curved in the apex; wavy or undulate on one margin as seen in valve view; transversely striate. Fig. 425....
....*EUNOTIA*

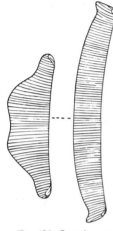

Frustules are slightly bowed and are undulate on one or both margins as seen in valve view. The face of the valves is transversely striate. The polar nodules are conspicuous and from them to the ventral (concave) margin a short raphe extends. There are many species common in especially soft water habitats.

Fig. 425. *Eunotia* spp., 2 cell shapes in valve view.

548a (546) Raphe located in a canal...........................549
548b Raphe not located in a canal...........................554

549a Frustules spirally twisted; raphe accordingly spiral; cells with a keel. Fig. 426...........
.... *CYLINDROTHECA*

Fig. 426. *Cylindrotheca* sp., valve view.

549b Frustules not spirally twisted.............................550

550a Raphe not in a keel.......................................551

550b Raphe in a keel or wing..................................552

551a Raphe in a canal without pores; frustule broadest on the girdle side and usually seen lying in this position; a clear area in the girdle zone boarded by prominent costae, margins usually with a swelling in the midregion as seen in girdle view. Fig. 427....
.... RHOPALODIA

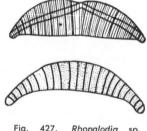

In this genus the cells are much different in shape as seen in girdle and valve views. In valve view the frustule is narrow with the poles bowed. The ventral margin is almost straight, except for the narrow, curved poles, the dorsal (convex) margin with a swelling in the midregion. The valve bears a keel to one side and in this lies the raphe. The valves are coarsely costate, the costae alternating with striae. In girdle view the cells are elongate, somewhat sub-quadrate in general outline but with a swelling on each side in the midregion. The girdle is smooth, but extending in from the margin are coarse costae which, in the polar regions converge toward the center of the wall. The genus is entirely fresh-water in distribution, but apparently only 2 species have been found in the United States.

Fig. 427. Rhopalodia sp., valve view, of 2 species.

551b Raphe in a canal with pores; lanceolate or elliptic in valve view. (See Fig. 398.)...................................DENTICULA

552a (550) Keels on margins of valves opposite one another; quadrangular in cross section. (See Fig. 415.).........HANTZSCHIA

552b Keels on alternate margins of valve.......................553

553a Frustules occurring in colonies; keel central. Fig. 428.........
....BACILLARIA

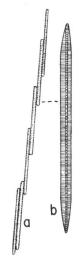

The species illustrated here is placed by some diatomists in the genus *Nitzschia* (Fig. 429). The narrowly elongate cells, with produced apices are united side by side to form ribbons. The cells slide back and forth along the sides of the frustules and draw the ribbon out into an extended, pseudofilamentous arrangement—then slide back and extend in the opposite direction; hence the name, "carpenter's rule" diatom. The keel is central or nearly so and is conspicuously punctate. The raphe is in the keel and is diagonally opposite the raphe in the other valve. Species are both marine and brackish.

Fig. 428. *Bacillaria paradoxa* Gmel., (a) diagram of cells sliding out to form elongate colony; (b) single cell, valve view.

553b Frustules solitary; keel excentric, diagonally opposite one another; rhomboid in cross section. Fig. 429.........*NITZSCHIA*

The frustules of this genus are narrowly linear and tapered at the poles in both valve and girdle views. The cells may be straight or slightly sigmoid. Along one margin of a valve is a keel which is opposite the unkeeled margin of the other valve. The raphe lies within the keel. The fissure of the raphe has a row of pores that open into the cell cavity. These are called carinal dots. There are prominent transverse rows of puncta on the valve faces. Although commonly solitary, *Nitzschia* often occurs in gelatinous tube-like strands.

Fig. 429. *Nitzschia* sp., valve view showing location of marginal keel.

554a (548) Frustules asymmetrical in either the transverse or the longitudinal axis; key- or wedge-shaped in valve view, slightly larger at one end than the other................................555

554b Frustules symmetrical in both axes......................556

555a Striae composed of puncta in a double series, interrupted near the margin of the valves so that a longitudinal marginal line is formed; attached. Fig. 430......................_GOMPHONEIS_

These cells are wedge-shaped or cuneate, unsymmetrical in both girdle and valve views (transversely). There is an elongate, axial field which is enlarged in the midregion. The frustules are very similar to _Gomphonema_ (Fig. 431) but there is a fine but definite line running parallel with the margin of the valve. Frustules attached or free-floating.

Fig. 430. _Gomphoneis herculeana_ (Ehr.) Cleve, valve view showing raphe. with curvature in the midregion.

555b Striae composed of puncta in a single series; attached on branched stalks, or floating. Fig. 431....................._GOMPHONEMA_

Species in this genus have frustules that are wedge-shaped or clavate, larger at one end than the other. In both girdle and valve view the frustules are transversely unsymmetrical. The elongate axial field is enlarged in the midregion where there is often an eccentric, coarse punctum. There are coarse striae extending inward from the valve margins. The cells are usually found attached on branched, gelatinous stalks at their narrow end. Compare with _Gomphoneis_ (Fig. 430).

Fig. 431. _Gomphonema lanceolatum_ var. _insignis_ (Greg.) Cl.

557a Frustules quadrangular in girdle view; usually in zig-zag chains; longitudinally septate, the septa with openings in the center and at the poles. Fig. 432..........................*DIATOMELLA*

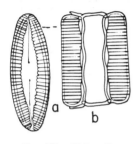

In valve view frustules are narrowly elongate, broadly rounded at the poles and enlarged in the midregion. In girdle view the cells are rectangular. There are 2 intercalary bands and 2 longitudinal septa. The valves have transverse rows of striae. Frustules may be solitary or in zig-zag chains.

Fig. 432. *Diatomella* sp., (a) valve view; (b) girdle view showing intercalary bands.

557b Frustules narrowly rectangular in girdle view, naviculoid in valve view; septa with large central opening and parallel linear openings which form 2 lateral series of minute, transverse canals. Fig. 433...*MASTOGLOIA*

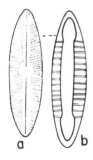

Frustules in this genus are symmetrical in both longitudinal and transverse axes. They are elongate-elliptic in valve view; rectangular in girdle view. The girdle is smooth. There is a raphe in a straight, clear axial field which is enlarged in the midregion. There are 2 longitudinal septa. In valve view there are transverse striae on either side of the axial field.

Fig. 433. *Masto gloia Danseii* Thw. (a) valve view; (b) diagram showing internal septum. (Redrawn from Smith.)

559a Valve with an enlarged, undecorated central area on the region of the central nodule; frustule broadly elliptic; valve costate. (See Fig. 399.).......................................*DIPLONEIS*

559b Valve without an enlarged clear area in the central region; valve not costate; frustules linear-lanceolate.....................560

560a Central nodule greatly elongated, the raphe appearing in 2 relatively short sections in the apical regions. Fig. 434...........
....*AMPHIPLEURA*

These are elongate and narrow, boat-shaped cells in valve view. The conspicuous differentiating character is the greatly elongated central nodule that extends 2/3 of the length of the valve and is divided to form 2 parallel extensions near the poles. The valve has minute transverse rows of punctations which can be seen only under special optical conditions, hence it appears smooth under ordinary magnification.

Fig. 434. *Amphipleura pelluci-da* Kuetz., valve view showing greatly elongated central nodule. (Redrawn from Boyer.)

560b Central nodule shorter, with 2 siliceous ribs extending toward the apices; raphe lying within the ribs. Fig. 435....*FRUSTULIA*

Like *Amphipleura* (Fig. 434) *Frustulia* has an elongate central nodule but it is relatively shorter (less than ½ the length of the cell). The cells are boat-shaped in valve view; rectangular in girdle view and without intercalary bands. Two ribs from the polar nodule run parallel to the raphe and unite with the polar nodules. Frustules are either solitary or lie side by side in a gelatinous, tubular colony.

Fig. 435. *Frustulia rhomboides* (Ehr.) DeToni, valve view showing raphe between two ribs. (Redrawn from Smith.)

561a (558) Valves with "wings," bearing a sigmoid keel, '8'-shaped in girdle view. (See Fig. 421.).....................*AMPHIPRORA*

561b Valves without a keel....................................562

562a Transverse valve markings interrupted, thus the frustule shows longitudinal lines paralleling the margins of the valves......563

562b Transverse markings not so interrupted....................565

563a Interruption of transverse lines forming a zig-zag pattern or line. Fig. 436 ....*ANOMOEONEIS*

The frustules are elongate boat-shaped in valve view with narrowly rounded (sometimes capitate) apices, whereas they are rectangular in girdle view. In the valve view a narrow axial field (clear of wall markings) is enlarged in the midregion. Lateral to the central field are fine, transverse striae which are interrupted by clear spaces in such a way that a zig-zag pattern is formed over the face of the valve. This is a freshwater genus; benthic or in the tychoplankton.

Fig. 436. Ano-moeoneis *sphaerophera* var. *sculpta* O. Null. (Redrawn from Reimer.)

563b Interruptions not forming zig-zag patterns....................564

564a Transverse markings formed of puncta. Fig. 437.......NEIDIUM

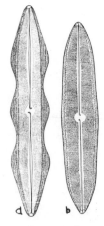

These boat-shaped cells in valve view show prominent, but discontinuous transverse striae. They are conspicuously interrupted by blank places in two lateral lines just within the margins of the valves. There is a clear, linear axial field which is enlarged in the midregion. At the central nodule the raphe forms 2 hooks which turn in the opposite direction. The frustules are rectangular in girdle view. Compare with *Caloneis* (Fig. 438), another strictly freshwater genus.

Fig. 437. (a) *Neidium magellanicum* Cl., valve view showing curvature of raphe in midregion. (Redrawn from Frenguelli.) (b) *N. iridis* var. *subundulata* (A. Cl.-Eul.) Reimer. (Redrawn from Reimer.)

564b Transverse markings of continuous lines. Fig. 438...CALONEIS

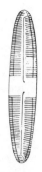

Cells are elongate cigar-shaped, but slightly widened in the midregion where the axial field is also enlarged. There are both central and polar nodules. There are parallel transverse striae extending from the lateral margins of the valve. The frustules are rectangular in girdle view. Just within the margins of the valve is a parallel line which crosses the transverse striae. There are many species in both fresh water habitats and in salt water.

Fig. 438. *Caloneis bacillum* (Grun.) Cleve, valve view showing clear area in midregion and curvature of raphe. (Redrawn from Foged.)

565a (562) Clear area in longitudinal axis sigmoid. Fig. 439 . . . .
. . . . *SCOLIOPLEURA*

The outstanding characteristic of this genus is the sigmoid axial field. Within this lies a sigmoid raphe. There may be a line on either side of the axial field bordering the transverse striae. The species are marine or brackish.

Fig. 439. *Scoliopleura* sp., valve view with sigmoid raphe.

565b Clear area of axial field not sigmoid 566

566a Valves with costae forming the transverse markings; costae punctate. Fig. 440 . . . . *BREBISSONIA*

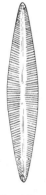

These cells are attached by branched, gelatinous strands to a substrate, sometimes aquatic plants. The cells are lanceolate-boat-shaped in valve view; quadrangular in girdle view. The 2 sections of the raphe lie in a clear, longitudinal axial field and between 2 parallel ridges (which are inconspicuous). Very prominent striae extend from the margins of the valve toward the axial field.

Fig. 440. *Brebissonia Boeckii* (Ehr.) Grun., valve view showing raphe between parallel ridges. (Redrawn from Boyer.)

566b Valves with ornamentation formed by puncta, or without evident markings 567

567a Lateral valve markings strongly oblique, interrupted in the mid-region by an undecorated area over the central nodule which extends to the margins of the valves. Fig. 441.....*STAURONEIS*

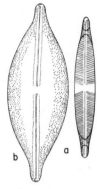

These are mostly naviculoid cells (in valve view), with either capitate or acutely rounded poles. The conspicuous feature (the stauros) is a broad central nodule which extends to both lateral margins of the valve. In this region alone there are no transverse striae which are prominent and which converge from the lateral margins. There is a straight raphe lying in a fairly wide, clear axial field. Common and widely distributed in the United States; occurs also in salt water.

Fig. 441. (a) *Stauroneis parvula* var. *prominula* Grun., valve view showing transverse stauros. (Redrawn from Foged.); (b) *S. Stodderi* Lewis. (Redrawn from Reimer.)

567b Central undecorated clear area not extending to the margins of the valve...568

568a Transverse ornamentations composed of costae, the axial field usually broad. Fig. 442.........................PINNULARIA

These frustules vary considerably in shape but mostly they are naviculoid with broadly rounded poles in valve view. Some species are enlarged in the midregion. The conspicuous feature is the prominent transverse costae on either side of a relatively wide, straight axial field. The raphe in this field is sigmoid. In girdle view the frustules are rectangular with truncate poles. Some species have cells which are perhaps the largest among freshwater diatoms.

Fig. 442. Pinnularia borealis Ehr., valve view showing costae. (Redrawn from Foged.)

568b Transverse ornamentations composed of puncta, the axial field narrow and linear, the raphe straight. Fig. 443......NAVICULA

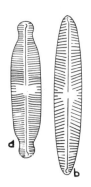

This is a large genus with many species in fresh water and are widely distributed. The cells vary considerably in shape but in general they are naviculoid or cigar-shaped, with narrowly rounded or capitate poles; sometimes distinctly rostrate. The frustules are eu- or tychoplanktonic or may occur in films on submerged objects. Compare with Pinnularia (Fig. 442). The striae or rows of punctae are convergent toward the central clear area of the axial field which is distinctly enlarged in the midregion. The field in general is straight and narrow and the raphe is straight. In girdle view the frustules are rectangular.

Fig. 443. Navicula Petersenii Hustedt; (b) N. digitoradiata fa. minor Foged, valve view. (Redrawn from Foged.)

A Check List of the More Common Genera of Fresh-Water Algae According to Families Orders and Phyla

I. PHYLUM (DIVISION) CHLOROPHYTA

A. SUB-DIVISION CHLOROPHYCEAE

1. Order Volvocales

Family Polyblepharidaceae
Brachiomonas
p. 38, fig. 28
Dunaliella
p. 41, fig. 36
Heteromastix
p. 42, fig. 37
Pedinomonas
p. 40, fig. 34
Polyblepharides
p. 42, fig. 39
Pyramimonas
p. 42, fig. 38
Stephanoptera
p. 41, fig. 35

Family Chlamydomonadaceae
Carteria
p. 40, fig. 33
Chlamydomonas
p. 39, fig. 31
Chlorogonium
p. 37, fig. 27
Lobomonas
p. 38, fig. 29
Platymonas
p. 40, fig. 32
Sphaerellopsis
p. 39, fig. 30

Family Phacotaceae
Cephalomonas
p. 36, fig. 24
Dysmorphococcus
p. 35, fig. 23
Phacotus
p. 36, fig. 25
Pteromonas
p. 35, fig. 22
Scotiella
p. 94, fig. 145
Wislouchiella
p. 37, fig. 26

Family Volvocaceae
Eudorina
p. 33, fig. 19
Gonium
p. 29, fig. 11
Pandorina
p. 31, fig. 15
Platydorina
p. 29, fig. 10
Pleodorina
p. 33, fig.20
Stephanoon
p. 32, fig. 18
Volvox
p. 31, fig. 16

Family Spondylomoraceae
Chlamydobotrys (See
Pyrobotrys)

Pascheriella
p. 30, fig. 12
Pyrobotrys
p. 30, fig. 14
Spondylomorum
p. 30, fig. 13

Family Sphaerellaceae
Haematococcus
p. 34, fig. 21
Stephanosphaera
p. 32, fig. 17

2. Order Tetrasporales

Family Palmellaceae
Askenasyella
p. 52, fig. 57
Asterococcus
p. 53, fig. 59
Dispora
p. 57, fig. 67
Gloeocystis
p. 47, fig. 48
Hormotila
p. 107, fig. 174
Palmella
p. 45, fig. 43
Palmodictyon
p. 49. fig. 52
Sphaerocystis
p. 54, fig. 62

Family Tetrasporaceae
Apiocystis
p. 45, fig. 44
Schizochlamys
p. 51, fig. 55
Tetraspora
p. 44, fig. 42

Family Chlorangiaceae
Chlorangium
p. 60, fig. 74
Malleochloris
p. 77, fig. 109
Prasinocladus
p. 108, fig. 176
Stylosphaeridium
p. 77, fig. 110

3. Order Ulotrichales

Family Ulotrichaceae
Binuclearia
p. 113, fig. 185
Geminella
p. 114, fig. 186
Hormidiopsis
p. 113, fig. 184
Hormidium
p. 116, fig. 190
Radiofilum
p. 114, fig. 187
Raphidonema
p. 115, fig. 189

II. PHYLUM (DIVISION) EUGLENOPHYTA

III. PHYLUM (DIVISION) PYRRHOPHYTA

IV. PHYLUM (DIVISION) CRYPTOPHYTA

HOW TO KNOW THE FRESH-WATER ALGAE

VII. PHYLUM (DIVISION) CYANOPHYTA

VIII. PHYLUM (DIVISION) RHODOPHYTA

INDEX AND PICTURED GLOSSARY

ATTENUATE: narrowing to a point or becoming reduced in diameter. Fig. 447.

Figure 447

Attheya 225
  Zachariasi 225
Audouinella 140
  violacea 140
Aulosira 201
  laxa 201
AUTOSPORES: spore-like bodies cut out of the contents of a cell which are small replicas of the parent cell and which only enlarge to become mature plants.
AXIAL: along a median line bisecting an object either transversely or longitudinally (especially the latter, e.g. an axial chloroplast). Fig. 448

Figure 448

B

Bacillaria 241
  paradoxa 241
BACILLIFORM: rod-shaped
Bambusina 98
  Brebissonii 98
Banana 126
Bangia 140
  fuscopurpurea 140
Basicladia 130,
  also 8
  Chelonum 130
BASIC WATER: hard water, containing an abundance of dissolved minerals or chemical elements.
Batrachospermum 118, also 1, 119, 122, 137, 140
  Boryanum 118
  moniliforme 118
  vagum 118
Biddulphia 220
  laevis 220

BILOBED: with two lobes or extensions.
Binuclearia 113
  tatrana 113
BIPAPILLATE: with two small protrusions; nipples.
BISCUIT-SHAPED: a thickened pad; pillow-shaped.
BIVALVE (wall); wall of cell which is in two sections, one usually slightly larger than the other. (See Melosira, Fig. 401).
Bladderwort: see Utricularia
BLEPHAROPLAST: a granular body in a swimming organism from which a flagellum arises. (See flagellum)
BLOOM: See Water Bloom.
Blue-green Algae 14, 15, 180
Bohlinia 89; also 94
  echidna 89
Borzia 186
  trilocularis 186
Bostrychia 139
  scorpioides 139
Botrydiopsis 151; also 157
  arhiza 151
  eriensis 151
Botrydium 146; also 24, 76
  granulatum 146
  Wallrothii 146
Botryococcus 51; also 142
  Braunii 51
Brachiomonas 38
  Westiana 38
Brebissonia 247
  Boeckii 247
BRISTLE: a stiff hair; a needle-like spine.
Brown Algae, see Phaeophyta
Bulbochaete 134; also 111
  congener 134
  insignis 134
Bumilleria 145
  exilis 145
  sicula 145
Bumilleriopsis 152; also 153
  brevis 152

C

Caloneis 246
  bacillum 246
Calothrix 184; also 194
  atricha 184
  Braunii 184
  epiphytica 184
Campylodiscus 220
  hibernicus 220
CAPITATE: with an enlargement or a head at one end. Fig. 449

Figure 449

Capsosira 195
  Brebissonii 195
CAROTENE: Orange-yellow plant pigment of which there are four kinds in algae; a hydrocarbon, $C_{40}H_{56}$.

CARPOGONIUM: female sex organ in the red algae; a flask-shaped cell with an extension, the trichogyne.
Carteria 40
  cordiformis 40
  Klebsii 40
CARTILAGINOUS: tough but pliable; resilient.
CELLULOSE: an insoluble carbohydrate, $C_6H_{12}O_5$, of

which most plant cell walls are composed.
CENTRAL BODY: the central region of a blue-green algal cell, relatively unpigmented and containing nuclear granules.
CENTRALES: a sub-class of the Diatomaceae (Bacillariophyceae) which includes cells with radial symmetry and radiately disposed wall markings; cells round in end view, 216, 218, 219, 224
Centritractus 153
  belonophorus 153
Centronella 226
  Reichelti 226
Cephaleuros 126; also 8
  virescens 126
Cephalomonas 36
  granulata 36
Cerasterias 95
  irregulare 95
Ceratium 170
  hirundinella 170
Ceratoneis 228
Ceratophyllum 192
Chaetoceros 216
  Elmorei 216
Chaetonema 122
  irregulare 122
Chaetopeltis 123
  orbicularis 123
Chaetophora 134; also 122, 135
  elegans 134
  incrassata 134
Chaetosphaeridium 59; also 76, 107
  globosum 59
Chamaesiphon 203; also 204
  incrustans 203
Chamaesiphonaceae 206
Chantransia 140
Chara 23; also 156
  Braunii 23
  canescens 23
  coronata 23
  excelsa 23
Characeae 1, 12, 22
Characiopsis 147; also 72, 149, 72, 78, 147
  acuta 147
  cylindrica 147
  spinifer 147

Figure 450

CONJUGATION: sexual re-
production between cells
which become joined or
"yoked" together, t h e
gametes (sex cells) moving
in an amoeboid fashion,
Fig. 451

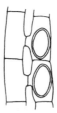

Figure 451

CONJUGATION TUBES: tubes which are put out by one or both cells involved in sexual reproduction, providing for the uniting of gametes; See Conjugation.
Conochaete 58; also 59
  comosa 58
CONSTRICTED: cut in or incised, usually from two opposite points on a cell so that an isthmus is formed between two parts or cell halves; indented as at the joints between cells of a filament. Figs. 452, 456.

Figure 452

CONTRACTILE VACUOLE: a small v a c u o l e (cavity) which is bounded by a membrane that pulsates, expanding and contracting.
Copepod 7
Coronastrum 48; also 58
  aestivale 48
C O R T E X; CORTICATING CELLS: cells superimposed on the main filament, or upon the axial part of a plant body; investing cells; e.g. Chara (Fig. 2); Batrachospermum (F i g. 195).
Coscinodiscus 219; also 218
  lacustris 219
Cosmarium 85; also 5, 52, 84, 86, 98, 107
  margaritatum 85
  panamense 85
Cosmocladium 52
  tuberculatum 52
C R E N U L A T E: wavy with small scallops; with small crenations.
CRESCENT: an arc of a circle; a curved figure t a p e r i n g to horn-like points from a wider, cylindrical midregion. S e e lunate.
CROWN CELLS: the cells formed at the tips of the investing elements that are spirally twisted about the oogonium in the Characeae.
Crucigenia 64; also 57
  rectangularis 64
  tetrapedia 64
Cryptomonas 169
  erosa 169
Cryptophyceae 14
Cryptophyta 15, 18

Ctenocladus 129
  circinnatus 129
CUP-SHAPED: a more or less complete plate (as a chloroplast) which lies just within the cell wall, open at one side to form a cup. Fig. 453

Figure 453

CUSHION: a pad; a thickened plate.
Cyanoderma bradypodis 8
Cyanophyta 7, 14, 17, 181 211, 212
Cyclonexis 177
  annularis 177
Cyclops
Cyclotella 218
  Meneghiniana 218
CYLINDRICAL: a f i g u r e, round in cross section, elongate w i t h parallel lateral margins when seen from the side, the ends square or truncate. See subcylindrical.
Cylindrocapsa 117
  geminella var. minor 117
Cylindrocystis 80; also 81
  Brebissonii 80
Cylindrospermum 198
  majus 198
  marchicum 198
Cylindrotheca 239
Cymatopleura 221
  elliptica 221
Cymbella 234
  cistula 234
CYST: a thick-walled resting cell or stage of an organism.
Cystodinium 167
  cornifax 167

D

Dactylococcopsis 213
  acicularis 213
  fascicularis 213
Dactylococcus 61; also 67
  infusionum 61
Dactylothece 50; also 87
  confluens 50
Dasygloea 190
  amorpha 190
DAUGHTER CELLS: cells produced directly from the

division of a primary or parent cell; cells produced from the same mother cell.
DAUGHTER C O L O N Y: a group of cells closely arranged, h a v i n g b e e n formed from the division of a parent cell.
Debarya 104
Denticula 223; also 240
  elegans 223
  tenuis 223
Derepyxis 163
  dispar 163
Dermatophyton, See Ulvella
Dermocarpa 205
  prasina 205
  rostrata 205
Desmatractum 78; also 86
  bipyramidatum 78
Desmidium 99; also 98
  Baileyi 99; also 98
  Grevillii 99
Desmids 5
Desmonema 202
  Wrangelii 202
Diachros 150; also 157
  simplex 150
Diatoma 230
  vulgare 230
Diatomaceae; Diatoms 7; preparation 13, 159; structure 216
Diatomella 243
Diceras 161
  phaseolus 161
Dichothrix 193
  gypsophila 193
Dichotomosiphon 136
  tuberosus 136
DICHOTOMOUS: dividing or b r a n c h e d by repeated forkings, usually into two equal portions or segments.
Dicranochaete 59; also 77
  reniformis 59
Dictyosphaerium 54; also 68
  pulchellum 54
Dimorphococcus 53; also 68
  cordatus 53
  lunatus 53
Dinobryon 159; also 160, 177, 178
  sertularia 159
Dinoflagellatae. 167, 169 170, 172, 173
Diplocolon 203
  Heppii 203
Diploneis 223; also 243
  elliptica 223
DISC; DISC-SHAPED: a flat (usually circular) figure; a circular plate.
Dispora 57
  crucigenioides 57
DISTAL: the forward or anterior end or region as opposed to the basal end.
DIVISION (ot the plant kingdom) defined 2, 3
Docidium 80
  Baculum 80
  undulatum 80
DORSAL: the back or upper surface or part as opposed to the under or lower (ventral) surface or side.

INDEX

DORSIVENTRAL: referring to differentiation into an upper (dorsal) and a lower (ventral) surface.
Draparnaldia 135
  glomerata 135
Draparnaldiopsis 135
  salishensis 135
Drying Specimens
Dunaliella 41; also 24
  salina 41
DWARF MALE: a minute male plant (as in the Oedogoniaceae) growing on or near the female sex organ (oogonium) in a larger filament.
Dysmorphococcus 35
  variabilis 35

E

ECCENTRIC: arranged without a common center; located to one side of center.
Echinosphaerella 87; also 154
  limnetica 87
Economic importances 1, 2
Elakatothrix 46; also 73, 87 also
  americana 46
  gelatinosa 46
  viridis 46
ELLIPSOID: an ellipse, a plane figure with curved margins, the poles more sharply rounded than the lateral margins of an elongate figure. Fig. 454

Figure 454

ENCYSTED: See cyst.
ENDOPHYTE: living within the cells or internally among the cells of a plant, 7, 8
ENDOSPORES: non-m o t i l e spores, cut out in indefinite numbers within a plant cell, or, as in *Chamaesiphon*, cut off from the tip of the protoplast and liberated one by one.
ENDOZOIC: living within the cells or among the cells or tissues of an animal
Enteromorpha 106
  intestinalis 106
Entocladia 121; also 123
  polymorpha 121
EPIPHYTE: living upon a plant, sometimes living internally also, 8, 205
Epipyxis 160
  Tabellariae 160

Epithemia 233
EPIZOIC: living on or attached to an animal, 8
Eremosphaera 91
  viridis 91
Errerella 66
  bornhemiensis 66
Euastropsis 43; also 63
  Richteri 43
Euastrum 84; also 5, 86
  pectinatum var. *inevolutum* 84
  pinnatum 84
Eucapisis 208
  alpina 208
Eudorina 33; also
  elegans 33
  unicocca 33
Euglena 28; also 24, 25, 27, 60, 143
  convoluta 28
  elastica 28
Euglenophyta 2, 15, 17, 25
Eunotia 239
EUPLANKTON: true or open-water plankton (floating) organisms. See plankton.
Eutreptia 27
  viridis 27
Excentrosphaera 93
  viridis 93
Exuviaella 169
  compressa 169
EYE-SPOT: a granular or complex of granules (red or brown) sensitive to light and related to responses to light by swimming organisms or spores, 26

F

FAA (Preservative), 12
FALSE BRANCH: a branch formed by lateral growth of one or both ends of a broken filament; a branch not formed by lateral division of cells in an unbroken filament.
FALSE FILAMENT: an arrangement of cells to form a short or loose thread; not forming a definite linear series of cells.
Family, defined 3
FIBRIL: a fine thread.
FILAMENT: a thread of cells; one or more rows of cells; in the blue-green algae the thread of cells together with a sheath that may be present, the thread of cells alone referred to as a trichome, which see.
FISSION: cell division by constriction not involving nuclear or mitotic division.
FLAGELLAR VACUOLES: cavities in the cytoplasm at the anterior end of a motile cell at the base of the flagellum, which see.
FLAGELLUM: a relatively coarse, whip-like organ of locomotion, arising from

a special granule, the blepharoplast, w i t h i n a cell.
FLANGE: a longitudinal bulge or wing-like vertical extension from the surface of a cell (or organism).
FLASK-LIKE: broad at the base and abruptly or gradually narrowed to a neck-like extension.
FLORIDEAN STARCH: a food reserve produced by the red algae (Rhodophyta) different from the starches produced by other plants.
FOLIOSE: leaf-like; a flat or curled, expanded thallus.
Formalin (preservative), 12
Fragilaria 231
  capucina 231
Franceia 65; also 88, 94
  Droescheri 65
Fremyella; See *Microchaete*
Fridaea 133
  torrenticola 133
Frustulia 244
  rhomboides 244
FUCOXANTHIN: a brown pigment predominant in the Phaeophyta.
FUSIFORM: a figure broadest in the midregion and gradually tapering to both poles which may be acute or bluntly rounded; shaped like a spindle. Fig. 455

Figure 455

G

GAMETANGIUM: any cell, specialized or unspecialized, which produces gametes (male or female sex cells).
GAMETE: a sex cell; cells which unite to produce a fertilized egg or zygospore, which see.
Geminella 114; also 115
  interrupta 114
  mutabilis 114
Genicularia 81; also 82, 103
  elegans 81
GENICULATE; GENICULATION: bent as a knee-joint; bending or abruptly curved.
Genus, defined 3
GIRDLE VIEW: see Valve.
Glaucocystis 142; also 207
  duplex 142
  Nostochinearum 142
Glenodinium 174
  Kulczynski 174
Gloeobotrys 157
  limneticus 157

INDEX

Gloeocapsa 209
    punctata 209
Gloeochaete 141; also 142, 207
    Wittrockiana 141
Gloeochloris, See Chlorosaccus
Gloeocystis 47; also 44, 45, 51, 54, 55, 92, 107, 142
    ampla 47
    gigas 47
    major 47
Gloeodinium 168
Gloeotaenium 69; also 94
    Loitelsbergerianum 69
Gloeothece 215; also 214
    linearis 215
Gloeotrichia 192; also 193
    echinulata 192
    natans 192
    Pisum 192
Glycerin, in preservative; in mounts.
GLYCOGEN: a starch-like storage product questionably identified in food granules of the Cyanophyta.
Golenkinia 69; also 88
    paucispina 69
    radiata 69
Gomontia 127
    Holdenii 127
Gomphoneis 242
    herculeana 242
Gomphonema 242
    lanceolatum var. insignis 242
Gomphosphaeria 208; also 213
    aponina 208
    lacustris 208
Gonatozygon 82
    aculeatum 82
Gonatozygaceae 81, 82
Gongrosira 127; also 129
    Debaryana 127
Goniochloris 156
    sculpta 156
Gonium 29
    pectorale 29
Gonyaulax 173
    palustre 173
Gonyostomum 25
    semen 25
GREGARIOUS: an association; groupings of individuals not necessarily joined together but closely associated.
GULLET: a canal leading from the opening of flagellated cells into the reservoir in the anterior end. (See Euglena, Fig. 9)
Gymnodinium 171; also 172
    fuscum 171
    palustre 171
Gymnozyga, See Bambusina
Gypsum: granules of calcium sulphate which occur in the vacuoles of some desmids. (See Closterium, Fig. 97)
Gyrodinium 171
    pusillum 171
Gyrosigma 235
    acuminatum 235

H

HAEMATOCHROME: a red or orange pigment, especially in some Chylorophyta and Euglenophyta, which masks the green chlorophyll, 9, 24, 34, 127, 143
Haematococcus 34; also 24, 38, 143
    lacustris 34
Hammatoidea 183
    yellowstonensis 183
Hantzschia 233; also 240
    amphioxys 233
Hapalosiphon 197; also 196
    hibernicus 197
HARD WATER: abundantly supplied with dissolved minerals; with a pH above neutral (7.0).
Hemidinium 174
    nasutum 174
Herbarium Specimens
Heterococcus 131
    arcticus 131
HETEROCYST: an enlarged cell in some of the filamentous blue-green algae, usually empty and different in shape from the vegetative cells. Fig. 456

Figure 456

HETEROGAMETE: a gamete (sex cell) clearly different in respect to maleness or femaleness (antherozoid, sperm and egg).
Heterokontae 146, 148
Heteromastix 42
    angulata 42
HOLD-FAST CELL: a basal cell of a filament or thallus, differentiated to form an attaching organ.
Holopedium 210
    irregulare 210
HORIZONTAL GROWTH: growth more or less at right angles to outwardly or upwardly projecting filaments or parts; usually growth parallel with a substrate to which a plant is attached.
Hormidiopsis 113
    ellipsoideum 113
Hormidium 116; also 113, 114
    Klebsii 116
Hormotila 107
    mucigena 107
Hot Springs 8, 187
H-SHAPED SECTIONS: segments of filaments or terminal cells of filaments which result from separation of cells, one from the other, at the midregion rather than at the

cross walls, the cell wall being composed of two sections which adjoin and overlap midway between the end walls. (See Figs. 194, 240); also in a chloroplast shape where there are two broad sections lying along the side walls and connected by a narrow cross band. Fig. 457.

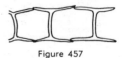

Figure 457

Hyalobryon 160
    mucicola 160
Hyalotheca 98; also 99, 149
    dissiliens 98
    mucosa 98
Hydra
Hydrocera 217
    triquetra 217
Hydrocoleum 190
    homeotrichum 190
    oligotrichum 190
Hydrodictyon 63
    reticulatum 63
Hydrurus 158
    foetidus 158
Hypnodinium 168
    sphaericum 168

I

INCISED: MEDIAN INCISION: cut in; with a narrow cut from the margin, Fig. 458

Figure 458

Indian Turnip 75
INFOLDED: as in cross walls of a filamentous alga which are not smooth, even membranes but have folds extending back into the cavity of the cell. Desmidium and certain species of Spirogyra have this type of wall; replicate.
INTERCALARY: arranged in the same series, as spores or heterocysts which occur in series with the vegetative cells rather than being terminal or lateral.
INTERNODE: the space or section of a filament or thallus extending between branch-bearing or enlarged portions (nodes).

INDEX

INTERSTICES: openings or spaces between adjoined cells, or between clusters of cells; openings in the mucilage which incloses cells in colonies.

INTESTINIFORM: a thallus, in the form of a tube, often crinkled, sometimes branched.

INVAGINATION: concavity; a depression from an otherwise smooth or plane surface.

IODINE TEST: application of a weak solution of iodine (Lugol's, *e.g.*) to determine presence of starch; starch-iodide which is formed when iodine is applied to cells of the Chlorophyta, appears as a blue-black substance, 13, 24.

ISODIAMETRICAL: a figure with all planes having an equal diameter or nearly so.

ISOGAMETE: a sex cell which shows no detectable differentiation in respect to maleness or femaleness.

J

JOINT: point or plane where two cells or elements adjoin.

Jack-in-the-pulpit, see *Aris-aema.*

K

KELP: common name for the larger brown sea weeds (Phaeophyta).

Kentrosphaera 93
  Bristolae 93
Kirchneriella 55; also 62, 93
  lunaris 55
  obesa var, *major* 55

L

Lagerheimia 88; also 65, 93
  longiseta 88
  quadriseta 88
Lagynion 162; also 163
  reductum 162
  triangularis var. *pyramid-atum* 162
LAMELLA; LAMELLATE: with layers; with plates lying against one another.

LAMANARIN: a polysaccharide carbohydrate used as food storage in Phaeophyta.

LAMINATE: plate-like; layered.

LATERAL CONJUGATION: reproduction involving the formation of a connecting tube around the end wall of two adjacent cells in the same filament so

that the contents of the cells may fuse to form a zygospore.

Lemanea 137
  annulata 137
Lemna 7
  trisulca 7, 44
Lepocinclis 27
  acuta 27
  glabra fa. *minor* 27
Leptosira 128
  Mediciana 128
LEUCOSIN: a whitish food reserve characteristic of many of the Chrysophytam especially the Heterokontae; gives a metallic lustre to cell contents.

Leuvenia 151
  natans 151
LICHEN: A duplex plant thallus formed by a fungus and an alga living in close association.

Lime (Marl Deposits)
LINEAR SERIES: cells or units arranged in a single row.

Lobomonas 38
  rostrata 38
LOBULE: a small lobe; a secondary division of a lobe.

LONGITUDINAL FURROW: a groove in the dinoflagellate cell which extends parallel with the long axis.

LORICA: a shell-like structure of varying shapes which houses an organism, has an opening through which organs of locomotion are extended. See *Dysmorphococcus*, Fig. 23; *Trachelomonas*, Fig. 459

Figure 459

LUNATE: crescent-shaped; as of the new moon in shape.

Lyngbya 182, also 188, 189
  Birgei 182
  contorta 182

M

Macrocystis 2
Magnolia 126
Malleochloris 77; also 108
  sessilis 77

Mallomonas 163
  acaroides 163
  caudata 163
  pseudocoronata 163
MANNITOL: 16
Mare's Eggs 201
Marl 23
Marssoniella 213
  elegans 213
Massartia 172
  Musei 172
Mastogloia 243
  Danseii 243
MEDIAN INCISION: See Incision.
Melosira 224
  granulata 224
Meridion 227
  circulare 227
Meringosphaera 154
  spinosa 154
Merismopedia 208; also 210
  convoluta 208
  elegans var. *major* 208
  glauca 208
Mesotaeniaceae 82
Mesotaenium 50; also 83
  Greyii 50
  macrococcum 50
METABOLIC: plastic, changing shape in motion as in many *Euglena*.
METABOLISM: referring to the physiological activities within a living cell.
Micractinium 66
  pusillum 66
  quadrisetum 66
Micrasterias 83; also 5, 97
  americana var. *Boldtii* 83
  foliacea 83,
  radiata 83
Microchaete 197; also 201
  diplosiphon 197
  robusta 197
Microcoleus 190
  lacustris 190
  vaginatus 190
MICROCRUSTACEAN: copepods, water fleas, Cladocera, etc., microscopic members of the Class Crustacea.
Microcystis 210; also 211
  aeruginosa 210
  flos-aquae 210
MICROFAUNA: microscopic animals; see Microcrustacea.
MICRON: a unit of microscopical measurement; one 1/1000 of a millimeter, determined by using a micrometer in the eyepiece of the microscope which has been calibrated with a standard stage micrometer; expressed by the symbol μ.
Microspora 118; also 4, 111, 145
  floccosa 118
  Loefgrenii 118
  Willeana 118
Microsporaceae 4
Microthamnion 131
  Kuetzingianum 131
  strictissimum 31

265

ly and symmetrically curved but more sharply so than the lateral margins. Fig. 464

Figure 464

OVOID: shaped like an egg; a curved figure broader at one end than at the other. Fig. 465

Figure 465

P

Pachycladon 95; also 96
  umbrinus 95
Palmella 45; also 48
  miniata 45
  mucosa 45
Palmellaceae 107
Palmella-stage of Chlamydomonas 47
Palmellococcus 92; also 94
  miniatus 92
Palmodictyon 49; also 108, 119
  varium 49
  viride 49
Pandorina 31; also 32, 33
  charkowiensis 31
  morum 31
PARAMYLUM: a solid, starch-like storage product in the Euglenophyta, 15, 27
PARASITIC: living on or in another organism at the expense of the host, often pathogenic, 8
PARIETAL: along the wall; arranged at the circumference; marginal as opposed to central or axial in location. Fig. 466

Figure 466

Pascheriella 30; also 32
  tetras 30
PEAR-SHAPED: a figure which is elongate and ovate, wider at one end than at the other, usually distinctly narrowed in the midregion.
PECTIN: a gelatinous carbohydrate deposited in the cell or in the cell wall of many algae.
Pectodictyon 49
  cubicum 49
PECTOSE: See Pectin
Pediastrum 63; also 43, 64
  biradiatum var. emarginatum fa. convexum 63
  Boryanum 63
  obtusum 63
  simplex 63
  tetras 63
PEDICEL: the outer membranous covering as in the Euglenophyta; a skin.
Pedinomonas 40
  rotunda 40
Penium 81
  margaritaceum 81
PENNALES: a subclass of the Diatomaceae in which the cells are bilaterally symmetrical and in which wall decorations are bilateral in arrangement from a longitudinal axis.
PERFORATE: with openings; with pores.
Perforating Algae 7
PERIDININ: a brown pigment characteristic of the Dinoflagellata,
Peridinium 173; also wisconsinense 173
PERIPHERY: the outer boundary; the surrounding outer part.
PERIPLAST: See Pellicle
Perone 147
  dimorpha 147
Peronia 238
Peroniella 149; also 156
  Hyalothecae 149
Phacotus 36; also 35
  lenticularis 36
Phacus 26
  curvicauda 26
  triqueter 26
Phaeophyta 2, 16, 18
Phaeoplaca 178
  thallosa 178
Phaeosphaera 179
  perforata 179
Phaeothamnion 158
  confervicola 158
Phormidium 189
  ambiguum 189
  favosum 189
  inundatum 189
PHOTOSYNTHESIS: physiological process by which plants with chlorophyll synthesize carbohydrates in the presence of light.
PHYCOCYANIN: a blue pigment found in the Cyano-

phyta, and in some Rhodophyta.
PHYCOERYTHRIN: a red pigment found in the Rhodophyta, and in some Cyanophyta.
PHYCOPYRRIN: a red or reddish-brown, water-soluble pigment in the chromatophores of the Dinoflagellata.
Phyllobium 75
  sphagnicola 75
Phyllosiphon 75; also 8, 136
  Arisari 75
Phylum, defined 3, Phyla of Algae, 14
Phymatodocis 99
  Nordstedtiana 99
Physolinum 125
  monilia 125
PIGMENTATION; PIGMENTS: colored substances either localized in special bodies (plastids) within the cell, or in solution within the cytoplasm, 5.
PIGMENT-SPOT: See Eyespot.
Pinnularia 249
  borealis 249
Pithophora 129; also 133
  Mooreana 129
  Oedogonia 129
PLACODERM DESMIDS: referring to those desmids which have the cell wall composed of two sections that are adjoined in the midregion of the cell where there often is a constriction so that "semicells" are formed.
PLANE (END WALLS): smooth, not infolded walls; opposite of replicate. Fig. 467

Figure 467

PLANKTON: organisms drifting in the water, or if swimming, not able to move against currents.
Plankton Net, 9
Planktosphaeria 55; also 54, 70
  gelatinosa 55
PLASTID: a body or organelle of the cell, either containing pigments or in some instances colorless.
PLATE: sections, polygonal in shape, composing the cell wall of some Dinoflagellata (the thecate or

armored dinoflagellates). Fig. 468

Figure 468

POLAR; POLE: referring to the two opposite ends of a cell or of an organism (or colony); differentiated regions of a globular cell; the ends of an axis.
POLYGONAL: many-sided.
POLYHEDRAL: a figure with more than four sides.
POSTERIOR: toward the rear; the end opposite the forward (anterior) end of a cell or of an organism.
Preserving; Preserving Fluids, 12
PROCESS: an extension of a cell or of a cell wall, or of a thallus; a horn, arm or abrupt protrusion from a plane surface or from an angle. Fig. 469

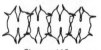

Figure 469

PROTONEMA: the filamentous stage in the development of moss plants (gametophytes), often similar to certain filamentous algae.
PROTOPLAST: the living part of the cell; the cell membrane and its contents, usually inclosed by a cell wall of dead material.
PSAMMON: the micro organisms inhabiting sandy beaches, especially above the high-water level, 7
PSEUDOCILIA: meaning false cilia; flagella-like structures not used for locomotion as in *Apiocystis* and *Tetraspora*.
PSEUDOPARENCHYMATOUS: a false cushion; a pillowlike mound of cells (usually attached) which actually is a compact series of short, often branched filaments. Fig. 470

Figure 470

PSEUDOPODIUM: meaning a false foot; locomotory organ formed by lobe-like extensions of the protoplasm, found in some Chrysophyta and in the Sarcodina Protozoa.
PSEUDOVACUOLE: meaning a false vacuole; a pocket in the cytoplasm of many blue-green algae which contains gas or mucilage; is light refractive. See *Microcystis*, p. 210, Fig. 377.

PUNCTATE: minute, pinpoint pores or holes in the cell wall; minute pits either extending completely through the wall or not. Fig. 471

Figure 471

PYRAMIDAL; PYRAMIDATE: in the shape of a pyramid; a pointed, 4-sided figure with a broad base. See Fig. 472

Figure 472

PYRENOID: a protein body around which starch or paramylum collects in a cell, usually buried in a chloroplast but sometimes free within the cytoplasm.
PYRIFORM: see Pear-shaped. Fig. 473

Figure 473

Q

QUADRATE: four-sided; with a general outline showing four sides.

R

Raciborskia 166; also 165
 bicornis 166
RADIATE: extending out-
 ward in several planes
 from a common center;
 extending in one plane
 in several directions from
 a common point.
Radiofilum 114
 conjunctivum 114
 flavescens 114
Ragweed 75
RAPHE: a longitudinal fissure
 in the wall of diatom cells
 (the shell known as a
 frustule); diatoms belonging to the Pennales may
 show a longitudinal cleft
 in one or both valves of
 the wall.
Raphidiopsis 191
 curvata 191
Raphidonema 115
 nivale 115
RECTANGULAR: a f i g u r e
 with four right angles.
RECTILINEAR: arranged in
 straight rows in two directions.
Red Snow, See Snow.
RENIFORM: kidney-shaped;
 bean-shaped. Fig. 474

Figure 474

REPLICATE: infolded; folded back as in the cross
walls of some species of
Spirogyra; not a plane
or straight wall. Fig. 475

Figure 475

RESERVOIR: cavity in the
 anterior end of flagellated
 cells from which the or-
 gans of locomotion arise.
RETICULATE: n e t t e d; arranged to form a network;
 with openings. Fig. 476

Figure 476

Rhabdoderma 214
 lineare 214
Rhizochrysis 165; also 178
 limnetica 165
Rhizoclonium 110; also 112,
 126, 133
 hieroglyphicum 110
 Hookeri 110
RHIZOID; RHIZOIDAL: root-
 like; a downward projecting root-like branch or
 cell usually without regu-
 larity.
R H I Z O P O D I A L: irregularly branched, root-like
 extensions of protoplasm
 used for locomotion.
Rhizosolenia 225
 eriensis 225
Rhodochytrium 75; also 24,
 143
 spilanthidis 75
Rhododendron 126
Rhodophyta 16, 18, 137,
 138, 139, 140, 142
Rhoicosphenia 237
 curvata 237
Rhopalodia 240
Riccia 7
 fluitans 7
Ricciocarpus 7
 natans 7
Rivularia 193; also 192
Rivulariaceae 184
Romeria 188
 elegans var. nivicola 188
Rotifer 7
Roya 82
 obtusa 82

S

SACCATE: like a sac; bal-
lon-like cell or a colony
of cells, or plant body.
Fig. 477

Figure 477

SACCODERM DESMID: false
 desmids; cells which have
 plane, unpitted walls all
 in one piece. See Placo-
 derm Desmid.
Sacconema 192
 rupestre 192
SARCINA ARRANGEMENT:
 cells arranged in the form
 of a cube.
SCALARIFORM: ladder-like;
 sexual reproduction by
 conjugation tubes formed

between cells of two filaments, forming a ladder-
 like figure.
Scenedesmus 65; also 5,
 43, 67
 bijuga var. alternans 65
 incrassatulus var. mononae
 65
 opoliensis 65
 quadricauda 65
Schizochlamys 51; also 150
 gelatinosa 51
Schizogoniaceae; Schizogoni-
 ales 100
Schizogonium 100; also 106
 crenulatum 100
 murale 100
Schizomeris 109; also 119
 Leibleinii 109
Schizothrix 191; also 190
 tinctoria 191
Schroederia 72; also 78
 ancora 72
 Judayi 72
 setigera 72
Scoliopleura 247
Scotiella 94; also 35
 nivalis 94
SCROBICULATE; SCROBICU-
 LATION: with saucer-like
 depressions in a plane
 surface (cell wall), sometimes deep. Fig. 478

Figure 478

Scytonema 201; also 194,
 202
 Archangelii 201
Scytonemataceae 185, 202
Scytonematopsis 194
 hydonoides 194
Sea Weed 18
Sea Wrack 2
Selenastrum 62; also 55, 73
 gracile 62
SEMICELL: a cell-half, as in
 the Placoderm desmids in
 which the cell has two
 parts that are mirror
 images of one another,
 the two parts often con-
 nected by a narrow isth-
 mus.
SEPTUM: a cross-partition,
 cross wall or a membrane
 complete or incomplete
 through the short diam-
 eter of a cell, sometimes
 parallel with the long
 axis.
SERRATE: toothed; jagged.
SETA: a hair, usually arising from within a cell
 wall; or a hair-like exten-

sion formed by tapering of a filament of cells to a fine point. Fig. 479

Figure 479

SHEATH: a covering, usually of mucilage, soft or firm; the covering of a colony of cells, or an envelope about one or more filaments of cells.

SICKLE-SHAPED: a c u t e l y curved; cresvent - shaped but curved more sharply than an arc of a circle. Fig. 480

Figure 480

S I P H O N; SIPHONOUS: a tube; a thallus without cross partitions.
Sirodotia 119
  suecica 119
Sirogonium 103
  sticticum 103
SKEIN: a web-like expanse; a thin m e m b r a n o u s growth.
Sloth 8
Snow Algae 8, 89
Sorastrum 69
  americanum 69
  spinulosum 69
Species, defined 3
Sphaerellopsis 39
  fluviatilis 39
Sphaerocystis 54
  Schroeteri 54
Sphaeroplea 112
  annulina 112
Sphaerozosma 97
  excavata 97
Sphagnum 11, 75, 79, 98, 118, 147, 163
SPICULE: a scale or needle in the wall of cells as a decoration: a sliver, usually siliceous.
SPINDLE-SHAPED: see Fusiform.

SPINE: a sharply-pointed projection from the cell wall.
Spirogyra 103; also 3, 81, 101, 102, 109, 126
  aequinoctialis 103
  rhizobrachiales 103
Spirotaenia 81
  condensata 81
Spirulina 181; also 182
  laxissima 181
  princeps 181
  subsalsa 181
Spondylomorum 30
  quaternarium 30
Spondylosium 98
  planum 98
  pulchrum 98
Sponge 74
SPORANGIUM: a cell (sometimes an unspecialized vegetative cell) w h i c h gives rise to spores; the case which forms about the zygospores in the Zygnematales.
Starch 14, 15, 18
STARCH-TEST: S e e Iodine Test.
STAR-SHAPED: See Stellate.
Staurastrum 84, 85
  cornutum 84
  leptocladum 85
  rotula 84
Stauroneis 248
  parvula var. prominula 248
  Stodderi 248
STELLATE: with radiating projections from a common center; star-like.
Stephanodiscus 219; also 218
  niagarae 219
Stephanoon 32
  Askenasii 32
Stephanoptera 41
  gracilis 41
Stephanosphaera 32
  pluvialis 32
Stichococcus 113
  bacillaris 113
Stichosiphon 204
  regularis 204
Stigeoclonium 122; also 116, 121, 122, 135
  flagelliferum 122
Stigonema 196
  muscicola 196
  ocellatum 196
  turfaceum 196
Stinging Cells 25
STIPE: a stalk, usually slender.
Stipitococcus 148
  urceolatus 148
  vasiformis 148
Stone-wort 1, 23
STRATIFIED: with layers
Strombomonas 26
Stylodinium 167
  globosum 167
Stylosphaeridium 77
  stipitatum 77
SUB-APICAL: slightly below the apex or below the anterior end.
SUBCYLINDRICAL: a figure which is elongate with

lateral margins that are parallel for most of their length. See Cylindrical.
SUBFLAGELLAR: located at the base of or just below the point of origin of flagella.
SUBQUADRANGULAR: n o t quite square, or with four rounded angles.
SUBSPHERICAL: not quite spherical. See Oblate.
SULCUS: groove or depression in cells of Dinoflagellata. (S e e Peridinium, Fig. 300)
Surirella 222; also 236
  oblonga 222
  ovalis 222
SUTURE: a groove between plates, as in some Dinoflagellata; a cleft-like crack or line in some zygospores of the Zygnemataceae.
Symploca 189
  muscorum 189
Syncrypta 176
  volvox 176
Synechococcus 212
  aeruginosus 212
Synechocystis 207
  aquatilis 207
Synedra 232
Synura 176
  Adamsii 176
  uvella 176

T

Tabellaria 229; also 230
  fenestrata 229
Tea 126
TEGUMENT: a skin; a firm outer covering.
Terpsinoe 224
  americana 224
TEST: a shell or covering external to the cell itself. See Lorica.
TETMEMORUS 79
  laevis 79
Tetracyclus 229
  lacustris 229
Tetradsemus 67
  Smithii 67
  wisconsinense 67
Tetradinium 165; also 166
  javanicum 165
  simplex 165
Tetraedron 96; also 5, 95, 167
  asymmetricum 96
  limneticum 96
  lobulatum var. crassum 96
  regulare var. bifurcatum 96
  regulare var. granulatum 96
TETRAGONAL: with four angles which are arranged in two opposite pairs.
Tetragoniella 155
  gigas 155
TETRAHEDRON: See Tetragonal.
Tetrallantos 56; also 67
  Lagerheimii 56

270

INDEX

U

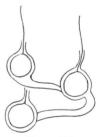

Figure 485

V

Figure 483

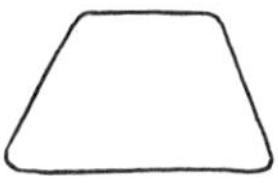

Figure 481

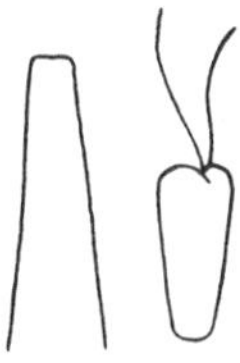

Figure 482

Figure 484

INDEX

stages involved in repro-
duction, especially sexual
reproduction.

VENTRAL: the under or
lower side or surface of
an organism or cell.

VERMIFORM: long, narrow
and crooked in shape;
worm-like.

VERRUCA: a warty projec-
tion; a protrusion which
bears knobs or spines.
Fig. 486

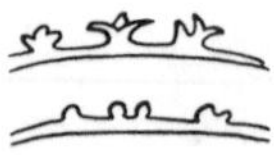

Figure 486

VERRUCOSE: roughened;
with irregular thickenings
on the surface. Fig. 487

Figure 487

VESICLE: a sac or balloon-
like cell or thallus.
Volvocaceae 29
Volvocales 33, 37, 94
Volvox 31; also 177
 tertius 31

W

Water Bloom: a profuse
growth of planktonic algae
which cloud or color the
water, often forming floating scums, 1, 28, 31, 51,
199, 227
Water Net, Hydrodictyon
Westella 68
 botryoides 68
WHORL: several parts,
branches or leaves arising
at one level from around
the axis.
Wislouchiella 37
 planctonica 37
Wollea 199
 saccata 199

X

Xanthidium 86
 cristatum var. uncinatum
 86
Xanthophyceae 137, 141
XANTHOPHYLL: a yellow
pigment of several kinds
associated with chloro-
phyll, $C_{40}H_{56}O_2$.

Xenococcus 205
 Schousbei 205

Y

Yellow-brown Algae 15

Z

Zoochlorella, See Chlorella
ZOOSPORE: an animal-like
spore equipped with
flagella and usually with
an eye-spot.
Zygnema 101; also 3
 pectinatum 101
Zygnemataceae 3
Zygnematales 103
Zygnemopsis 101
 decussata 101
 desmidioides 101
Zygogonium 102
 ericetorum 102
ZYGOSPORE: spore resulting
from the union of gametes
(sex cells); a resting stage
involving a thickened
wall.